Dynamics

Jan J. Tuma, Ph.D.
Engineering Consultant
Boulder, Colorado

 QUANTUM PUBLISHERS, INC.

257 PARK AVENUE SOUTH, NEW YORK, N.Y. 10010

254906

Preface

This book, *Dynamics*, and its companion volume, *Statics*, present the theory and applications of the engineering mechanics of rigid bodies and are designed to serve as textbooks for college courses at the introductory and intermediate levels.   Moreover, the numerous illustrative problems make these books very useful supplements to all current standard texts in this subject.

The contents of *Dynamics* is divided into eleven chapters.   The first four chapters deal with the kinematics and kinetics of a particle in the plane and in space, and the fifth chapter develops the dynamics of systems of particles.   Next, the study of motion in moving reference axes is introduced in the sixth chapter.   This provides the foundation of rigid body dynamics, which is discussed in the subsequent four chapters.   The last chapter treats of linear vibrations of mechanical systems as a special application of the principles of the dynamics of lumped masses.

Each chapter consists of three parts: the theory, the illustrative problems, and the review problems.   The theory section includes clear statements of definitions, theorems, governing equations and methods of solution.   A wide variety of solved problems illustrates virtually every topic considered in that chapter, supplies the pertinent derivations and proofs, and illuminates the fine points and potential difficulties.   The large number of review problems enables the student to test his understanding of the theory and his proficiency in applying the acquired knowledge.   The only mathematical background required of the reader is elementary calculus.   This overall approach makes the book suitable not only as a text in a structured classroom situation, but also as a supplement to all other texts in the subject.

As in the first volume, *Statics*, the algebraic, vectorial and matrix forms of analysis are gradually developed in this volume and their advantages and disadvantages demonstrated by comparative examples.

The material included in this book is more than can be covered in most courses.   Consequently, some topics of Chapter 3 (transformation matrices), of Chapter 4 (transport matrices), of Chapters 9 and 10 (general motion of rigid bodies) and of Chapter 11 (vibration with damping) may be omitted at the introductory level and left for future reference or reading assignments.

In the organization and preparation of the material presented in this book, I have been assisted by many individuals.   In particular, I take pleasure in acknowledging the help of my former colleagues, Professors M. N. Reddy, A. Lassker, R. K. Munshi, G. Alberti, and J. Hutt. I wish also to express my gratitude to Daniel Schaum and Nicolas Monti for their excellent editorial cooperation.

JAN J. TUMA

Boulder, Colorado

Contents

Dynamics

Chapter 1

Kinematics of Particles, Plane Motion

1.1 GENERAL CONSIDERATIONS

Definitions

Dynamics, defined as the systematic study of motion of material particles (bodies), is traditionally divided into two parts called kinematics and kinetics.

Kinematics is concerned with the space-time relationship of the motion (geometry of motion) without regard to causes (forces and/or moments) required to produce or maintain the motion.

Kinetics is concerned with the causes required to produce and maintain the motion and consequently is the study of force-space-time relationships.

Basic Concepts

Three *basic concepts* of dynamics are space, time and force.

(1) *Space* is the region in which the motion takes place. The measure of space is length and in engineering the space is three-dimensional.

(2) *Time* is the measure of succession of events related to an arbitrarily selected datum (start, beginning). The measure of time is a fraction of one day (hour, minute, second) and in engineering the time is independent of the motion of the observer.

(3) *Force* is the action of one body on another, interpreted as the push or pull. The weight of a body is the most typical example of force and in engineering the weight of a body is independent of its geographical location.

Associated Concepts

In addition to the basic concepts introduced above, three *associated concepts* are necessary in the dynamic analysis; they are the notions of particle, body and configuration.

(a) *Particle* is the small amount of matter assumed to occupy a single point in space.

(b) *Rigid body* is a system of particles in a given and fixed position relative to each other (which does not change under the action of causes).

(c) *Configuration* is the arrangement of particles in a system which may or may not be a function of time, forces, moments, temperature and/or moisture content.

Physically, all engineering systems (structures, machines, etc.) are never absolutely rigid but deform (change shape) under the action of causes. Since in many cases these changes in configuration are small, they may be disregarded and the representation of the given system by a rigid body is admissible. The dynamic analysis in this book is based on the assumption that all bodies involved are rigid (rigid body mechanics).

1

Analytical Model

For the analysis, the real system is replaced by an *analytical (mathematical) model* which represents symbolically the physical characteristics of the real system (idealization of the real system).

In this model, the particles are represented by points, bodies by lines, areas or volumes, forces by single-headed vectors (Fig. 1-1) and moments by double-headed vectors (Fig. 1-2).

All components of the analytical model are given or assumed in selected units of measure and if vectorial in character, they are governed by sign conventions of the respective reference system (Sections 1.4 and 3.1).

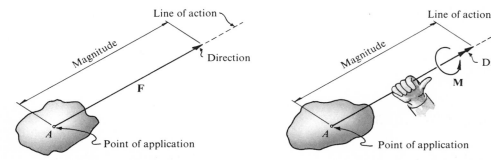

Fig. 1-1   Force vector $\mathbf{F}_m$.   **Fig. 1-2**   Moment vector $\mathbf{M}_m$.

Kinematic Quantities

Three linear vectors used in kinematics of particles are *position vector* $\mathbf{r}$, *velocity vector* $\mathbf{v}$, and *acceleration vector* $\mathbf{a}$.

Definition 1.1: *Linear position vector* defining at time t the position of a particle in motion with respect to an arbitrarily selected origin 0 (Fig. 1-3) is

$$\mathbf{r}(t) = \mathbf{r} = r\mathbf{e}_r \qquad (1\text{-}1)$$

where r is the *position radius* and $\mathbf{e}_r$ is the *radial unit vector*.

Definition 1.2: *Linear velocity vector* defining at time t the time rate of change in linear position of a particle in motion with respect to an arbitrarily selected origin 0 (Fig. 1-3) is

$$\mathbf{v}(t) = \lim_{\Delta t \to 0} \frac{\Delta \mathbf{r}(t)}{\Delta t} = \frac{d\mathbf{r}}{dt} = \dot{\mathbf{r}} = v\mathbf{e}_v \qquad (1\text{-}2)$$

where $v = dr/dt$ is the *speed* (velocity scalar) and $\mathbf{e}_v$ is the *velocity unit vector*.

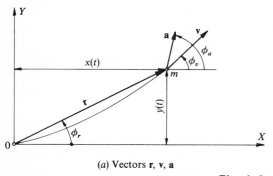

(a) Vectors $\mathbf{r}$, $\mathbf{v}$, $\mathbf{a}$ (b) Unit vectors $\mathbf{e}_r$, $\mathbf{e}_v$, $\mathbf{e}_a$

Fig. 1-3   Kinematic vectors.

Definition 1.3: *Linear acceleration vector* defining at time t the time rate of change in linear velocity of a particle in motion with respect to an arbitrarily selected origin 0 (Fig. 1-3) is

$$\mathbf{a}(t) = \lim_{\Delta t \to 0} \frac{\Delta \mathbf{v}(t)}{\Delta t} = \frac{d\mathbf{v}}{dt} = \dot{\mathbf{v}} = \dot{v}\mathbf{e}_a = \frac{d^2\mathbf{r}}{dt^2} = \ddot{\mathbf{r}} = a\mathbf{e}_a \qquad (1\text{-}3)$$

where $a = dv/dt$ is the *acceleration scalar* and $\mathbf{e}_a$ is the *acceleration unit vector*.

Equations $(1\text{-}1)$ to $(1\text{-}3)$ are known as the *kinematic equations of motion* and their validity presumes that $\mathbf{r}(t)$ is a continuous, single-valued vector function of the scalar variable t in the given interval.

In general, the velocity vector is tangent to the path of motion and the acceleration vector deviates from this tangent (except in rectilinear motion, where all vectors are collinear).

For a particular value of t (at a particular instant) these vectors are designated as the instantaneous position, velocity and acceleration vectors, respectively.

1.2   GEOMETRY OF PLANE PATH

Equation of Path

The *path of motion* is usually given by an equation (or a set of equations) in the cartesian or polar system of coordinates and expressed in the respective scalar form as

$$x = x(t), \ y = y(t) \qquad \text{or} \qquad r = r(\theta), \ \theta = \theta(t) \qquad (1\text{-}4),(1\text{-}5)$$

The *positive direction* of the curve given by $(1\text{-}4)$ or $(1\text{-}5)$ is that in which the particle moves when the time t increases.

Properties of Path

The *arc element* of the path (Fig. 1-4) is

$$ds = \sqrt{\dot{x}^2 + \dot{y}^2}\, dt \qquad \text{or} \qquad ds = \dot{\theta}\sqrt{r^2 + r^{*2}}\, dt = \sqrt{(r\dot{\theta})^2 + \dot{r}^2}\, dt \qquad (1\text{-}6),(1\text{-}7)$$

where $\dot{x} = dx(t)/dt$, $\dot{y} = dy(t)/dt$, $r^* = dr(\theta)/d\theta$, $\dot{\theta}(t) = d\theta(t)/dt$, $\dot{r}(t) = dr(t)/dt$.

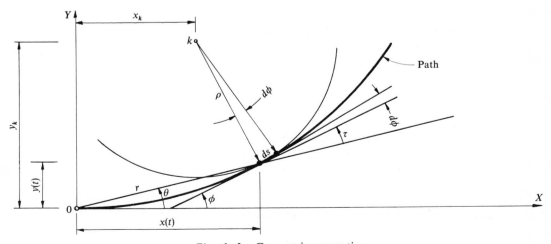

Fig. 1-4   Geometric properties.

The *direction functions* of the path are

$$\tan \phi = \dot{y}/\dot{x}, \qquad \sin \phi = \dot{y}/\sqrt{\dot{x}^2 + \dot{y}^2}, \qquad \cos \phi = \dot{x}/\sqrt{\dot{x}^2 + \dot{y}^2} \qquad (1\text{-}8)$$

or

$$\tan \tau = r/r^*, \qquad \sin \tau = r/\sqrt{r^2 + r^{*2}}, \qquad \cos \tau = \dot{r}/\dot{\theta}\sqrt{r^2 + r^{*2}} \qquad (1\text{-}9)$$

where ϕ, θ and τ are the angles shown in Fig. 1-4.

The *radius of curvature* of the path (Problem 1.2) is

$$\rho = \frac{[\dot{x}^2 + \dot{y}^2]^{3/2}}{\dot{x}\ddot{y} - \ddot{x}\dot{y}} \qquad \text{or} \qquad \rho = \frac{[r^2 + r^{*2}]^{3/2}}{r^2 + 2r^{*2} - rr^{**}} \qquad (1\text{-}10), (1\text{-}11)$$

and the *coordinates of the center of curvature* (Problem 1.3) are

$$x_k = x - \frac{\dot{y}(\dot{x}^2 + \dot{y}^2)}{\dot{x}\ddot{y} - \ddot{x}\dot{y}}, \qquad y_k = y + \frac{\dot{x}(\dot{x}^2 + \dot{y}^2)}{\dot{x}\ddot{y} - \ddot{x}\dot{y}} \qquad (1\text{-}12)$$

or

$$\left.\begin{aligned}
x_k &= r \cos \theta - \frac{(r^2 + r^{*2})(r \cos \theta + r^* \sin \theta)}{r^2 + 2r^{*2} - rr^{**}} \\[2ex]
y_k &= r \sin \theta - \frac{(r^2 + r^{*2})(r \sin \theta - r^* \cos \theta)}{r^2 + 2r^{*2} - rr^{**}}
\end{aligned}\right\} \qquad (1\text{-}13)$$

where $\ddot{x} = d^2x(t)/dt^2$, $\ddot{y} = d^2y(t)/dt^2$, $r^{**} = d^2r(\theta)/d\theta^2$.

1.3 ABSOLUTE RECTILINEAR MOTION

General Case

The simplest and yet the most important motion in engineering is the *straight-line (rectilinear) motion*. The path is a straight line, $x = x(t)$, $y = 0$, so the position, velocity and acceleration vectors are respectively

$$\mathbf{r} = x\mathbf{i}, \qquad \mathbf{v} = \dot{x}\mathbf{i}, \qquad \mathbf{a} = \ddot{x}\mathbf{i} \qquad (1\text{-}14)$$

Special Cases

If $\mathbf{a}$ = constant, the motion is called *uniformly accelerated motion* and

$$\mathbf{v} = \mathbf{v}_0 + \mathbf{a}t, \qquad \mathbf{r} = \mathbf{v}_0 t + \mathbf{a}t^2/2 = (\mathbf{v}_0 + \mathbf{v})t/2 \qquad (1\text{-}15)$$

where $\mathbf{v}_0$ is the velocity at $t = 0$.

If $\mathbf{a} = 0$ and $\mathbf{v}$ = constant, the motion is called *uniform motion* and

$$\mathbf{v} = \mathbf{v}_0, \qquad \mathbf{r} = \mathbf{v}_0 t \qquad (1\text{-}16)$$

Because of the constant and collinear direction of all vectors, the algebraic form of (*1-14*), (*1-15*) and (*1-16*) is commonly used.

1.4   ABSOLUTE CURVILINEAR MOTION

General Case

If the path of motion is a *plane curve*, the motion is said to be *plane curvilinear motion*.   The study of this motion in three different coordinate systems is presented in this section.

(*a*) *Cartesian coordinates* (Fig. 1-5).   In terms of $x = x(t)$, $y = y(t)$, $z = 0$, equations (*1-1*) to (*1-3*) are

$$\left.\begin{array}{l} \mathbf{r} = x\mathbf{i} + y\mathbf{j} = r_x\mathbf{i} + r_y\mathbf{j} = r\mathbf{e}_r \\ \mathbf{v} = \dot{\mathbf{r}} = \dot{x}\mathbf{i} + \dot{y}\mathbf{j} = v_x\mathbf{i} + v_y\mathbf{j} = v\mathbf{e}_v \\ \mathbf{a} = \dot{\mathbf{v}} = \ddot{\mathbf{r}} = \ddot{x}\mathbf{i} + \ddot{y}\mathbf{j} = a_x\mathbf{i} + a_y\mathbf{j} = a\mathbf{e}_a \end{array}\right\} \qquad (1\text{-}17)$$

where

$$r = \sqrt{x^2 + y^2}, \qquad v = \sqrt{\dot{x}^2 + \dot{y}^2}, \qquad a = \sqrt{\ddot{x}^2 + \ddot{y}^2} \qquad (1\text{-}18)$$

are the respective magnitudes and $\mathbf{e}_r$, $\mathbf{e}_v$, $\mathbf{e}_a$ are the unit vectors introduced in Fig. 1-3*b*.

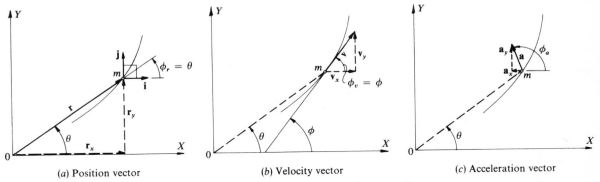

(a) Position vector   (b) Velocity vector   (c) Acceleration vector

Fig. 1-5   Kinematic vectors in cartesian coordinates.

A particular property of this form of equations of motion is the time independence of $\mathbf{i}$, $\mathbf{j}$, i.e. $d\mathbf{i}/dt = 0$, $d\mathbf{j}/dt = 0$.

(*b*) *Polar coordinates* (Fig. 1-6).   In terms of $r = r(\theta)$, $\theta = \theta(t)$, $z = 0$, equations (*1-1*) to (*1-3*) are

$$\left.\begin{array}{l} \mathbf{v} = \dot{\mathbf{r}} = \dot{r}\mathbf{e}_r + r\dot{\theta}\mathbf{e}_\theta = v_r\mathbf{e}_r + v_\theta\mathbf{e}_\theta \\ \mathbf{a} = \dot{\mathbf{v}} = \ddot{\mathbf{r}} = (\ddot{r} - r\dot{\theta}^2)\mathbf{e}_r + (r\ddot{\theta} + 2\dot{r}\dot{\theta})\mathbf{e}_\theta = a_r\mathbf{e}_r + a_\theta\mathbf{e}_\theta \end{array}\right\} \qquad (1\text{-}19)$$

where v_r, v_θ are the magnitudes of the radial and transverse components of $\mathbf{v}$, respectively, a_r, a_θ

6 DYNAMICS

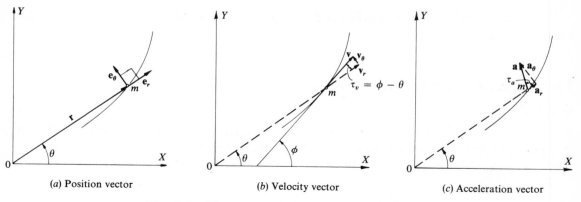

Fig. 1-6 Kinematic vectors in polar coordinates.

are the analogical components of **a**, and $\mathbf{e}_r$, $\mathbf{e}_\theta$ are the unit vectors along and normal to **r** respectively. The derivatives of these unit vectors are

$$\dot{\mathbf{e}}_r = \dot{\theta}\mathbf{e}_\theta, \qquad \dot{\mathbf{e}}_\theta = -\dot{\theta}\mathbf{e}_r \qquad\qquad (1\text{-}20)$$

as shown in Problem 1.14.

(c) *Curvilinear coordinates* (Fig. 1-7).   An alternative form of the equations of motion is in terms of the tangential unit vector $\mathbf{e}_t$, the normal unit vector $\mathbf{e}_n$, and the curvilinear coordinate $s = s(t)$.   Analytically,

$$\left.\begin{array}{l} \mathbf{v} = v\mathbf{e}_t \\ \mathbf{a} = \dot{v}\mathbf{e}_t + v\dot{\mathbf{e}}_t = \dot{v}\mathbf{e}_t + (v^2/\rho)\mathbf{e}_n = a_t\mathbf{e}_t + a_n\mathbf{e}_n \end{array}\right\} \qquad (1\text{-}21)$$

where $v = ds/dt$, $\mathbf{e}_t = d\mathbf{r}/ds$, $\mathbf{e}_n = \rho\, d\mathbf{e}_t/ds$,
   s = curvilinear coordinate measured along the path from the origin of motion,
   ρ = radius of curvature of the path.

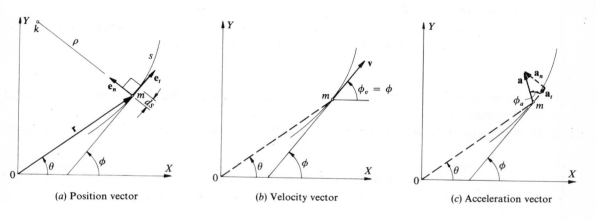

Fig. 1-7 Kinematic vectors in curvilinear coordinates.

1.5 RELATIVE MOTION

Classification

Definition 1.4: The *absolute motion of a particle* is a motion whose **r, v, a** are measured with respect to fixed coordinate axes.

Definition 1.5: The *relative motion of a particle* is a motion whose **r, v, a** are measured with respect to a moving point and/or rotating coordinate axes.

Relative Vectors

The *position vector* $\mathbf{r}_{nm}$, *velocity vector* $\mathbf{v}_{nm}$, and *acceleration vector* $\mathbf{a}_{nm}$ of the moving particle m with respect to another moving particle n (Fig. 1-8) are

$$\left. \begin{aligned} \mathbf{r}_{nm} &= \mathbf{r}_{0m} - \mathbf{r}_{0n} \\ \mathbf{v}_{nm} &= \dot{\mathbf{r}}_{0m} - \dot{\mathbf{r}}_{0n} = \mathbf{v}_{0m} - \mathbf{v}_{0n} \\ \mathbf{a}_{nm} &= \ddot{\mathbf{r}}_{0m} - \ddot{\mathbf{r}}_{0n} = \dot{\mathbf{v}}_{0m} - \dot{\mathbf{v}}_{0n} = \mathbf{a}_{0m} - \mathbf{a}_{0n} \end{aligned} \right\} \qquad (1\text{-}22)$$

In these equations $\mathbf{r}_{0m}, \mathbf{r}_{0n}, \mathbf{v}_{0m}, \mathbf{v}_{0n}, \mathbf{a}_{0m}, \mathbf{a}_{0n}$ are the absolute vectors of the particles m, n respectively, related to a fixed point 0 and $\mathbf{r}_{nm}, \mathbf{v}_{nm}, \mathbf{a}_{nm}$ are the relative vectors of the particle m related to a moving particle n.

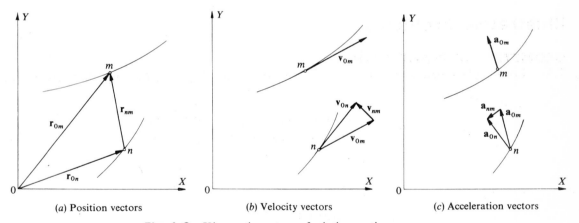

(a) Position vectors   (b) Velocity vectors   (c) Acceleration vectors

Fig. 1-8 Kinematic vectors of relative motion.

1.6 UNITS

General Symbols

All kinematic vectors and scalars are given in this section in terms of *units of length* L, *unit of time* T, and/or in radians.

In particular, **r** is given in L, **v** in L/T and **a** in L/T^2; θ, ϕ, τ in radians; $\dot{\theta}$ in rad/T, and $\ddot{\theta}$ in rad/T^2.

Specific Symbols

Three *systems of units* used in the kinematics of particles are listed in Table 1-1.

Table 1-1   Units of Kinematic Vectors

	Metric units MKS	Metric units CGS	British units FPS
L	Meter (m)	Centimeter (cm)	Foot (ft)
T	Second (sec)	Second (sec)	Second (sec)
r	(m)	(cm)	(ft)
v	(m)/(sec)	(cm)/(sec)	(ft)/(sec)
a	(m)/(sec)^2	(cm)/(sec)^2	(ft)/(sec)^2
θ	Radian (rad)	Radian (rad)	Radian (rad)
$\dot{\theta}$	(rad)/(sec)	(rad)/(sec)	(rad)/(sec)
$\ddot{\theta}$	(rad)/(sec)^2	(rad)/(sec)^2	(rad)/(sec)^2

Illustrative Problems

GEOMETRY OF PLANE PATH

1.1   For the plane path given by $x = 5t^2$, $y = 10t^3$, find $\dot{x}$, $\dot{y}$, $\ddot{x}$, $\ddot{y}$, ds, $\tan\phi$, $\sin\phi$, and $\cos\phi$.

By (*1-6*),

$$\dot{x} = d(5t^2)/dt = 10t \qquad \ddot{x} = d\dot{x}/dt = 10$$
$$\dot{y} = d(10t^3)/dt = 30t^2 \qquad \ddot{y} = d\dot{y}/dt = 60t$$

$$ds = \sqrt{\dot{x}^2 + \dot{y}^2}\, dt = t\sqrt{10^2 + 30^2 t^2}\, dt = 10t\sqrt{1 + 9t^2}\, dt$$

By (*1-8*),

$$\tan\phi = \dot{y}/\dot{x} = 30t^2/10t = 3t$$
$$\sin\phi = \dot{y}/\sqrt{\dot{x}^2 + \dot{y}^2} = 30t^2/t\sqrt{10^2 + 30^2 t^2} = 3t/\sqrt{1 + 9t^2}$$
$$\cos\phi = \dot{x}/\sqrt{\dot{x}^2 + \dot{y}^2} = 10t/t\sqrt{10^2 + 30^2 t^2} = 1/\sqrt{1 + 9t^2}$$

1.2   Derive the general expression (*1-10*), page 4, for the radius of curvature ρ of the plane path of Fig. 1-4.

By definition, the curvature of the curve given by $y = f(x)$ is

$$\kappa = \lim_{\Delta s \to 0} \frac{\Delta\phi}{\Delta s} = \lim_{\Delta x \to 0} \frac{\Delta\phi/\Delta x}{\Delta s/\Delta x} = \frac{d\phi/dx}{ds/dx} \qquad (1)$$

where $d\phi$ and ds are elements of the slope and arc of the path at m, respectively.

Since $ds/dx = \sqrt{1 + (dy/dx)^2}$, $dy/dx = \tan \phi$, then

$$\phi = \tan^{-1}\frac{dy}{dx}, \qquad \frac{d\phi}{dx} = \frac{d^2y/dx^2}{1 + (dy/dx)^2}$$

and the curvature in (1) can be written as

$$\kappa = \frac{(d^2y/dx^2)/[1 + (dy/dx)^2]}{\sqrt{1 + (dy/dx)^2}} = \frac{y''}{[1 + (y')^2]^{3/2}} \qquad (2)$$

where $y' = dy/dx$, $y'' = d^2y/dx^2$.

In terms of the radius of curvature ρ,

$$ds = \rho \, d\phi \qquad (3)$$

and on substituting in (1),

$$\kappa = 1/\rho \qquad (4)$$

Then (2) in terms of (4) yields

$$\rho = \frac{(1 + (y')^2)^{3/2}}{y''} \qquad (5)$$

If $x = x(t)$, $y = y(t)$,

$$y' = \frac{dy}{dt}\frac{dt}{dx} = \frac{dy/dt}{dx/dt} = \frac{\dot{y}}{\dot{x}} \qquad (6)$$

$$y'' = \frac{d(dy/dx)}{dx} = \frac{d(dy/dx)}{dt}\frac{dt}{dx} = \frac{d(\dot{y}/\dot{x})}{dt}\frac{1}{\dot{x}} = \frac{\dot{x}\ddot{y} - \ddot{x}\dot{y}}{(\dot{x})^3} \qquad (7)$$

and their substitution into (5) gives the radius of curvature as

$$\rho = \frac{[\dot{x}^2 + \dot{y}^2]^{3/2}}{\dot{x}\ddot{y} - \ddot{x}\dot{y}} \qquad (8)$$

1.3   Derive the general expressions (1-12) for the coordinates x_k, y_k of the center of curvature of the plane path of Fig. 1-4.

The center of curvature k is on the normal to the path at m, whose angle with the X axis is $\pi/2 + \phi$. Thus the coordinates of k are

$$x_k = x + \rho \cos(\pi/2 + \phi) = x - \rho \sin \phi$$
$$y_k = y + \rho \sin(\pi/2 + \phi) = y + \rho \cos \phi$$

In terms of $\sin \phi = y'/\sqrt{1 + y'^2}$, $\cos \phi = 1/\sqrt{1 + y'^2}$ and equations (6) and (8) of Problem 1.2, the coordinates of k are

$$x_k = x - \frac{\dot{y}(\dot{x}^2 + \dot{y}^2)}{\dot{x}\ddot{y} - \ddot{x}\dot{y}}, \qquad y_k = y + \frac{\dot{x}(\dot{x}^2 + \dot{y}^2)}{\dot{x}\ddot{y} - \ddot{x}\dot{y}}$$

1.4 For the plane path of Problem 1.1 find the equation of the radius of curvature ρ and the coordinates of the center of curvature. Use the results of Problems 1.1, 1.2, 1.3.

By *(1-10)*,

$$\rho = \frac{(\dot{x}^2 + \dot{y}^2)^{3/2}}{\dot{x}\ddot{y} - \ddot{x}\dot{y}} = \frac{t(\sqrt{10^2 + 30^2 t^2})^3}{300}$$

By *(1-12)*,

$$x_k = 5t^2 - \frac{30t^2(100t^2 + 900t^4)}{300t^2} = -5t^2 - 90t^4$$

$$y_k = 10t^3 + \frac{10t(100t^2 + 900t^4)}{300t^2} = 3.33t + 40t^3$$

1.5 For the plane path given by $r = b\theta$, $\theta = t$, find $\dot{r}$, $\dot{\theta}$, $\ddot{r}$, $\ddot{\theta}$, ds, $\tan\tau$, $\sin\tau$, and $\cos\tau$.

By *(1-7)*,

$$\dot{r} = \frac{dr}{d\theta}\frac{d\theta}{dt} = (b)(1) = b, \qquad \ddot{r} = 0, \qquad r^* = \frac{dr}{d\theta} = b = \dot{r}$$

$$\dot{\theta} = \frac{d\theta}{dt} = 1, \qquad \ddot{\theta} = 0$$

$$ds = (1)\sqrt{(bt)^2 + b^2}\,dt = b\sqrt{1 + t^2}\,dt$$

By *(1-9)*,

$$\tan\tau = r/r^* = bt/b = t$$
$$\sin\tau = r/\sqrt{r^2 + r^{*2}} = t/\sqrt{1 + t^2}$$
$$\cos\tau = \dot{r}/\dot{\theta}\sqrt{r^2 + r^{*2}} = 1/\sqrt{1 + t^2}$$

where τ is the angle between r and the tangent at m (Fig. 1-4).

1.6 For the plane path of Problem 1.5, find the equation of the radius of curvature ρ and the coordinates of the center of curvature. Use the results of Problem 1.5.

By *(1-11)*, and with $\dot{r} = r^*$,

$$\rho = \frac{[r^2 + \dot{r}^2]^{3/2}}{r^2 + 2\dot{r}^2 - r\ddot{r}} = \frac{b[1 + t^2]^{3/2}}{2 + t^2}$$

By *(1-13)*,

$$x_k = r\cos\theta - \frac{(r^2 + \dot{r}^2)(r\cos\theta + \dot{r}\sin\theta)}{r^2 + 2\dot{r}^2 - r\ddot{r}} = bt\cos t - \frac{b(1 + t^2)(t\cos t + \sin t)}{1 + 2t^2}$$

$$y_k = r\sin\theta - \frac{(r^2 + \dot{r}^2)(r\sin\theta - r\cos\theta)}{r^2 + 2\dot{r}^2 - r\ddot{r}} = bt\sin t - \frac{b(1 + t^2)(t\sin t - \cos t)}{1 + 2t^2}$$

ABSOLUTE RECTILINEAR MOTION

1.7   A particle moves along the path defined by $\mathbf{r} = [(1 + 2t + 3t^2 + 4t^3)\mathbf{i}]$ L.   Find the position, velocity, and acceleration vectors and their magnitudes at $t = 10$ T.

By (1-14), at $t = 10$ T,

$$\mathbf{r} = x\mathbf{i} = (1 + 20 + 300 + 4000)\mathbf{i} = (4321\,\mathbf{i})\,\text{L}$$
$$\mathbf{v} = \dot{x}\mathbf{i} = (2 + 6t + 12t^2)\mathbf{i} = (2 + 60 + 1200)\mathbf{i} = (1262\mathbf{i})\,\text{L/T}$$
$$\mathbf{a} = \ddot{x}\mathbf{i} = (6 + 36t)\mathbf{i} = (6 + 360)\mathbf{i} = (366\mathbf{i})\,\text{L/T}^2$$

where the magnitudes are $r = 4321$ L, $v = 1262$ L/T, $a = 366$ L/T^2.

1.8   A rectilinear motion of a particle is defined by the velocity vector $\mathbf{v}(t) = (2 + 3t^2)\mathbf{i}$, and the initial position vector $\mathbf{r}(0) = 10\mathbf{i}$.   Find the position vector $\mathbf{r}(t)$ and the acceleration vector $\mathbf{a}(t)$.

By definition, $\dot{\mathbf{r}}(t) = \mathbf{v}(t) = (2 + 3t^2)\mathbf{i}$.   Now

$$\int \dot{\mathbf{r}}(t)\,dt = \mathbf{i}\int (2 + 3t^2)\,dt + \mathbf{c} \qquad \text{and so} \qquad \mathbf{r}(t) = (2t + t^3)\mathbf{i} + \mathbf{c}$$

where $\mathbf{c}$ is the integration constant to be determined from the initial condition.
At $t = 0$, $\mathbf{r}(0) = 10\mathbf{i}$; and by (2), $\mathbf{c} = 10\mathbf{i}$.   Thus

$$\mathbf{r}(t) = (10 + 2t + t^3)\mathbf{i} \qquad \text{and} \qquad \mathbf{a}(t) = \ddot{\mathbf{r}}(t) = 6t\,\mathbf{i}$$

1.9   A rectilinear motion of a particle is defined by the acceleration vector $\mathbf{a}(t) = (6t)\mathbf{i}$, the initial position vector $\mathbf{r}(0) = 10\mathbf{i}$, and the initial velocity vector $\mathbf{v}(0) = 2\mathbf{i}$.   Find the expressions for the position vector $\mathbf{r}(t)$ and the velocity vector $\mathbf{v}(t)$.

By definition, $\ddot{\mathbf{r}}(t) = \mathbf{a}(t) = 6t\mathbf{i}$.   Then $\displaystyle\int \ddot{\mathbf{r}}(t)\,dt = \mathbf{i}\int 6t\,dt + \mathbf{c}_1$ from which $\dot{\mathbf{r}}(t) = 3t^2\mathbf{i} + \mathbf{c}_1$.

At $t = 0$, $\dot{\mathbf{r}}(0) = \mathbf{v}(0) = 2\mathbf{i} = \mathbf{c}_1$, and $\dot{\mathbf{r}}(t) = (2 + 3t^2)\mathbf{i}$.

Now $\displaystyle\int \dot{\mathbf{r}}(t)\,dt = \mathbf{i}\int (2 + 3t^2)\,dt + \mathbf{c}_2$ which gives $\mathbf{r}(t) = (2t + t^3)\mathbf{i} + \mathbf{c}_2$.

At $t = 0$, $\mathbf{r}(0) = 10\mathbf{i} = \mathbf{c}_2$, and so $\mathbf{r}(t) = (10 + 2t + t^3)\mathbf{i}$.

1.10   The solutions of Problems 1.8 and 1.3 reveal that the constants of integration are initial values of the respective motions.   If the initial vectors at $t = 0$ are $\mathbf{r}(0)$, $\mathbf{v}(0)$ and the acceleration vector at t is $\mathbf{a}(t)$, determine the general equations of this motion.

By definition,
$$\ddot{\mathbf{r}}(t) = \mathbf{a}(t) \tag{1}$$

The solution of this vector differential equation is found by successive integration as

$$\dot{\mathbf{r}}(t) = \int \mathbf{a}(t)\,dt + \mathbf{c}_1$$

$$\mathbf{r}(t) = \iint \mathbf{a}(t)\,dt\,dt + \mathbf{c}_1 t + \mathbf{c}_2 \tag{2}$$

Equation (I) and its integrals (2) are functions of t and are valid for any position on the t axis. The vector constants $\mathbf{c}_1$, $\mathbf{c}_2$ take on different values as the origin changes its position.

At $t = 0$, the integrals of $\mathbf{a}(t)$ vanish and

$$\mathbf{c}_1 = \dot{\mathbf{r}}(0), \qquad \mathbf{c}_2 = \mathbf{r}(0) \tag{3}$$

In terms of (3),

$$\left.\begin{array}{l} \ddot{\mathbf{r}}(t) = \mathbf{a}(t) \\[2mm] \dot{\mathbf{r}}(t) = \displaystyle\int_0^t \mathbf{a}(t)\, dt + \dot{\mathbf{r}}(0) \\[4mm] \mathbf{r}(t) = \displaystyle\int_0^t \int_0^t \mathbf{a}(t)\, dt\, dt + t\dot{\mathbf{r}}(0) + \mathbf{r}(0) \end{array}\right\} \tag{4}$$

In matrix form,

$$\begin{bmatrix} 1 \\ \mathbf{r}(t) \\ \dot{\mathbf{r}}(t) \end{bmatrix} = \begin{bmatrix} 1 \\ \displaystyle\int_0^t \int_0^t \mathbf{a}(t)\, dt\, dt & 1 & t \\ \displaystyle\int_0^t \mathbf{a}(t)\, dt & 0 & 1 \end{bmatrix} \begin{bmatrix} 1 \\ \mathbf{r}(0) \\ \dot{\mathbf{r}}(0) \end{bmatrix} \tag{5}$$

$$\underbrace{\phantom{\begin{bmatrix} 1 \\ \mathbf{r}(t) \\ \dot{\mathbf{r}}(t) \end{bmatrix}}}_{[A_t]} \qquad \underbrace{}_{[\hat{T}_{t0}]} \qquad \underbrace{\phantom{\begin{bmatrix} 1 \\ \mathbf{r}(0) \\ \dot{\mathbf{r}}(0) \end{bmatrix}}}_{[A_0]}$$

where $[A_0]$, $[A_t]$ are the kinematic vectors at $t = 0$, $t = t$ respectively, and $[\hat{T}_{t0}]$ is the kinematic transport matrix between the respective time stations, $t = 0$, $t = t$.

The integrals in $[\hat{T}_{t0}]$ designated as

$$\mathbf{r}_{t0} = \int_0^t \int_0^t \mathbf{a}(t)\, dt\, dt, \qquad \dot{\mathbf{r}}_{t0} = \int_0^t \mathbf{a}(t)\, dt \tag{6}$$

are constant values for the given time interval.

ABSOLUTE CURVILINEAR MOTION—CARTESIAN COORDINATES

1.11 The path of plane motion is given by $\mathbf{r}(t) = (bt)\mathbf{i} + (ct - gt^2/2)\mathbf{j}$, where b, c, g are known constants. Examine the motion.

Since $x(t) \neq 0$, $y(t) \neq 0$, but $z(t) = 0$, the motion is a plane curvilinear motion in the XY plane. By (1-17),

$$\mathbf{v} = \dot{\mathbf{r}} = b\mathbf{i} + (c - gt)\mathbf{j}$$
$$\mathbf{a} = \ddot{\mathbf{r}} = -g\mathbf{j}$$

and

$$r = [(bt)^2 + (ct - gt^2/2)^2]^{1/2}, \qquad v = [b^2 + (c - gt)^2]^{1/2}, \qquad a = g$$

If g is the acceleration due to gravity, $\mathbf{r}(t)$ represents the path of motion of a projectile having initial velocity $\mathbf{v}(0) = b\mathbf{i} + c\mathbf{j}$ (Fig. P-1.11).

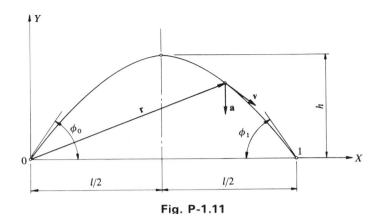

Fig. P-1.11

1.12   Using the results of Problem 1.11, determine the maximum height h of the path of motion of the projectile, the time t_l, distance l and velocity v_l of its landing (Fig. P-1.11).

The projectile touches the ground at 1 when
$$y(t) = ct - gt^2/2 = 0, \qquad x(t) = bt = l$$
from which $t_l = 2c/g$ and $l = 2bc/g$.

The final velocity of the projectile is $\mathbf{v}_l = b\mathbf{i} - c\mathbf{j}$, which must satisfy the condition
$$\tan \phi_0 = c/b = -\tan \phi_1$$
where ϕ_0 is the angle of path at 0 and ϕ_1 is its symmetrical counterpart at 1.

The maximum height is attained at $t_l/2 = c/g$ and is
$$h = y(t_l/2) = c^2/g - c^2/2g = c^2/2g$$
and its velocity there is $\mathbf{v}(t_l/2) = b\mathbf{i}$.

1.13   The path of a moving particle (Fig. P-1.13) is given by $\mathbf{r} = (R \cos \omega t)\mathbf{i} + (R \sin \omega t)\mathbf{j}$, where R and ω are constants.   Examine the motion.

By *(1-17)*, the velocity and acceleration are respectively

$$\mathbf{v} = \dot{\mathbf{r}} = (-R\omega \sin \omega t)\mathbf{i} + (R\omega \cos \omega t)\mathbf{j}$$
$$\mathbf{a} = \ddot{\mathbf{r}} = (-R\omega^2 \cos \omega t)\mathbf{i} - (R\omega^2 \sin \omega t)\mathbf{j} = -R\omega^2 \mathbf{r}$$

By *(1-18)*, the magnitudes of $\mathbf{r}$, $\mathbf{v}$, $\mathbf{a}$ are respectively

$$r = \sqrt{r_x^2 + r_y^2} = R\sqrt{(\cos \omega t)^2 + (\sin \omega t)^2} = R$$

$$v = \sqrt{v_x^2 + v_y^2} = R\sqrt{(-\sin \omega t)^2 + (\cos \omega t)^2} = R\omega$$

$$a = \sqrt{a_x^2 + a_y^2} = R\omega^2\sqrt{(-\cos \omega t)^2 + (\sin \omega t)^2} = R\omega^2$$

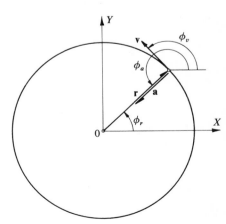

The slopes of $\mathbf{r}$, $\mathbf{v}$, $\mathbf{a}$ are respectively

$\tan \phi_r = r_y/r_x = (R \sin \omega t)/(R \cos \omega t) = \tan \omega t$
$\tan \phi_v = v_y/v_x = (R\omega \cos \omega t)/(-R\omega \sin \omega t) = -\cot \omega t$
$\tan \phi_a = a_y/a_x = (-R\omega^2 \sin \omega t)/(-R\omega^2 \cos \omega t) = \tan \omega t$

Fig. P-1.13

Since $\tan\phi_r \tan\phi_v = -1$, then $\mathbf{r}$ and $\mathbf{v}$ are perpendicular; this can be verified by $\mathbf{r}\cdot\mathbf{v} = 0$.

Since $\tan\phi_r = \tan\phi_a$, $\mathbf{r}$ and $\mathbf{a}$ are collinear but their vector expressions are of opposite signs. $\mathbf{a}$ is directed toward the center 0 from which $\mathbf{r}$ is measured and is therefore called the centripetal acceleration.

The path is a circle of radius R, the motion is uniform ($R\omega = $ constant); ω is called the angular speed, defined as the angle change per unit of time, $\dot\theta = d(\omega t)/dt = \omega$.

ABSOLUTE CURVILINEAR MOTION—POLAR COORDINATES

1.14 Derive the analytical relationships between the unit vectors $\mathbf{i}$, $\mathbf{j}$ of the cartesian system and the unit vectors $\mathbf{e}_r$, $\mathbf{e}_\theta$ of the polar system.

As $\mathbf{i}$, $\mathbf{j}$ are two normal vectors and $\mathbf{e}_r$, $\mathbf{e}_\theta$ are also two normal vectors, then from Fig. P-1.14 their relationships are given by the angular transformation matrices as

$$\begin{bmatrix}\mathbf{e}_r\\\mathbf{e}_\theta\end{bmatrix} = \begin{bmatrix}\cos\theta & \sin\theta\\-\sin\theta & \cos\theta\end{bmatrix}\begin{bmatrix}\mathbf{i}\\\mathbf{j}\end{bmatrix} \qquad \begin{bmatrix}\mathbf{i}\\\mathbf{j}\end{bmatrix} = \begin{bmatrix}\cos\theta & -\sin\theta\\\sin\theta & \cos\theta\end{bmatrix}\begin{bmatrix}\mathbf{e}_r\\\mathbf{e}_\theta\end{bmatrix} \qquad (1), (2)$$

As the particle moves, the magnitude and direction of $\mathbf{i}$, $\mathbf{j}$ remain constant but $\mathbf{e}_r$, $\mathbf{e}_\theta$ change their direction and magnitude, being always respectively collinear and normal to $\mathbf{r}$.

The time derivatives of (1) are

$$\dot{\mathbf{e}}_r = \dot\theta[(-\sin\theta)\mathbf{i} + (\cos\theta)\mathbf{j}] = \dot\theta\mathbf{e}_\theta$$
$$\dot{\mathbf{e}}_\theta = -\dot\theta[(\cos\theta)\mathbf{i} + (\sin\theta)\mathbf{j}] = -\dot\theta\mathbf{e}_r \qquad (3)$$

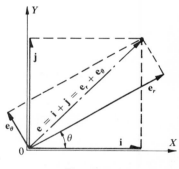

Fig. P-1.14

which are the relationships $(1$-$20)$.

In turn, the time derivatives of (2) must equal zero, i.e.

$$\mathbf{i} = \underbrace{\dot{\mathbf{e}}_r\cos\theta - \mathbf{e}_r\dot\theta\sin\theta}_{-\dot{\mathbf{e}}_\theta} - \underbrace{\dot{\mathbf{e}}_\theta\sin\theta - \mathbf{e}_\theta\dot\theta\cos\theta}_{\dot{\mathbf{e}}_r} = 0$$

$$\mathbf{j} = \underbrace{\dot{\mathbf{e}}_r\sin\theta + \mathbf{e}_r\dot\theta\cos\theta}_{-\dot{\mathbf{e}}_\theta} + \underbrace{\dot{\mathbf{e}}_\theta\cos\theta - \mathbf{e}_\theta\dot\theta\sin\theta}_{\dot{\mathbf{e}}_r} = 0 \qquad (4)$$

1.15 Derive the equations of plane motion $(1$-$19)$ in polar coordinates.

By definition,

$$\mathbf{r} = r\mathbf{e}_r$$
$$\mathbf{v} = \dot{\mathbf{r}} = \dot r\mathbf{e}_r + r\dot{\mathbf{e}}_r$$
$$\mathbf{a} = \dot{\mathbf{v}} = \ddot{\mathbf{r}} = \ddot r\mathbf{e}_r + \dot r\dot{\mathbf{e}}_r + \dot r\dot{\mathbf{e}}_r + r\ddot{\mathbf{e}}_r \qquad (1)$$

By (3) of Problem 1.14,

$$\dot{\mathbf{e}}_r = \dot\theta\mathbf{e}_\theta, \qquad \dot{\mathbf{e}}_\theta = -\dot\theta\mathbf{e}_r$$
$$\ddot{\mathbf{e}}_r = \ddot\theta\mathbf{e}_\theta + \dot\theta\dot{\mathbf{e}}_\theta = \ddot\theta\mathbf{e}_\theta - \dot\theta^2\mathbf{e}_r \qquad (2)$$

With (2), $\mathbf{v}$ and $\mathbf{a}$ in (1) become

$$\mathbf{v} = \dot r\mathbf{e}_r + r\dot\theta\mathbf{e}_\theta$$
$$\mathbf{a} = (\ddot r - r\dot\theta^2)\mathbf{e}_r + (r\ddot\theta + 2\dot r\dot\theta)\mathbf{e}_\theta$$

which are the desired equations $(1$-$19)$.

1.16 Using *(1-19)* derive the equations of plane circular motion.   Given: $r = R$, $\theta = \omega t$ where R, ω are constants.

First compute the derivatives of the position coordinates:

$$\dot{r} = \frac{d(R)}{dt} = 0, \qquad \ddot{r} = 0, \qquad \dot{\theta} = \frac{d(\omega t)}{dt} = \omega, \qquad \ddot{\theta} = 0$$

Then by *(1-19)*,

$$\mathbf{v} = \dot{r}\mathbf{e}_r + r\dot{\theta}\mathbf{e}_\theta = (0)\mathbf{e}_r + R\omega\mathbf{e}_\theta = R\omega\mathbf{e}_\theta$$
$$\mathbf{a} = (\ddot{r} - r\dot{\theta}^2)\mathbf{e}_r + (r\ddot{\theta} + 2\dot{r}\dot{\theta})\mathbf{e}_\theta = (0 - R\omega^2)\mathbf{e}_r + [R(0) + 2(0)(\omega)]\mathbf{e}_\theta = -R\omega^2\mathbf{e}_r$$

1.17 A particle moves along a spiral path given by $r = bt^2$ and $\theta = ct$, where b, c are given constants. Find the equations of this motion.

By *(1-19)*,

$$\mathbf{r} = bt^2\mathbf{e}_r$$
$$\mathbf{v} = \dot{r}\mathbf{e}_r + r\dot{\theta}\mathbf{e}_\theta = 2bt\mathbf{e}_r + bct^2\mathbf{e}_\theta$$
$$\mathbf{a} = (\ddot{r} - r\dot{\theta}^2)\mathbf{e}_r + (r\ddot{\theta} + 2\dot{r}\dot{\theta})\mathbf{e}_\theta = [2b - (bt^2)(c^2)]\mathbf{e}_r + [(bt^2)(0) + 2(2bt)(c)]\mathbf{e}_\theta$$
$$= b(2 - c^2t^2)\mathbf{e}_r + 4bct\mathbf{e}_\theta$$

The slopes with respect to $\mathbf{r}$ are

$$\tan\tau_v = v_\theta/v_r = bct^2/2bt = ct/2$$
$$\tan\tau_a = a_\theta/a_r = 4bct/b(2 - c^2t^2) = 4ct/(2 - c^2t^2)$$

which indicates that $\mathbf{v}$ is normal to $\mathbf{r}$ only for $t = \infty$ and $\mathbf{a}$ is normal to $\mathbf{r}$ only for $t = \sqrt{2}/c$.   For $t > \sqrt{2}/c$, the radial component of $\mathbf{a}$ is negative.

ABSOLUTE CURVILINEAR MOTION—CURVILINEAR COORDINATES

1.18 Derive the equations of plane motion in curvilinear coordinates *(1-21)*.

If the position vector of a particle is $\mathbf{r}(s)$ where $s = s(t)$ is the curvilinear coordinate measured along the path, then

$$\mathbf{v} = \dot{\mathbf{r}}(s) = \frac{d\mathbf{r}(s)}{ds}\frac{ds}{dt} = \dot{s}\mathbf{e}_t = v\mathbf{e}_t \tag{1}$$

where $\dot{s}$ is the speed and $\mathbf{e}_t = d\mathbf{r}(s)/ds$ is the unit tangent vector.
Similarly, from *(1)*,

$$\mathbf{a} = \ddot{\mathbf{r}}(s) = \dot{v}\mathbf{e}_t + v\dot{\mathbf{e}}_t \tag{2}$$

where $\dot{v} = d^2s/dt^2$ and $\dot{\mathbf{e}}_t = \dfrac{d\mathbf{e}_t}{ds}\dfrac{ds}{dt} = v\dfrac{d\mathbf{e}_t}{ds}$.

Since $\mathbf{e}_t \cdot \mathbf{e}_t = 1$, differentiation of this equation gives

$$\mathbf{e}_t \cdot \frac{d\mathbf{e}_t}{ds} + \frac{d\mathbf{e}_t}{ds} \cdot \mathbf{e}_t = 0 \qquad \text{or} \qquad 2\mathbf{e}_t \cdot \frac{d\mathbf{e}_t}{ds} = 0 \tag{3}$$

which shows that $\mathbf{e}_t$ and $d\mathbf{e}_t/ds$ are orthogonal vectors.

We denote

$$\frac{d\mathbf{e}_t}{d\theta} = \mathbf{e}_n \tag{4}$$

as the unit normal vector, and $d\mathbf{e}_t/(\rho\, d\theta) = d\mathbf{e}_t/ds = \mathbf{e}_n/\rho$. Then

$$\dot{\mathbf{e}}_t = \frac{d\mathbf{e}_t}{d\theta}\frac{d\theta}{dt} = \mathbf{e}_n\frac{d\theta}{ds}\frac{ds}{dt} = \mathbf{e}_n\frac{d\theta}{\rho\, d\theta}\dot{s} = \frac{v}{\rho}\mathbf{e}_n \tag{5}$$

In terms of (5), (2) becomes

$$\mathbf{a} = \dot{v}\mathbf{e}_t + (v^2/\rho)\mathbf{e}_n \tag{6}$$

Furthermore, using (4), the curvature of path is

$$\kappa = \frac{1}{\rho} = \frac{d\mathbf{e}_t/ds}{\mathbf{e}_n} = \left|\frac{d\mathbf{e}_t}{ds}\right| = \left|\frac{\dot{\mathbf{e}}_t}{\dot{s}}\right| \tag{7}$$

where $ds = \rho\, d\theta$.

From these derivations it may be concluded that the velocity vector $\mathbf{v}$ is tangential to the path and its magnitude is $v = \dot{s}$, whereas the acceleration vector $\mathbf{a}$ deviates from this tangent. Its tangential component $\mathbf{a}_t$ has magnitude $a_t = \dot{v} = \ddot{s}$ and its normal component has magnitude $a_n = v^2/\rho = \dot{s}^2/\rho$.

The magnitude of the acceleration is

$$a = \sqrt{a_t^2 + a_n^2} = [\dot{v}^2 + v^4/\rho^2]^{1/2} \tag{8}$$

1.19 A particle moves along the plane circular path given by $\mathbf{r} = R[(\cos \omega t)\mathbf{i} + (\sin \omega t)\mathbf{j}]$ where R, ω are given constants.   (a) Compute the unit vectors $\mathbf{e}_t$, $\mathbf{e}_n$ of this path in the curvilinear coordinate system.   (b) Find the velocity and acceleration vectors of the given circular motion.

(a) The time derivatives are

$$\dot{\mathbf{r}} = d\mathbf{r}/dt = -R\omega[(\sin \omega t)\mathbf{i} - (\cos \omega t)\mathbf{j}]$$

$$\dot{s} = ds/dt = \sqrt{\dot{x} + \dot{y}} = \sqrt{(-R\omega \sin \omega t)^2 + (R\omega \cos \omega t)^2} = R\omega$$

The tangent unit vector (1-21) is

$$\mathbf{e}_t = d\mathbf{r}/ds = \dot{\mathbf{r}}/\dot{s} = (-\sin \omega t)\mathbf{i} + (\cos \omega t)\mathbf{j}$$

The time derivative of $\mathbf{e}_t$ is

$$\dot{\mathbf{e}}_t = d\mathbf{e}_t/dt = -\omega[(\cos \omega t)\mathbf{i} + (\sin \omega t)\mathbf{j}]$$

The curvature κ (Problem 1.17) is

$$\kappa = \left|\frac{\dot{\mathbf{e}}_t}{\dot{s}}\right| = \sqrt{\left(\frac{-\cos \omega t}{R}\right)^2 + \left(\frac{-\sin \omega t}{R}\right)^2} = \frac{1}{R}$$

and the radius of curvature is $\rho = R$.

The normal unit vector (1-21) is

$$\mathbf{e}_n = \rho\, d\mathbf{e}_t/ds = \rho\dot{\mathbf{e}}_t/\dot{s} = (-\cos \omega t)\mathbf{i} - (\sin \omega t)\mathbf{k}$$

The analytical form of $\mathbf{e}_t$, $\mathbf{e}_n$ in terms of $\mathbf{i}$, $\mathbf{j}$ must be identical to that of Problem 1.14.

(b) By (1-21), the velocity and acceleration vectors are respectively

$$\mathbf{v} = v\mathbf{e}_t = \dot{s}\mathbf{e}_t = R\omega[(-\sin \omega t)\mathbf{i} + (\cos \omega t)\mathbf{j}]$$
$$\mathbf{a} = \dot{v}\mathbf{e}_t + v\dot{\mathbf{e}}_t = (0)\mathbf{e}_t + R\omega[(-\omega \cos \omega t)\mathbf{i} - (\omega \sin \omega t)\mathbf{j}]$$

Their magnitudes are $v = R\omega$, $a_t = 0$, $a_n = R\omega^2$.

RELATIVE MOTION

1.20   Referring to Fig. P-1.20, the position vector of car 2 traveling along X_B is given by $\mathbf{r}_{B2} = 60t\mathbf{i}$. Determine the linear and angular velocities and accelerations of this car with respect to a stationary observer posted at 1.

Linear equations of motion:

$$\mathbf{r}_{12} = 60t\mathbf{i} + 60\mathbf{j}, \qquad \dot{\mathbf{r}}_{12} = 60\mathbf{i}, \qquad \ddot{\mathbf{r}}_{12} = 0$$

Angular equations of motion:

$$\theta = \tan^{-1}\frac{60t}{60} = \tan^{-1} t, \qquad \dot{\theta} = \frac{d(\tan^{-1} t)}{dt} = \frac{1}{1 + t^2}, \qquad \ddot{\theta} = \frac{-2t}{(1 + t^2)^2}$$

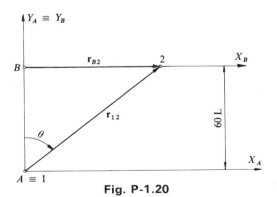

Fig. P-1.20   Fig. P-1.21

1.21   In Fig. P-1.21, the position vector of boat 2 traveling along X_B is $\mathbf{r}_{A2} = 80t^2\mathbf{i} + 60\mathbf{j}$ and the position vector of boat 1 circling around A is $\mathbf{r}_{A1} = 100[(\cos \omega t)\mathbf{i} + (\sin \omega t)\mathbf{j}]$.   Determine t and ω at which they collide (if such event is kinematically possible).

The vector condition of collision is $\mathbf{r}_{A1} = \mathbf{r}_{A2}$, which can be expressed algebraically as

$$r_{A1x} = r_{A2x} \qquad\qquad r_{A1y} = r_{A2y}$$
$$100 \cos \omega t = 80t^2 \qquad\qquad 100 \sin \omega t = 60$$

The solution is $t = 1\,\text{T}$, $\omega t = \cos^{-1} 0.8 = 53.1°$.

1.22   Consider (Fig. P-1.22) two airplanes flying at the same altitude along paths given by $\mathbf{r}_{A1} = 100t^2\mathbf{i} + 50t\mathbf{j}$ and $\mathbf{r}_{B2} = 200t^2\mathbf{i} - 100t\mathbf{j}$, respectively.   Find the relative position vector $\mathbf{r}_{12}$, relative velocity vector $\dot{\mathbf{r}}_{12}$, and relative acceleration vector $\ddot{\mathbf{r}}_{12}$ of these planes.

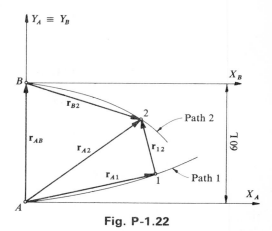

Fig. P-1.22

The position vector of airplane 2 relative to A is

$$\mathbf{r}_{A2} = \mathbf{r}_{AB} + \mathbf{r}_{B2} = 200t^2\mathbf{i} + (60 - 100t)\mathbf{j}$$

Then

$$\mathbf{r}_{12} = \mathbf{r}_{A2} - \mathbf{r}_{A1} = 100t^2\mathbf{i} + (60 - 150t)\mathbf{j}$$
$$\dot{\mathbf{r}}_{12} = 200t\mathbf{i} - 150\mathbf{j}$$
$$\ddot{\mathbf{r}}_{12} = 200\mathbf{i}$$

Problems

GEOMETRY OF PLANE PATH

1.23   For the hyperbolic plane path given by $x = a/\cos \omega t$ and $y = b \tan \omega t$, find $\dot{x}$, $\dot{y}$, $\ddot{x}$, $\ddot{y}$, ds and $\tan \phi$. $a, b, \omega =$ constants.

1.24   For the cycloidal plane path given by $x = R\omega t - b \sin \omega t$ and $y = R - b \cos \omega t$, find $\dot{x}$, $\dot{y}$, $\ddot{x}$, $\ddot{y}$, ds and $\tan \phi$. $R, b, \omega =$ constants.

1.25   For the elliptical plane path given by $x = a \cos \omega t$ and $y = b \sin \omega t$, find $\dot{x}$, $\dot{y}$, $\ddot{x}$, $\ddot{y}$, ds and $\tan \phi$. $a, b, \omega =$ constants.

1.26   For the hyperbolic plane path of Problem 1.23, find the equation of radius of curvature ρ and the coordinates of the center of curvature x_k, y_k.

1.27   For the cycloidal plane path of Problem 1.24, find the equation of the radius of curvature ρ and the coordinates of the center of curvature x_k, y_k.

1.28   For the elliptical plane path of Problem 1.25, find the equation of the radius of curvature ρ and the coordinates of the center of curvature x_k, y_k.

ABSOLUTE RECTILINEAR MOTION

1.29   The rectilinear motion of a particle is defined by $\mathbf{r}(t) = [(1 + 2t + 3t^2)\mathbf{i}]$ L.   Find the velocity and acceleration vector of this particle and compute its position, velocity and acceleration at $t = 10$ T.

1.30   The acceleration of a particle in rectilinear motion is $\mathbf{a} = 10$ L/T^2.   If the initial position vector is $\mathbf{r}_0 = [30\mathbf{i}]$ L and the initial velocity vector is $\mathbf{v}_0 = [50\mathbf{i}]$ L/T, find the general equations of this motion.

1.31   The uniformly decelerated motion of a particle is defined by $s(t) = v_0 t - at^2/2$.   Determine the time t_1 at which the particle will stop and the distance it will travel before it stops.

1.32   For the rectilinear motion of a particle given by $s(t) = s_0 + v_0 t + gt^2/2$, construct the kinematic transport matrix equation developed in Problem 1.10.

1.33   Using the results of Problem 1.32, compute the kinematic vectors at $t = 0, 2, 4$ sec.   Given: $s_0 = 0$, $v_0 = 10$ ft, $g = 32.2$ ft/sec^2.

1.34   For the rectilinear motion of a particle given by $s(t) = s_0 - v_0 t + gt^2/2$, construct the kinematic transport matrix equation developed in Problem 1.10.

1.35   Using the results of Problem 1.34, compute the kinematic vectors at $t = 0, 2, 4$ sec.   Given: $s_0 = 0$, $v_0 = 10$ ft, $g = 32.2$ ft/sec^2.

ABSOLUTE CURVILINEAR MOTION—CARTESIAN COORDINATES

1.36   A particle moves in an elliptical path $\mathbf{r} = (a \cos \omega t)\mathbf{i} + (b \sin \omega t)\mathbf{j}$.   Determine the velocity and acceleration vectors. a, b, ω = constants.

1.37   A particle moves on a hyperbola $\mathbf{r} = (a/\cos \omega t)\mathbf{i} + (b \tan \omega t)\mathbf{j}$.   Find the velocity and acceleration vectors. a, b, ω = constants.

1.38   The path of a particle is a cycloid $\mathbf{r} = (R\omega t - b \sin \omega t)\mathbf{i} + (R - b \cos \omega t)\mathbf{j}$.   Find the velocity and acceleration vectors. a, b, ω = constants.

1.39   A projectile is fired from a hill of height $h = 300$ m with the initial velocity $v_0 = 500$ m/sec at an angle $\phi_0 = 45°$ as shown in Fig. P-1.39.   Derive the algebraic equations of motion.   Consider $g = 9.8$ m/sec^2 and neglect air resistance.

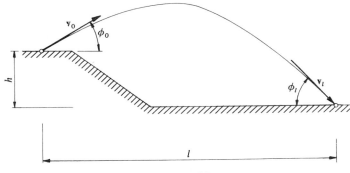

Fig. P-1.39

1.40   Referring to Fig. P-1.39, determine the distance l, speed v_l and time t_l of the landing.

1.41   Investigate the plane circular motion given by $\mathbf{r} = R[(\cos \omega t^2)\mathbf{i} + (\sin \omega t^2)\mathbf{j}]$.

ABSOLUTE CURVILINEAR MOTION—POLAR COORDINATES

1.42   A particle moves along a plane spiral path $r = a\theta$, $\theta = t^2$. Determine its velocity and acceleration vectors in polar coordinates. a = constant.

1.43   A particle moves along a plane curve defined as the lemniscate of Bernoulli (two-leaved rose, Fig. P-1.43) given by

$$r^2 = a^2 \cos 2\theta, \qquad \theta = t$$

Determine its velocity and acceleration vectors in polar coordinates. a = constant.

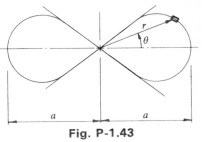

Fig. P-1.43

ABSOLUTE CURVILINEAR MOTION—CURVILINEAR COORDINATES

1.44   Derive the expressions of the unit tangent vector $\mathbf{e}_t$ and the unit normal vector $\mathbf{e}_n$ for the plane path given by $x = t^2$, $y = 4t$.

1.45   Derive the equations of motion for the plane elliptical path of Problem 1.25 in curvilinear coordinates.

1.46   Find the equations of motion for the plane hyperbolic path of Problem 1.23 in curvilinear coordinates.

1.47   Find the acceleration vector for the plane cycloidal path of Problem 1.24 in curvilinear coordinates.

RELATIVE MOTION

1.48   A ball is ejected vertically upward with an initial velocity 100 ft/sec. A second ball is ejected 4 seconds later with an initial velocity 200 ft/sec along the same vertical path.   Neglecting air resistance and taking $g = 32.2$ ft/sec^2, determine their relative position vector $\mathbf{r}_{21}$, their relative velocity $\mathbf{v}_{21}$, and the time of their collision.

1.49   The position vectors of two vehicles are given respectively by $\mathbf{r}_1 = (10t\mathbf{i} + 20t^2\mathbf{j})$ L   and $\mathbf{r}_2 = (-20t\mathbf{i} + 30t^2\mathbf{j})$ L.   Find the relative velocity $\dot{\mathbf{r}}_{12}$ and the relative acceleration $\ddot{\mathbf{r}}_{12}$ at $t = 10$ T.

1.50   In Fig. P-1.50, car 1 moves on a circular path of radius R with an angular velocity ω, and car 2 moves on a concentric elliptic path of $a = 3R$ and $b = 2R$ with the same angular velocity ω.   Compute the extreme values of $\dot{\mathbf{r}}_{12}$ and $\ddot{\mathbf{r}}_{12}$.

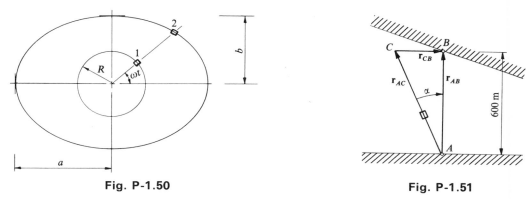

Fig. P-1.50

Fig. P-1.51

1.51   Determine the direction angle α the ferry boat of Fig. P-1.51 must take upstream in crossing the river of 600 m width if its own speed is 10 km/hr and the speed of the current is 5 km/hr.   Also compute the time and velocity of crossing.

1.52   Refer to Fig. P-1.52.   Compute the angle α and the initial speed v_m of the missile fired from the ground level at A, so that it will hit at $t = t_p$ an approaching airplane moving with constant speed v_p at constant altitude h.   Assume the firing occurs at $t = 0$ and when the plane is first observed in position $C(l,h)$.   Given: v_p, l, h, t_p, g.

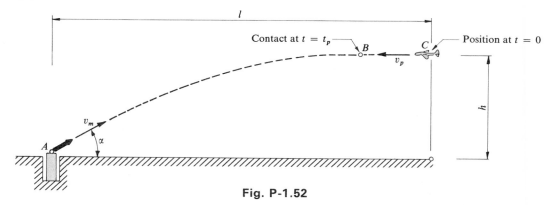

Fig. P-1.52

Chapter 2

Kinetics of Particles, Plane Motion

2.1 AXIOMS OF MECHANICS

Newton's Laws

Kinetics of particles, defined as the study of causes required to produce and/or sustain their motion, is based on Newton's laws of motion. Their verbal and analytical formulations (in modified form) are given below.

Definition 2.1: *Newton's First Law* A particle remains at rest or in a uniform rectilinear motion, unless compelled by unbalanced causes (forces and/or moments) to change this state.

Definition 2.2: *Newton's Second Law* The acceleration of a particle acted upon by an unbalanced cause (force or moment) is proportional to the magnitude of the cause and has its direction.   Analytically,

$$\mathbf{F} = \frac{d(m\mathbf{v})}{dt} = \frac{d\mathbf{G}}{dt} \qquad (2\text{-}1)$$

where m is the mass of the particle, $\mathbf{v}$ is its velocity vector, and $\mathbf{G} = m\mathbf{v}$ is its linear momentum.   If $m =$ constant,

$$\mathbf{F} = m\frac{d\mathbf{v}}{dt} = m\mathbf{a} \qquad (2\text{-}2)$$

where $\mathbf{a}$ is the acceleration of the particle.

Definition 2.3: *Newton's Third Law* The forces of action and reaction at the point of contact of two particles are equal in magnitude and opposite in direction.   Analytically,

$$\mathbf{F}_{ab} = \mathbf{F}_{ba}$$

where $\mathbf{F}_{ab}$ is the force of particle b acting on the particle a, and $\mathbf{F}_{ba}$ is the force of particle a acting on the particle b.

These laws presume the existence of a *basic frame of reference* with respect to which the motion is measured, and a *reference event* with respect to which the time is measured.   Although the theory of relativity caused a complete reformulation of Newtonian mechanics, Newton's laws provide a satisfactory conceptual basis for the dynamic analysis of mechanical systems when the velocities are far below that of light (3×10^8 m/sec).

Force and Mass

In *Newtonian mechanics*, the mass m of a particle is assumed to be a constant quantity,* determined experimentally from the relationship

$$m = W/g \qquad (2\text{-}3)$$

where W is the weight of the particle and g is the acceleration due to gravity.

For *engineering purposes*, g is taken as

$$g = 980\ \text{cm/sec}^2 \equiv 32.2\ \text{ft/sec}^2 \equiv 386\ \text{in/sec}^2 \qquad (2\text{-}4)$$

and its variation with geographical location is disregarded.

Although an exact *definition of force* is not available, the action of one particle on another, interpreted as the push or pull, is called force.

Kinetic Units

Table 2-1 gives four consistent systems of units. The MKS system is rapidly gaining universal preference, and the FPS system is rarely used.

Table 2-1   Systems of Units

	(A) Gravitational systems (length, time, force)		(B) Absolute systems (length, time, mass)	
	Metric units MKS	British units FPS	Metric units CGS	British units FPS
Length L	Meter (m)	Foot (ft)	Centimeter (cm)	Foot (ft)
Force F	Kilogram (kg)	Pound (lb)	Dyne	Poundal
Time T	Second (sec)	Second (sec)	Second (sec)	Second (sec)
Mass M	$(\text{kg})(\text{m})^{-1}(\text{sec})^2$	$(\text{lb})(\text{ft})^{-1}(\text{sec})^2$	Gram (g)	Pound (lb)

Three less familiar units are defined below:

Dyne   The force which when acting on 1 g of mass produces in it an acceleration of 1 cm/sec^2 is called a dyne (10^5 dynes $= 1$ newton).

Slug   The mass of a body weighing 32.2 lb at the earth's surface is called a slug.

Poundal   The force which when acting on 1 lb of mass produces in it an acceleration of 1 ft/sec^2 is called a poundal.

Conversion relationships between these systems of units are given in the Appendix.

---

*According to the theory of relativity, the mass is a function of the speed of the particle and approaches infinity as the speed of the particle approaches the speed of light. For the range of speeds of engineering systems the mass variation is completely insignificant and therefore the mass is considered constant.

2.2 EQUATIONS OF MOTION

Classification of Problems

In the kinetic analysis of particles in motion, three distinct types of problems occur:

(I) *Kinetic problem of the first kind*, in which the kinematics of motion is given and the causes of motion must be determined.

(II) *Kinetic problem of the second kind*, in which the causes of motion are given and the kinematics of motion must be determined.

(III) *Kinetic problem of the third kind*, in which only a part of each type of information is given and the remaining part must be determined (mixed problem).

The problems of the first and second kind are the prime concern of this chapter.

Problem of the First Kind

If $\mathbf{r}(t)$, $\mathbf{v}(t)$, $\mathbf{a}(t)$ and the mass m of the particle are known, the associated force (cause) is given by *(2-2)* as

$$\mathbf{F}(t) = m\ddot{\mathbf{r}}(t) \tag{2-5}$$

where $\mathbf{F}(t)$ is called the *force function* and $m\ddot{\mathbf{r}}(t)$ is the *inertial function*.

Problem of the Second Kind

If $\mathbf{F}$ and m are known, the acceleration of the particle is given by *(2-2)* as

$$\ddot{\mathbf{r}}(t) = \mathbf{F}/m \tag{2-6}$$

where

$$\mathbf{F} = \mathbf{F}(t, s, \dot{s}, \ddot{s}) \tag{2-7}$$

may be one or several functions.

According to the analytical form of $\mathbf{F}$, several distinct forms of *(2-6)* are recognized and listed in Table 2-2.

Table 2-2 Governing Equations—Problem of the Second Kind

Case	Causes	Equations	Problems
1	$\mathbf{F}$ is a constant	$\ddot{\mathbf{r}}(t) = \mathbf{C}/m$	2.1–2.8
2	$\mathbf{F}$ is a function of time	$\ddot{\mathbf{r}}(t) = \mathbf{F}(t)/m$	2.9–2.10
3	$\mathbf{F}$ is a function of position	$\ddot{\mathbf{r}}(t) = \mathbf{F}(s)/m$	2.11–2.12
4	$\mathbf{F}$ is a function of velocity	$\ddot{\mathbf{r}}(t) = \mathbf{F}(\dot{s})/m$	2.13–2.14

Note: Additional cases may be obtained by superposition. For example, $\ddot{\mathbf{r}}(t) = [\mathbf{F}_1(t) + \mathbf{F}_2(s)]/m$, etc.

2.3   MOMENTUM AND IMPULSE

Linear Momentum

Definition 2.4: The *linear momentum* **G** of a particle in motion is the product of its mass m and its velocity **v**.

$$\mathbf{G} = m\mathbf{v} = m\dot{\mathbf{r}} \qquad (2\text{-}8)$$

Definition 2.5: The *time derivative* $\dot{\mathbf{G}}$ *of the linear momentum* of a particle in motion is by (*2-1*) the force **F** causing the motion.

$$\dot{\mathbf{G}} = m\dot{\mathbf{v}} = m\ddot{\mathbf{r}} = \mathbf{F} \qquad (2\text{-}9)$$

Angular Momentum

Definition 2.6: The *angular momentum* **H** of a particle in motion is the vector product of its position vector **r** and its linear momentum **G**.

$$\mathbf{H} = \mathbf{r} \times \mathbf{G} = (\mathbf{r} \times \mathbf{v})m = (\mathbf{r} \times \dot{\mathbf{r}})m \qquad (2\text{-}10)$$

Definition 2.7: The *time derivative* $\dot{\mathbf{H}}$ *of the angular momentum* of a particle in motion is by (*2-1*) the moment **M** causing the motion.

$$\dot{\mathbf{H}} = \mathbf{r} \times \dot{\mathbf{G}} = \mathbf{r} \times \mathbf{F} = \mathbf{M} \qquad (2\text{-}11)$$

Conservation of Momentum

If the resultant of forces acting on a particle in motion is zero ($\mathbf{F} = 0$), then

$$\dot{\mathbf{G}} = m\dot{\mathbf{v}} = \mathbf{F} = 0 \qquad \text{and} \qquad \mathbf{G} = \text{constant} \qquad (2\text{-}12)$$

which leads to the principle of conservation of linear momentum stated below.

Definition 2.8: The *linear momentum* **G** of a particle in motion *is conserved* (is constant) if the resultant of forces acting on the particle is zero.

If the resultant of moments acting on a particle in motion is zero ($\mathbf{M} = 0$), then

$$\dot{\mathbf{H}} = \mathbf{r} \times \dot{\mathbf{G}} = \mathbf{M} = 0 \qquad \text{and} \qquad \mathbf{H} = \text{constant} \qquad (2\text{-}13)$$

which leads to the principle of conservation of angular momentum stated below.

Definition 2.9: The *angular momentum* **H** of a particle in motion *is conserved* if the resultant of moments acting on the particle is zero.

Linear Impulse

The *time integral of the force* **F** acting on a particle in motion between limits t_1 and t_2, called the linear impulse, is

$$\int_{t_1}^{t_2} \mathbf{F}\, dt = \int_{t_1}^{t_2} \dot{\mathbf{G}}\, dt = m[\mathbf{v}_2 - \mathbf{v}_1] = \mathbf{G}_2 - \mathbf{G}_1 \qquad (2\text{-}14)$$

where $\mathbf{v}_1$, $\mathbf{v}_2$ and $\mathbf{G}_1$, $\mathbf{G}_2$ are the velocities and linear momenta of the particle at t_1 and t_2 respectively.

Definition 2.10: The *linear impulse* of a particle in motion corresponding to the time interval $t_2 - t_1$ is the change in its linear momentum during this time interval.

Angular Impulse

The *time integral of the moment* **M** acting on a particle in motion between limits t_1 and t_2, called the angular impulse, is

$$\int_{t_1}^{t_2} \mathbf{M} \, dt = \int_{t_1}^{t_2} \dot{\mathbf{H}} \, dt = \mathbf{r}_2 \times \mathbf{G}_2 - \mathbf{r}_1 \times \mathbf{G}_1 = \mathbf{H}_2 - \mathbf{H}_1 \qquad (2\text{-}15)$$

where $\mathbf{r}_1$, $\mathbf{r}_2$ and $\mathbf{H}_1$, $\mathbf{H}_2$ are the position vectors and angular momenta of the particle at t_1 and t_2 respectively.

Definition 2.11: The *angular impulse* of a particle in motion corresponding to the time interval $t_2 - t_1$ is the change in its angular momentum during this time interval.

2.4   POWER, WORK, ENERGY

Power

By definition, the scalar product of the force **F** acting on a particle in motion and its velocity **v**, is called the *power P*, i.e.

$$P = \mathbf{F} \cdot \mathbf{v} = d(\tfrac{1}{2}mv^2)/dt = \dot{T} \qquad (2\text{-}16)$$

where v is the speed.

Kinetic Energy

By definition, the scalar function T in (*2-16*) is called the *kinetic energy* of the particle (energy of motion), i.e.

$$T = \tfrac{1}{2}mv^2 \qquad \text{or} \qquad T = \tfrac{1}{2}m\mathbf{v} \cdot \mathbf{v} \qquad (2\text{-}17)$$

Definition 2.12: The *power* of the resultant force on a particle equals the time rate of change in the kinetic energy of the particle.

Mechanical Work and Kinetic Energy

The *total mechanical work U* done by the force **F** in moving a particle along a given path from 1 to 2 is defined analytically by the following three integrals.

(*a*) *Displacement Integral:*

$$U = \int_{s_1}^{s_2} \mathbf{F} \cdot d\mathbf{r} = \tfrac{1}{2}m(v_2^2 - v_1^2) = T_2 - T_1 \qquad (2\text{-}18a)$$

where s_1, s_2 are the curvilinear coordinates of 1, 2 respectively, v_1, v_2 are the initial and terminal speeds respectively, and $T_2 - T_1$ is the change in kinetic energy.

(*b*) *Velocity Integral:*

$$U = \int_{v_1}^{v_2} \mathbf{G} \cdot d\mathbf{v} = \tfrac{1}{2}m(v_2^2 - v_1^2) = T_2 - T_1 \qquad (2\text{-}18b)$$

where **G** is the linear momentum (*2-8*) and v_1, v_2, T_1, T_2 have the same meaning as in (*2-18a*).

(*c*) *Time Integral:*

$$U = \int_{t_1}^{t_2} P \, dt = \tfrac{1}{2}m(v_2^2 - v_1^2) = T_2 - T_1 \tag{2-18c}$$

where P is the power (*2-6*) and v_1, v_2, T_1, T_2 have again the same meaning as in (*2-18a*).

The identity of these results leads to

Definition 2.13: The *total mechanical work done* by the force **F** in moving the particle along a given path from 1 to 2 equals the *change in kinetic energy*.

$$U = T_2 - T_1 \tag{2-18}$$

Mechanical Work and Potential Energy

In general the value of the line integral in (*2-18a*) depends on the path of integration and consequently this path must be known in advance. A special case arises when the force **F** is a function of position only and the product **F** · *d***r** is an exact differential. In such a case the *force field* is said to be *conservative* and in cartesian coordinates

$$\mathbf{F} = -\nabla V(x,y) = -\frac{\partial V(x,y)}{\partial x}\mathbf{i} - \frac{\partial V(x,y)}{\partial y}\mathbf{j} \tag{2-19}$$

where $V(x,y)$ is called the *potential energy* (energy of position) and ∇ is a differential operator called the *gradient*.

The work integral (*2-18a*) can be then expressed as

$$U = \int_{s_1}^{s_2} \mathbf{F} \cdot d\mathbf{r} = -\int_{x_1}^{x_2} \frac{\partial V(x,y)}{\partial x}\,dx - \int_{y_1}^{y_2} \frac{\partial V(x,y)}{\partial y}\,dy = -\int_{s_1}^{s_2} dV(x,y) = V_1 - V_2 \tag{2-20}$$

where $(V_1 - V_2)$ is the *change in potential energy* of **F** as it moves from 1 to 2.

The interpretation of (*2-20*) leads to the following conclusions.

Definition 2.14: The total mechanical work done by the force defined by (*2-19*) in moving the particle from 1 to 2 is *independent of path* and equals the negative change in potential energy (Fig. 2-1).

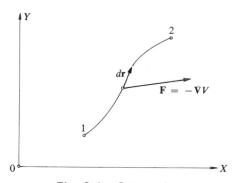

Fig. 2-1 Open path.

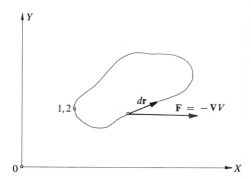

Fig. 2-2 Closed path.

Definition 2.15: The total mechanical work done by the force defined by (*2-19*) in moving the particle along a *closed path* (1 $\equiv$ 2) equals zero (Fig. 2-2).

$$\oint \mathbf{F} \cdot d\mathbf{r} = 0 \qquad\qquad (2\text{-}21)$$

Conservation of Energy

When a particle is acted upon by a force defined by (*2-19*), the *work-energy equations* (*2-18*) and (*2-20*) may be combined into

$$T_2 - T_1 = V_1 - V_2 \qquad \text{or} \qquad T_1 + V_1 = T_2 + V_2 \qquad\qquad (2\text{-}22)$$

where the sum of kinetic and potential energy $T_1 + V_1 = E$, $T_2 + V_2 = E$ is called the *total energy E.*

Definition 2.16: In a *conservative force field* the total energy remains constant (principle of conservation of energy).

Illustrative Problems

EQUATIONS OF MOTION, CONSTANT FORCE

2.1 Consider a particle of mass m acted upon by a force of constant magnitude and direction in the XY plane. Derive the scalar form of its equations of motion. Given: F_x, F_y = constant components of force, x_0, y_0 = position coordinates at $t = 0$, $\dot{x}_0, \dot{y}_0$ = velocities at $t = 0$ (Fig. P-2.1).

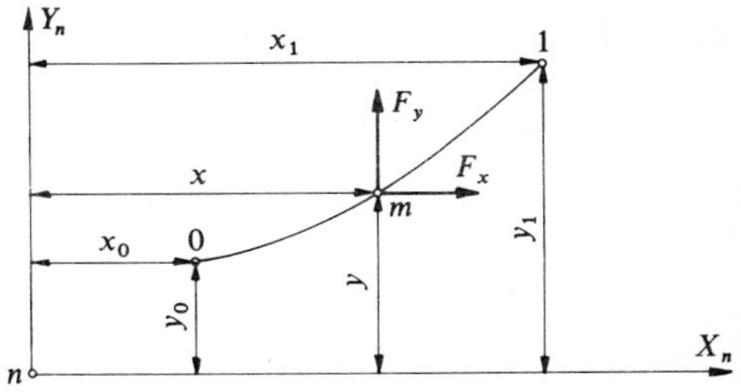

Fig. P-2.1

By (*2-6*),

$$\ddot{x} = F_x/m = \ddot{x}_0 \qquad\qquad \ddot{y} = F_y/m = \ddot{y}_0 \qquad\qquad (1a, b)$$

Integrating,

$$\dot{x} = A_1 + \ddot{x}_0 t \qquad\qquad \dot{y} = B_1 + \ddot{y}_0 t \qquad\qquad (2a, b)$$
$$x = A_1 t + A_2 + \ddot{x}_0 t^2/2 \qquad\qquad y = B_1 t + B_2 + \ddot{y}_0 t^2/2 \qquad\qquad (3a, b)$$

At $t = 0$, $x = x_0$, $\dot{x} = \dot{x}_0$, $\ddot{x} = \ddot{x}_0$, $y = y_0$, $\dot{y} = \dot{y}_0$, $\ddot{y} = \ddot{y}_0$. Then from (*2*), $A_1 = \dot{x}_0$, $B_1 = \dot{y}_0$; from (*3*), $A_2 = x_0$, $B_2 = y_0$. Hence

$$\dot{x} = \dot{x}_0 + \ddot{x}_0 t \qquad\qquad \dot{y} = \dot{y}_0 + \ddot{y}_0 t \qquad\qquad (4a, b)$$
$$x = x_0 + \dot{x}_0 t + \ddot{x}_0 t^2/2 \qquad\qquad y = y_0 + \dot{y}_0 t + \ddot{y}_0 t^2/2 \qquad\qquad (5a, b)$$

2.2 Compute the time t_1 required for the particle of Problem 2.1 to attain a speed v_1. Given: initial velocities $\dot{x}_0, \dot{y}_0$; constant accelerations $\ddot{x}_0, \ddot{y}_0$; and the speed v_1 at $t = t_1$.

By (4) of Problem 2.1,

$$t_1 = (\dot{x}_1 - \dot{x}_0)/\ddot{x}_0 \qquad\qquad t_1 = (\dot{y}_1 - \dot{y}_0)/\ddot{y}_0 \tag{1}$$

where $\dot{x}_1, \dot{y}_1$ are the components of the given speed and are related by

$$v_1 = \sqrt{\dot{x}_1^2 + \dot{y}_1^2} \tag{2}$$

From (1),

$$\dot{x}_1 = \dot{x}_0 + \ddot{x}_0 t_1 \qquad\qquad \dot{y}_1 = \dot{y}_0 + \ddot{y}_0 t_1 \tag{3}$$

which when put into (2) yields

$$v_1^2 = \dot{x}_0^2 + 2\dot{x}_0\ddot{x}_0 t_1 + \ddot{x}_0^2 t_1^2 + \dot{y}_0^2 + 2\dot{y}_0\ddot{y}_0 t_1 + \ddot{y}_0^2 t_1^2$$

$$0 = t_1^2 \underbrace{(\ddot{x}_0^2 + \ddot{y}_0^2)}_{a^2} + 2t_1 \underbrace{(\dot{x}_0\ddot{x}_0 + \dot{y}_0\ddot{y}_0)}_{b^2} + \underbrace{(\dot{x}_0^2 + \dot{y}_0^2) - v_1^2}_{c^2} \tag{4}$$

and so in terms of a, b, c the required time is

$$t_1 = \frac{-b^2 \pm \sqrt{b^4 - a^2c^2}}{a^2} \tag{5}$$

2.3   Reduce Problem 2.1 to the rectilinear motion of Fig. P-2.3.   Given: $F_x = F, x_0, \dot{x}_0$, all constant.

The equations of motion are

$$x = x_0 + \dot{x}_0 t + Ft^2/2m = x_0 + \dot{x}_0 t + \ddot{x}_0 t^2/2 \tag{1}$$

$$\dot{x} = \dot{x}_0 + Ft/m = \dot{x}_0 + \ddot{x}_0 t \tag{2}$$

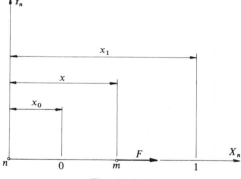

Fig. P-2.3

The time required to attain velocity $v_1 = \dot{x}_1$ is, from (2),

$$t_1 = (\dot{x}_1 - \dot{x}_0)/\ddot{x}_0 \tag{3}$$

which is the reduced equation (5) of Problem 2.2.
In turn, the velocity $\dot{x}_1$ at t_1 is, from (1) and (2),

$$\dot{x}_1 = x_1/t_1 - x_0/t_1 + \ddot{x}_0 t_1/2$$

which in terms of (3) is

$$\dot{x}_1 = \sqrt{2\ddot{x}_0(x_1 - x_0) + \dot{x}_0^2} \tag{4}$$

For $x_0 = 0, \dot{x}_0 = 0, \dot{x}_1 = \sqrt{2\ddot{x}_0 x_1}$.

2.4   An object of mass m is released at 0 (Fig. P-2.4) at the elevation h above the ground and falls freely.   Neglecting air resistance, find its equations of motion.   Given: m, h and g (acceleration due to gravity).

By (2-6), where $F = W = mg$, we have $m\ddot{y} = W$ and $\ddot{y} = g$.

By (4) and (5) of Problem 2.1 and with $y_0 = 0$, $\dot{y}_0 = 0$, $\ddot{y}_0 = g$, we get $\dot{y} = gt$, $y = gt^2/2$.

The time of landing (when $y = h$) is $t_1 = \sqrt{2h/g}$ and the velocity of landing is $\dot{y} = gt_1 = \sqrt{2gh}$.

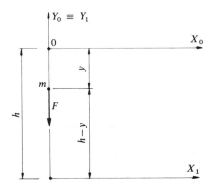 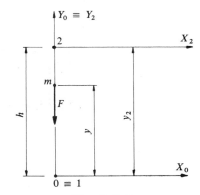

Fig. P-2.4   **Fig. P-2.5**

2.5   An object of mass m is ejected vertically upward from the base at ground level with velocity $\dot{y}_0$ (Fig. P-2.5). Neglecting air resistance, find the equations of motion. Given: $m, g, \dot{y}_0$.

By (2-6), where $F = -W = -mg$,

$$m\ddot{y} = -W \qquad \text{and} \qquad \ddot{y} = -g \qquad (1)$$

By (4) and (5) of Problem 2.1 and with $y_0 = 0$, $\dot{y}_0 \neq 0$,

$$\dot{y} = \dot{y}_0 - gt, \qquad y = \dot{y}_0 t - gt^2/2 \qquad (2),(3)$$

The mass will reach a point where $\dot{y} = 0$ and then fall freely. From (2) above,

$$0 = \dot{y}_0 - gt_2 \qquad \text{or} \qquad t_2 = \dot{y}_0/g \qquad (4)$$

is the time required to reach the highest point. The vertical coordinate y_2 of this point is given by (3) as

$$y_2 = \dot{y}_0 t_2 - gt_2^2/2 = \dot{y}_0^2/g - g\dot{y}_0^2/2g^2 = \dot{y}_0^2/2g$$

The time for the descent is given by the free-fall equation of Problem 2.4, with $h = y_2$,

$$t_1 = \sqrt{2y_2/g} = \sqrt{2\dot{y}_0^2/2g^2} = \dot{y}_0/g$$

which must give the velocity of landing equal to the velocity of ejection, i.e.

$$\dot{y}_1 = gt_1 = \dot{y}_0$$

The velocity in terms of y is given by (4) of Problem 2.3 where the Y axis is substituted for the X axis and the acceleration is $-g$, i.e.

$$\dot{y} = \sqrt{\dot{y}_0^2 - 2gy}$$

2.6 A projectile of mass m is fired with initial velocity v_0 at an angle ϕ_0 with the horizontal (Fig. P-2.6). Find the equations of motion.   Given: m, g, v_0, ϕ_0.

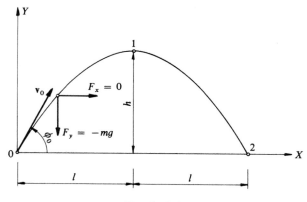

Fig. P-2.6

By (2-6), with $F_x = 0$, $F_y = -mg$,

$$m\ddot{x} = 0 \qquad\qquad m\ddot{y} = -mg \qquad\qquad (1a, b)$$

By (4) and (5) of Problem 2.1 and with $\dot{x}_0 = v_0 \cos \phi_0$, $\dot{y}_0 = v_0 \sin \phi_0$, $x_0 = 0$, $y_0 = 0$,

$$\dot{x} = v_0 \cos \phi_0 \qquad\qquad \dot{y} = v_0 \sin \phi_0 - gt \qquad\qquad (2a, b)$$

$$x = (v_0 \cos \phi_0)t \qquad\qquad y = (v_0 \sin \phi_0)t - gt^2/2 \qquad\qquad (3a, b)$$

Solving (3a) for t and substituting in (3b), the equation of the trajectory (path) is

$$y = x \tan \phi_0 - \frac{gx^2}{2v_0^2 \cos^2 \phi_0} \qquad\qquad (4)$$

which is the equation of a parabola with axis parallel to the Y axis.

2.7 Investigate the properties of the trajectory of the projectile in Problem 2.6.

At the vertex $1(x_1, y_1)$ of the trajectory given by (4) of Problem 2.6,

$$\frac{dy}{dx} = \frac{d}{dx}\left(x \tan \phi_0 - \frac{gx^2}{2v_0^2 \cos^2 \phi_0}\right) = \tan \phi_0 - \frac{gx}{v_0^2 \cos^2 \phi_0} = 0 \qquad (1)$$

The coordinates of 1, computed from the above equation and from (4) of Problem 2.6, are

$$x_1 = \frac{v_0^2}{2g} \sin 2\phi_0 = l, \qquad y_1 = \frac{v_0^2}{2g} \sin^2 \phi_0 = h \qquad\qquad (2a, b)$$

The time t_1 required to reach vertex 1 and the time t_2 required to hit point 2 on the ground are computed by (3a) of Problem 2.6 and (2a) of this problem and are found to be

$$t_1 = l/(v_0 \cos \phi_0), \qquad t_2 = 2l/(v_0 \cos \phi_0)$$

The distance $\overline{02} = 2l$, called the range, is $2l = (v_0^2/g) \sin 2\phi_0$.

2.8   Investigate the effect of ϕ_0 on the motion of the projectile in Problem 2.6 (Fig. P-2.8).

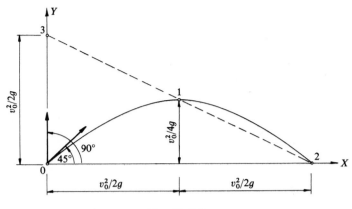

Fig. P-2.8

(a) For $\phi_0 = 0$, the solutions of Problems 2.6 and 2.7 are not applicable.

(b) For $\phi_0 = \pi/4$,

$$x_1 = v_0^2/2g, \qquad y_1 = v_0^2/4g,$$
$$2l = v_0^2/g, \qquad t_2 = v_0\sqrt{2}/g \quad \text{(maximum range)}$$

(c) For $\phi_0 = \pi/2$,

$$x_1 = 0, \qquad y_1 = v_0^2/2g,$$
$$2l = 0, \qquad t_2 = 2v_0/g \quad \text{(maximum time)}$$

Case (c) is equivalent to Problem 2.5.

EQUATIONS OF MOTION, F(t)

2.9   Consider a particle of mass m acted upon by a force whose direction and magnitude vary with time.   Derive the scalar form of equations of motion for this particle.   Given: $F_x = F_x(t)$, $F_y = F_y(t)$, x_0, y_0, $\dot{x}_0$, $\dot{y}_0$ and m.

By (2-6),

$$\ddot{x} = (1/m)F_x(t) \qquad\qquad \ddot{y} = (1/m)F_y(t) \qquad\qquad (1a, b)$$

Integrating,

$$\dot{x} = \frac{1}{m}\int_0^t F_x(t)\, dt + A_1 \qquad\qquad \dot{y} = \frac{1}{m}\int_0^t F_y(t)\, dt + B_1 \qquad (2a, b)$$

$$x = \frac{1}{m}\int_0^t\int_0^t F_x(t)\, dt\, dt + A_1 t + A_2 \qquad y = \frac{1}{m}\int_0^t\int_0^t F_y(t)\, dt\, dt + B_1 t + B_2 \qquad (3a, b)$$

At $t = 0$, $x = x_0$, $\dot{x} = \dot{x}_0$, $y = y_0$, $\dot{y} = \dot{y}_0$.

From (2), $A_1 = \dot{x}_0$, $B_1 = \dot{y}_0$; from (3), $A_2 = x_0$, $B_2 = y_0$. Then the equations of motion are

$$\dot{x} = \dot{x}_0 + \frac{1}{m}\int_0^t F_x(t)\,dt \qquad\qquad \dot{y} = \dot{y}_0 + \frac{1}{m}\int_0^t F_y(t)\,dt \qquad\qquad (4a, b)$$

$$x = x_0 + \dot{x}_0 t + \frac{1}{m}\int_0^t\int_0^t F_x(t)\,dt\,dt \qquad\qquad y = y_0 + \dot{y}_0 t + \frac{1}{m}\int_0^t\int_0^t F_y(t)\,dt\,dt \qquad (5a, b)$$

2.10 Using the general equations of motion derived in Problem 2.9 investigate the motion produced by $F_x = F\cos\omega t$, $F_y = F\sin\omega t$, where ω is a given constant. Initial conditions are: $x_0 = 0$, $y_0 = 0$, $\dot{x}_0 = 0$, $\dot{y}_0 = 0$, and m is a given constant.

By (1), (2) and (3) of Problem 2.9, and with the given initial conditions,

$$\ddot{x} = (F/m)\cos\omega t \qquad\qquad \ddot{y} = (F/m)\sin\omega t$$
$$\dot{x} = (F/m\omega)\sin\omega t \qquad\qquad \dot{y} = (F/m\omega)(1 - \cos\omega t)$$
$$x = (F/m\omega^2)(1 - \cos\omega t) \qquad\qquad y = (F/m\omega^2)(\omega t - \sin\omega t)$$

The position vector is

$$\mathbf{r} = \underbrace{x_1\mathbf{i} + y_1\mathbf{j}}_{\substack{\text{uniform}\\\text{rectilinear}\\\text{motion}}} + \underbrace{x_2\mathbf{i} + y_2\mathbf{j}}_{\substack{\text{uniform}\\\text{circular}\\\text{motion}}}$$

where $x_1 = F/m\omega^2$, $y_1 = (F/m\omega^2)\omega t$, $x_2 = -(F/m\omega^2)\cos\omega t$, $y_2 = -(F/m\omega^2)\sin\omega t$.

EQUATIONS OF MOTION, F(s)

2.11 Consider a particle of mass m acted upon by a force whose direction and magnitude vary with position. Derive the scalar form of the equations of motion of this particle. Given: $F_x = F(x)$, $F_y = F(y)$, $x_0, y_0, \dot{x}_0, \dot{y}_0$ and m.

By (2-6),

$$\ddot{x} = (1/m)F(x) \qquad\qquad \ddot{y} = (1/m)F(y) \qquad\qquad (1a, b)$$

Since the force components are functions of x and y, the integration must be performed with respect to these variables. For this purpose,

$$\ddot{x} = \frac{dv_x}{dt} = \frac{dv_x}{dx}\frac{dx}{dt} = v_x\frac{dv_x}{dx} \qquad\qquad \ddot{y} = \frac{dv_y}{dt} = \frac{dv_y}{dy}\frac{dy}{dt} = v_y\frac{dv_y}{dy} \qquad (2a, b)$$

and so equations (1) become

$$v_x\,dv_x/dx = (1/m)F(x) \qquad\qquad v_y\,dv_y/dy = (1/m)F(y) \qquad\qquad (3a, b)$$

Integrating,

$$v_x^2/2 = \frac{2}{m}\int_0^x F(x)\,dx + A_1 \qquad\qquad v_y^2/2 = \frac{1}{m}\int_0^y F(y)\,dy + B_1$$

$$v_x = \frac{dx}{dt} = \underbrace{\sqrt{\frac{2}{m}\int_0^x F(x)\,dx + 2A_1}}_{\psi(x)} \qquad v_y = \frac{dy}{dt} = \underbrace{\sqrt{\frac{2}{m}\int_0^y F(y)\,dy + 2B_1}}_{\psi(y)} \qquad (4a,b)$$

from which

$$t = \int_0^x \frac{dx}{\psi(x)} \qquad\qquad t = \int_0^y \frac{dy}{\psi(y)} \qquad (5a,b)$$

where A_1, B_1 must be determined from the initial conditions of motion (Problem 2.12).

2.12 A particle of mass m is attached to the linear springs of stiffness k as shown in Fig. P-2.12. Derive its equations of motion in terms of the initial conditions x_0, y_0, $\dot{x}_0$, $\dot{y}_0$.

First allow the particle to move downward by

$$y_{st} = (W/2k)\cos\alpha$$

under the action of its weight.

Then select this position of static equilibrium as the datum of motion, from which x_0, y_0, $\dot{x}_0$, $\dot{y}_0$ but also x, y, $\dot{x}$, $\dot{y}$, $\ddot{x}$, $\ddot{y}$ are measured. At this new position,

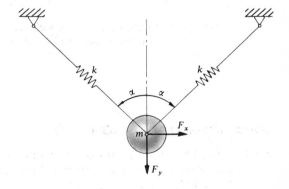

Fig. P-2.12

$$F_x = -(2k\sin\alpha)x \qquad \text{and} \qquad F_y = -(2k\cos\alpha)y$$

and by (1) of Problem 2.11,

$$\ddot{x} = \underbrace{-(1/m)(2k\sin\alpha)}_{\lambda_x^2}x \qquad\qquad \ddot{y} = \underbrace{-(1/m)(2k\cos\alpha)}_{\lambda_y^2}y \qquad (1a,b)$$

By (4) of Problem 2.11,

$$v_x^2/2 = -\lambda_x^2(x^2 - x_0^2)/2 + A_1 \qquad\qquad v_y^2/2 = -\lambda_y^2(y^2 - y_0^2)/2 + B_1 \qquad (2a,b)$$

where $A_1 = v_{0x}^2/2 = \dot{x}_0^2/2$ and $B_1 = v_{0y}^2/2 = \dot{y}_0^2/2$.

From these equations,

$$\frac{dx}{dt} = \sqrt{\dot{x}_0^2 - \lambda_x^2(x^2 - x_0^2)} \qquad\qquad \frac{dy}{dt} = \sqrt{\dot{y}_0^2 - \lambda_y^2(y^2 - y_0^2)} \qquad (3a,b)$$

By (5) of Problem 2.11,

$$dt = \frac{dx}{\sqrt{\dot{x}_0^2 - \lambda_x^2(x^2 - x_0^2)}} \qquad\qquad dt = \frac{dy}{\sqrt{\dot{y}_0^2 - \lambda_y^2(y^2 - y_0^2)}}$$

$$t = (1/\lambda_x)\left[\sin^{-1}\tau_x x - \sin^{-1}\tau_x x_0\right] \qquad t = (1/\lambda_y)\left[\sin^{-1}\tau_y y - \sin^{-1}\tau_y y_0\right] \qquad (4a, b)$$

where $\tau_x = \dfrac{1}{\sqrt{\dot{x}_0^2/\lambda_x^2 + x_0^2}}$ and $\tau_y = \dfrac{1}{\sqrt{\dot{y}_0^2/\lambda_y^2 + y_0^2}}$.

Solving for x and y in (4),

$$x = (1/\tau_x)\sin(\lambda_x t + \phi_x) \qquad\qquad y = (1/\tau_y)\sin(\lambda_y t + \phi_y) \qquad (5a, b)$$

where*

$$\phi_x = \sin^{-1}\tau_x x_0 = \tan^{-1}(\lambda_x x_0/\dot{x}_0) \qquad \phi_y = \sin^{-1}\tau_y y_0 = \tan^{-1}(\lambda_y y_0/\dot{y}_0)$$

are the phase angles, i.e. for $t = 0$ we have $\sin\phi_x = \tau_x x_0$, $\sin\phi_y = \tau_y y_0$.

These equations define the free plane vibration of the particle of mass m and are further studied in Chapter 11.

EQUATIONS OF MOTION, $F(\dot{s})$

2.13 Consider a particle of mass m acted upon by a force whose direction and magnitude vary with the velocity of motion. Derive the scalar form of its equations of motion. Given: $F_x = F(\dot{x})$, $F_y = F(\dot{y})$, x_0, y_0, $\dot{x}_0$, $\dot{y}_0$ and m.

By (2-6),

$$\ddot{x} = (1/m)F(\dot{x}) \qquad\qquad \ddot{y} = (1/m)F(\dot{y}) \qquad\qquad (1a, b)$$

Since the force components are functions of $\dot{x} = v_x$, $\dot{y} = v_y$, the integrations (as in Problem 2.11) must be performed with respect to these variables. Thus

$$dv_x/dt = (1/m)F(v_x) \qquad\qquad dv_y/dt = (1/m)F(v_y) \qquad\qquad (2a, b)$$

from which

$$t = m\int_{v_{0x}}^{v_x} \frac{dv_x}{F(v_x)} \qquad\qquad t = m\int_{v_{0y}}^{v_y} \frac{dv_y}{F(v_y)} \qquad\qquad (3a, b)$$

where $v_{0x} = \dot{x}_0$ and $v_{0y} = \dot{y}_0$.

---

*J. J. Tuma, "Engineering Mathematics Handbook", McGraw-Hill, New York, 1970, p. 73.

From (3),

$$v_x = dx/dt = \phi_x(t) \qquad\qquad v_y = dy/dt = \phi_y(t) \qquad\qquad (4a, b)$$

and

$$x - x_0 = \int_0^t \phi_x(t)\, dt \qquad\qquad y - y_0 = \int_0^t \phi_y(t)\, dt \qquad\qquad (5a, b)$$

2.14 Consider the motion of the projectile of Problem 2.6 moving in a medium offering a resistance linearly proportional to the velocity of motion. Given: m, g, v_0, ϕ_0, and c = constant of resistance.

By (2-6), with $F_x = -c\dot{x}$, $F_y = -c\dot{y} - mg$,

$$m\ddot{x} = -c\dot{x} \qquad\qquad m\ddot{y} = -c\dot{y} - mg \qquad\qquad (1a, b)$$

By (2) and (3) of Problem 2.13,

$$d\dot{x}/dt = -(1/m)c\dot{x} \qquad\qquad d\dot{y}/dt = -(1/m)c\dot{y} - g$$

and by integration

$$t = -\frac{m}{c} \int_{\dot{x}_0}^{\dot{x}} \frac{d\dot{x}}{\dot{x}} = -\frac{m}{c} \ln\left(\frac{\dot{x}}{\dot{x}_0}\right) \qquad\qquad t = -\frac{m}{c} \int_{\dot{y}_0}^{\dot{y}} \frac{d\dot{y}}{\dot{y} + mg/c} = -\frac{m}{c} \ln\left(\frac{\dot{y} + mg/c}{\dot{y}_0 + mg/c}\right) \qquad (2a, b)$$

or

$$\dot{x} = \dot{x}_0 e^{-ct/m} \qquad\qquad \dot{y} = -\frac{mg}{c} + \left(\dot{y}_0 + \frac{mg}{c}\right) e^{-ct/m} \qquad\qquad (3a, b)$$

where $\dot{x}_0 = v_0 \cos\phi_0$ and $\dot{y}_0 = v_0 \sin\phi_0$.
By integration,

$$x = x_0 + (m\dot{x}_0/c)(1 - e^{-ct/m}) \qquad\qquad (4a)$$
$$y = y_0 - mgt/c + (m/c)(\dot{y}_0 + mg/c)(1 - e^{-ct/m}) \qquad\qquad (4b)$$

LINEAR MOTION WITH CONSTRAINTS

2.15 A force P acts on a block of weight $W = mg$ moving up along the inclined plane of Fig. P-2.15. Neglecting friction, determine the equations of motion of the block with respect to 0. Given: P, m, g, α, x_0, $\dot{x}_0$.

By (2-6), in the X_n, Y_n system,

$$F_x = P \cos\alpha - mg \sin\alpha, \qquad\qquad F_y = -P \sin\alpha - mg \cos\alpha + N = 0 \qquad\qquad (1)$$

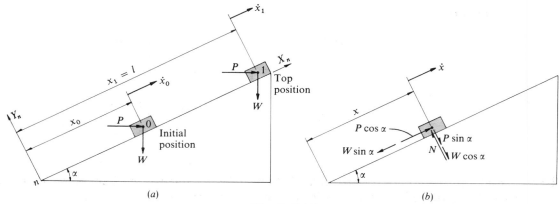

Fig. P-2.15

where N is the constraint (reaction of the plane), and

$$\ddot{x} = (P \cos \alpha - mg \sin \alpha)/m \tag{2}$$
$$\dot{x} = (P \cos \alpha - mg \sin \alpha)t/m + A_1 \qquad\qquad A_1 = \dot{x}_0 \tag{3}$$
$$x = (P \cos \alpha - mg \sin \alpha)t^2/2m + A_1 t + A_2 \qquad A_2 = x_0 \tag{4}$$

For a tangential force along the inclined plane, replace $P \cos \alpha$ by P and $P \sin \alpha$ by zero.

2.16 Consider Problem 2.15 for the special condition $P \cos \alpha > mg \sin \alpha$ and find the time t_1 and the velocity x_1 at which the block reaches the top of the plane. Given: $P, m, g, \alpha, x_0, \dot{x}_0$, and $x_1 = l$.

For $x_0 > 0$, $\dot{x}_0 > 0$ and $P \cos \alpha > mg \sin \alpha$, the velocity given by (3) of Problem 2.15 is

$$\dot{x} = \underbrace{(P \cos \alpha - mg \sin \alpha)t/m}_{F_1} + \dot{x}_0$$

The time t_1 required for the block to reach the top at a distance l from n given by (4) of Problem 2.15 is

$$t_1 = (-\dot{x}_0 + \sqrt{\dot{x}_0^2 - 2F_1(x_0 - l)/m})/(F_1/m)$$

which for $x_0 = 0$, $\dot{x}_0 = 0$, is $t_1 = \sqrt{2ml/F_1}$.
The velocity at t_1 is

$$\dot{x}_1 = \sqrt{\dot{x}_0^2 - 2F_1(x_0 - l)/m}$$

which, for $x_0 = 0$ and $\dot{x}_0 = 0$, is $\dot{x}_1 = \sqrt{2F_1 l/m}$, and $\dot{x}_1 t_1/2$ must equal l.

2.17 Consider Problem 2.16 for the specific condition $P \cos \alpha < mg \sin \alpha$ and find the time t_2 at which the block will stop on the way up.

For $x_0 > 0$, $\dot{x}_0 > 0$ and $P \cos \alpha < mg \sin \alpha$, the time of $\dot{x}_2 = 0$ computed from (3) of Problem 2.15 is

$$t_2 = \dot{x}_0 m/\underbrace{(mg \sin \alpha - P \cos \alpha)}_{F_2}$$

and the position, by (4) of Problem 2.15, is

$$x_2 = -F_2 t_2^2/2m + \dot{x}_0 t_2 + x_0 = \dot{x}_0^2 m/2F_2 + x_0$$

where $x_2 < l$.   For $x_2 > l$ the block overruns the top without stopping.

If $F_2 = 0$, the block remains in motion with constant velocity $\dot{x}_0$, $t_2 = \infty$, $x_2 = \infty$, and again the block overruns the top without stopping.

CIRCULAR MOTION WITH CONSTRAINTS

2.18   A block of weight $W = mg$ acted upon by a force $P = mg(1 + \cos \theta)$ moves along a cylindrical surface of radius $R + e$ in a plane normal to the axis of the cylinder as shown in Fig. P-2.18a. Neglecting friction, derive the equations of motion of this block in polar coordinates.   Given: m, g, R, θ_0, $\dot{\theta}_0$.

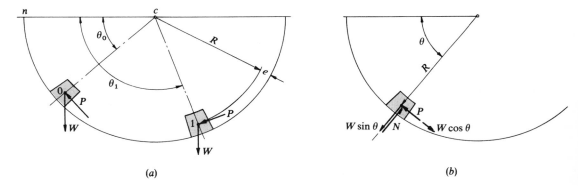

(a)   (b)

Fig. P-2.18

From Fig. P-2.18b,

$$F_\theta = mg \cos \theta - mg(1 + \cos \theta) = -mg \tag{1}$$
$$F_R = mg \sin \theta - N \quad (N = \text{constraint}) \tag{2}$$

and by (2-6) in polar coordinates

$$mR\ddot{\theta} = -mg \quad \text{or} \quad \ddot{\theta} = -g/R$$
$$\dot{\theta} = -(g/R)t + \dot{\theta}_0, \quad \theta = -(g/R)t^2/2 + \dot{\theta}_0 t + \theta_0 \tag{3},(4)$$

where θ_0 and $\dot{\theta}_0$ are given constants.

For $P = 0$, (1) becomes $mR\ddot{\theta} = mg \cos \theta$.   Solution of this differential equation is shown in Problem 4.11, page 91.

2.19   Determine the time t_1 and the angle θ_1 at which the block of Problem 2.18 stops.

For $\theta_1 = 0$, equation (3) of Problem 2.18 becomes

$$0 = -(g/R)t_1 + \dot{\theta}_0 \quad \text{and so} \quad t_1 = R\dot{\theta}_0/g$$

In terms of t_1, equation (3) of Problem 2.18 gives the angle θ_1 at which the block stops:

$$\theta_1 = -(g/R)t_1^2/2 + \dot\theta_0 t_1 + \theta_0 = -(g/R)(R^2\dot\theta_0^2/2g^2) + \dot\theta_0(R\dot\theta_0/g) + \theta_0 = \dot\theta_0^2 R/2g + \theta_0$$

For $R = 100$ ft, $g = 32.2$ ft/sec^2, $\dot\theta_0 = 0.500$ rad/sec, $\theta_0 = 0.873$ rad, we get $t_1 = 1.55$ sec, $\theta_1 = 1.261$ rad, where $\theta_0 = 50°$ and $\theta_1 = 72.2°$.

FUNCTION RESISTANCE

2.20 Include the effect of kinetic friction (Fig. P-2.20) in the equations of motion of Problem 2.15. Given: P, m, g, α, x_0, $\dot x_0$, and μ_k = coefficient of kinetic friction.

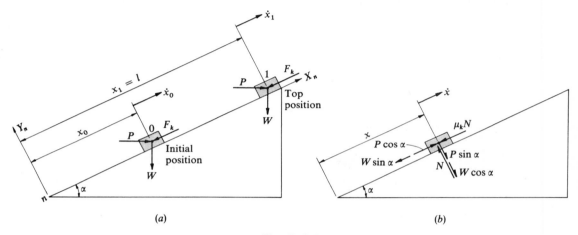

Fig. P-2.20

The friction force is

$$F_k = N\mu_k = (P \sin \alpha + mg \cos \alpha)\mu_k$$

and must be included in (2) of Problem 2.15.   Then

$$\ddot x = \underbrace{[P(\cos \alpha - \mu_k \sin \alpha) - mg(\sin \alpha + \mu_k \cos \alpha)]}_{F}/m \tag{1}$$

$$\dot x = (F/m)t + \dot x_0 \tag{2}$$

$$x = (F/m)t^2/2 + \dot x_0 t + x_0 \tag{3}$$

For a tangential force acting along the inclined plane, $F = P - mg(\sin \alpha + \mu_k \cos \alpha)$ in (1), (2) and (3).

2.21 A block of weight W slides from rest at 0 under its weight down an inclined plane $\overline{01}$, and stops at 2 on a horizontal plane $\overline{12}$ as shown in Fig. P-2.21.   Determine the position coordinate of point 2, x_2, measured from 1 on the horizontal plane.   Assume the terminal velocity of the block on $\overline{01}$, $\dot s_1$, equals the initial velocity on $\overline{12}$, $\dot x_1$.   Given: $01 = l = 100$ m, $g = 9.8$ m/sec^2, $\alpha = \pi/4$, $\mu_k = 0.3$ = coefficient of kinetic friction.

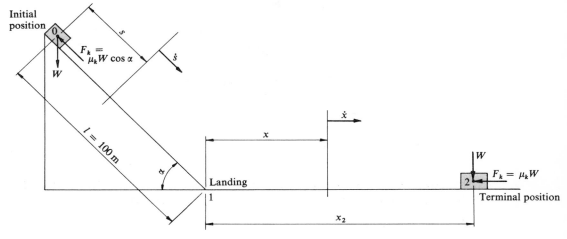

Fig. P-2.21

The equations of motion on the $\overline{01}$ plane are

$$\ddot{s} = (mg \sin \alpha - \mu_k mg \cos \alpha)/m = a \qquad\qquad (1)$$
$$\dot{s} = at, \qquad s = at^2/2 \qquad\qquad (2),(3)$$

where $a = g(\sin \alpha - \mu_k \cos \alpha)$.

The equations of motion on the $\overline{12}$ plane are

$$\ddot{x} = -(\mu_k mg)/m = -b \qquad\qquad (4)$$
$$\dot{x} = -bt + \dot{x}_1, \qquad x = -bt^2/2 + \dot{x}_1 t \qquad\qquad (5),(6)$$

where $b = \mu_k g$ and by definition, $\dot{x}_1 = \dot{s}_1 = at_1$.

The time of sliding from 0 to 1 is, by (3),

$$t_1 = \sqrt{2s_1/a} = \sqrt{2l/a}$$

where $s_1 = \overline{01} = l$.

The block stops at 2 when, by (5),

$$\dot{x}_2 = 0 = -bt_2 + \dot{x}_1 = -bt_2 + at_1 \qquad \text{or} \qquad t_2 = at_1/b = \sqrt{2al}/b$$

The position of 2 is, by (6),

$$x_2 = -bt_2^2/2 + \dot{x}_1 t_2 = al/b = l(\sin \alpha - \mu_k \cos \alpha)/\mu_k$$

For $l = 100$ m, $\sin 45° = \cos 45° = 0.707$, $\mu_k = 0.3$, $x_2 = \dfrac{100(0.707 - 0.3 \times 0.707)}{0.3} = 165$ m.

MOMENTUM AND IMPULSE

2.22 A mass of 1000 kg moves on a straight path from the initial speed 1000 m/sec to 2000 m/sec in 10 sec. Compute the linear impulse required to produce this change (kg_m = mass of 1 kg).

By (2-2) and (2-14), the linear impulse is

$$\text{L.I.} = \int_{t_1}^{t_2} F(t)\, dt = \int_{t_1}^{t} \frac{d}{dt}(mv)\, dt = \left[mv \right]_{t_1}^{t_2} = mv_2 - mv_1$$

where $mv_1 = G_1$, $mv_2 = G_2$ are the linear momenta at t_1, t_2 respectively.
Here $G_1 = (1000)(1000) = 10^6$ kg$_m$-m/sec, $G_2 = (1000)(2000) = 2 \times 10^6$ kg$_m$-m/sec and

$$\text{L.I.} = G_2 - G_1 = 10^6 \text{ kg}_m\text{-m/sec}$$

which shows that the time $t = 10$ sec is not required for this form of calculation of L.I.

2.23 A mass of 1000 kg moves on a straight path under the action of a force of 1×10^5 kg for 10 sec. If its velocity at $t = 10$ sec is 2000 m/sec, what was its initial velocity?

The linear impulse (2-14) is

$$\text{L.I.} = \int_0^{10} (1 \times 10^5)\, dt = 1 \times 10^6 = m(v_2 - v_1)$$

Since $v_2 = 2000$ m/sec, $m = 1000$ kg$_m$, we obtain $v_1 = 1000$ m/sec.

2.24 The position vector of a mass of 1000 kg is $\mathbf{r} = [10t^2\mathbf{i} + 20t\mathbf{j}]$ m. Determine its linear momentum at $t_1 = 10$ sec and $t_2 = 20$ sec, the corresponding forces and their linear impulse.

The velocity vector is

$$\dot{\mathbf{r}} = [20t\mathbf{i} + 10\mathbf{j}] \text{ m/sec}$$

The linear momenta (2-8) are

$$\mathbf{G}_1 = (1000)(20t_1\mathbf{i} + 10\mathbf{j}) = 1000[200\mathbf{i} + 10\mathbf{j}] \text{ kg}_m\text{-m/sec}$$
$$\mathbf{G}_2 = (1000)(20t_2\mathbf{i} + 10\mathbf{j}) = 1000[400\mathbf{i} + 10\mathbf{j}] \text{ kg}_m\text{-m/sec}$$

The corresponding forces (2-9) are

$$\mathbf{F} = \dot{\mathbf{G}} = m\ddot{\mathbf{r}} = (20{,}000\mathbf{i}) \text{ kg} = \mathbf{F}_1 = \mathbf{F}_2$$

which in turn must satisfy the linear impulse equation (2-14):

$$\text{L.I.} = \int_{t_1}^{t_2} \mathbf{F}\, dt = \left[(20{,}000t)\mathbf{i} \right]_{10}^{20} = [200{,}000\mathbf{i}] \text{ kg}_m\text{-m/sec}$$

2.25 Determine the angular momenta in Problem 2.24 at $t_1 = 10$ sec and $t_2 = 20$ sec, the corresponding moments and the angular impulse.

The angular momenta (2-10) are

$$\mathbf{H} = \mathbf{r} \times \mathbf{G} = \begin{vmatrix} \mathbf{i} & \mathbf{j} & \mathbf{k} \\ 10t^2 & 10t & 0 \\ 20{,}000t & 10{,}000 & 0 \end{vmatrix} = [(-100{,}000t^2)\mathbf{k}] \text{ kg}_m\text{-m}^2\text{/sec}$$

$$\mathbf{H}_1 = \mathbf{r}_1 \times \mathbf{G}_1 = [-10 \times 10^6 \mathbf{k}] \text{ kg}_m\text{-m}^2\text{/sec}, \qquad \mathbf{H}_2 = \mathbf{r}_2 \times \mathbf{G}_2 = [-40 \times 10^6 \mathbf{k}] \text{ kg}_m\text{-m}^2\text{/sec}$$

The angular impulse (*2-15*) is

$$\text{A.I.} = \mathbf{H}_2 - \mathbf{H}_1 = (-30 \times 10^6 \mathbf{k}) \, \text{kg}_m\text{-m}^2/\text{sec}$$

The corresponding moments (*2-11*) are

$$\mathbf{M} = \dot{\mathbf{H}} = \mathbf{r} \times \mathbf{F} = \begin{vmatrix} \mathbf{i} & \mathbf{j} & \mathbf{k} \\ 10t^2 & 10t & 0 \\ 20{,}000 & 0 & 0 \end{vmatrix} = [(-2 \times 10^5 t)\mathbf{k}] \, \text{kg-m}$$

$$\mathbf{M}_1 = [-2 \times 10^6 \mathbf{k}] \, \text{kg-m}, \qquad \mathbf{M}_2 = [-4 \times 10^6 \mathbf{k}] \, \text{kg-m}$$

which in turn must satisfy the angular impulse equation (*2-15*):

$$\text{A.I.} = \int_{t_1}^{t_2} \mathbf{M} \, dt = \left[(-2 \times 10^5 t^2/2)\mathbf{k} \right]_{10}^{20} = [-30{,}000\mathbf{k}] \, \text{kg}_m\text{-m}^2/\text{sec}$$

WORK AND ENERGY

2.26 Derive the displacement integral form of the work-energy equation (*2-18a*) for a particle of mass m.

By definition the force is $\mathbf{F} = m\ddot{\mathbf{r}}$ and the corresponding elemental work is $dU = \mathbf{F} \cdot d\mathbf{r}$ where $d\mathbf{r}$ is the element of path motion.

The total work between 1 and 2 (two arbitrary points of path) is

$$U = \int_{s_1}^{s_2} \mathbf{F} \cdot d\mathbf{r} = \int_{s_1}^{s_2} m\ddot{\mathbf{r}} \cdot d\mathbf{r}$$

$$= \int_{t_1}^{t_2} \left(m\frac{d\dot{\mathbf{r}}}{dt} \cdot \frac{d\mathbf{r}}{dt} \right) dt = \int_{t_1}^{t_2} \left(m\frac{d\mathbf{v}}{dt} \cdot \mathbf{v} \right) dt = m\int_{v_1}^{v_2} \dot{\mathbf{v}} \cdot d\mathbf{v} \qquad (1)$$

$$= \tfrac{1}{2}m\int_{v_1}^{v_2} d(\mathbf{v} \cdot \mathbf{v}) = m\left[v^2/2 \right]_{v_1}^{v_2} = \tfrac{1}{2}m(v_2^2 - v_1^2)$$

where s, t, v are the position coordinate, time and speed respectively and the subscripts 1, 2 identify the stations.

Since $T = \tfrac{1}{2}mv^2$ is by definition called the kinetic energy,

$$U = \int_{v_1}^{s_2} \mathbf{F} \cdot d\mathbf{r} = \tfrac{1}{2}m(v_2^2 - v_1^2) = T_2 - T_1 \qquad (2)$$

where T_1, T_2 are the kinetic energies at 1, 2 respectively.

2.27 Derive the velocity integral form of the work-energy equation for a particle of mass m.

By definition the linear momentum is $\mathbf{G} = m\mathbf{v}$ and the corresponding elemental work is $dU = \mathbf{G} \cdot d\mathbf{v}$ where $d\mathbf{v}$ is the elemental velocity.

The total work between 1 and 2 is

$$U = \int_{v_1}^{v_2} \mathbf{G} \cdot d\mathbf{v} = m \int_{v_1}^{v_2} \mathbf{v} \cdot d\mathbf{v} = \tfrac{1}{2}m(v_2^2 - v_1^2) \tag{1}$$

where the evaluation of the integral follows the pattern of Problem 2.26.   As before,

$$U = \int_{v_1}^{v_2} \mathbf{G} \cdot d\mathbf{v} = \tfrac{1}{2}m(v_2^2 - v_1^2) = T_2 - T_1 \tag{2}$$

2.28 Derive the time integral form of the work-energy equation $(2\text{-}18c)$ for a particle of mass m.

By definition the power is $P = \mathbf{F} \cdot \mathbf{v}$ and the corresponding elemental work is $dU = P\,dt$ where dt is the elemental time.

The total work between 1 and 2 is

$$U = \int_{t_1}^{t_2} P\,dt = \int_{t_1}^{t_2} \mathbf{F} \cdot \mathbf{v}\,dt = m \int_{t_1}^{t_2} \dot{\mathbf{v}} \cdot \mathbf{v}\,dt = m \int_{v_1}^{v_2} \mathbf{v} \cdot d\mathbf{v} = \tfrac{1}{2}m(v_2^2 - v_1^2) \tag{1}$$

where the evaluation of the integral follows the pattern of Problem 2.26.   Then

$$U = \int_{t_1}^{t_2} P\,dt = \tfrac{1}{2}m(v_2^2 - v_1^2) = T_2 - T_1 \tag{2}$$

2.29 Express the work-energy equations $(2\text{-}18a, b, c)$ in the cartesian system.

(a) *Displacement Integral:*

$$\mathbf{F} = F_x\mathbf{i} + F_y\mathbf{j}, \qquad d\mathbf{r} = dx\,\mathbf{i} + dy\,\mathbf{j}$$

$$U = \int_{s_1}^{s_2} \mathbf{F} \cdot d\mathbf{r} = \int_{x_1}^{x_2} F_x\,dx + \int_{y_1}^{y_2} F_y\,dy$$

$$= m \int_{t_1}^{t_2} \frac{d\dot{x}}{dt}\frac{dx}{dt}\,dt + m \int_{t_1}^{t_2} \frac{d\dot{y}}{dt}\frac{dy}{dt}\,dt$$

$$= m \int_{v_1}^{v_2} v_x\,dv_x + m \int_{v_1}^{v_2} v_y\,dv_y = \tfrac{1}{2}m(v_{2x}^2 - v_{1x}^2) + \tfrac{1}{2}m(v_{2y}^2 - v_{1y}^2)$$

$$= T_{2x} - T_{1x} + T_{2y} - T_{1y} = T_2 - T_1$$

(b) *Velocity Integral:*

$$\mathbf{G} = G_x\mathbf{i} + G_y\mathbf{j}, \qquad d\mathbf{v} = dv_x\,\mathbf{i} + dv_y\,\mathbf{j}$$

$$U = \int_{v_1}^{v_2} \mathbf{G} \cdot d\mathbf{v} = \int_{v_{1x}}^{v_{2x}} G_x\,dv_x + \int_{v_{1y}}^{v_{2y}} G_y\,dv_y$$

$$= m \int_{v_{1x}}^{v_{2x}} v_x \, dv_x + m \int_{v_{1y}}^{v_{2y}} v_y \, dv_y = \tfrac{1}{2}m(v_{2x}^2 - v_{1x}^2) + \tfrac{1}{2}m(v_{2y}^2 - v_{1y}^2)$$

$$= T_{2x} - T_{1x} + T_{2y} - T_{1y} = T_2 - T_1$$

(c)   *Time Integral:*

$$P = \mathbf{F} \cdot \mathbf{v} = F_x v_x + F_y v_y, \qquad dv_x = \dot{v}_x \, dt, \qquad dv_y = \dot{v}_y \, dt$$

$$U = \int_{t_1}^{t_2} P \, dt = \int_{t_1}^{t_2} F_x v_x \, dt + \int_{t_1}^{t_2} F_y v_y \, dt$$

$$= m \int_{t_1}^{t_2} \dot{v}_x v_x \, dt + m \int_{t_1}^{t_2} \dot{v}_y v_y \, dt = m \int_{v_{1x}}^{v_{2x}} v_x \, dv_x + m \int_{v_{1y}}^{v_{2y}} v_y \, dv_y$$

$$= \tfrac{1}{2}m(v_{2x}^2 - v_{1x}^2) + \tfrac{1}{2}m(v_{2y}^2 - v_{1y}^2) = T_{2x} - T_{1x} + T_{2y} - T_{1y} = T_2 - T_1$$

2.30   Figure P-2.30 shows a block of mass m moving along the X axis and pushed by a force $\mathbf{F}$ of magnitude 200 kg and whose line of action passes through point 2 on the Y axis.   Compute the work done between $x = 0$ and $x = +20$ m.

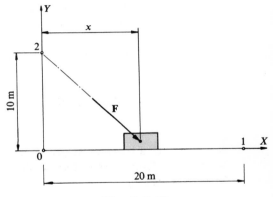

Fig. P-2.30

$$\mathbf{F} = \frac{200x}{\sqrt{x^2 + 100}}\, \mathbf{i} - \frac{2000}{\sqrt{x^2 + 100}}\, \mathbf{j}$$

$$\mathbf{r} = x\mathbf{i}, \qquad d\mathbf{r} = dx\, \mathbf{i}$$

$$U = \int_0^{20} \mathbf{F} \cdot d\mathbf{r} = \int_0^{20} \frac{200x \, dx}{\sqrt{x^2 + 100}}$$

$$= \left[200\sqrt{x^2 + 100} \right]_0^{20} = 2482 \text{ m-kg}$$

2.31   Using (2-18a), compute the velocity of a freely falling body dropped from a height $h = 100$ ft.

By (2-18a),

$$U = T_2 - T_1 \tag{1}$$

where

$$U = \int_0^h mg \, dy = hmg \tag{2}$$

$$T_2 = \tfrac{1}{2}mv_2^2 \neq 0, \qquad T_1 = \tfrac{1}{2}mv_1^2 = 0, \qquad T_2 - T_1 = \tfrac{1}{2}mv_2^2 \tag{3}$$

Then (1) in terms of (2) and (3) is

$$mgh = \tfrac{1}{2}mv_2^2 \qquad \text{and} \qquad v_2 = \sqrt{2hg} = \sqrt{2 \times 100 \times 32.2} = 80.25 \text{ ft/sec}$$

2.32 Refer to Fig. P-2.32. Compute the work required to move the block of mass m, constrained horizontally by a linear spring along the frictionless path parallel to the X axis, from $x = a$ to $x = b$. Given: $a, b, m,$ and $k =$ spring constant.

The force required to move the block is $F = k(x - a)$. The mechanical work is

$$U = \int_a^b k(x - a)\, dx = \left[k(x^2/2 - ax)\right]_a^b$$

$$= k(b^2/2 - ab - a^2/2 + a^2) = \tfrac{1}{2}k(b^2 - 2ab + a^2) = kl^2/2$$

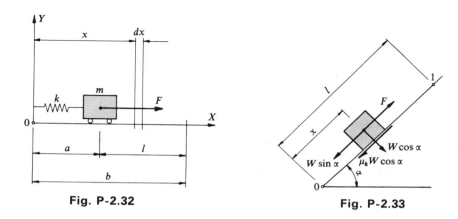

Fig. P-2.32   Fig. P-2.33

2.33 In Fig. P-2.33, a block of weight W is moving up under the action of force F on the inclined plane of angle α. Considering friction, determine the work required to move the block from 0 to 1. Given: W, α, l, μ_k.

The force F required for motion is

$$F = W \sin \alpha + \mu_k W \cos \alpha$$

By (2-18a),

$$U = \int_0^l F\, dx = W(\sin \alpha + \mu_k \cos \alpha)l$$

2.34 Referring to Problem 2.6, find by (2-18a) the terminal velocity of the projectile. Given: $v_1 =$ initial speed, $W =$ weight of projectile.

By (2-18a), $U = T_2 - T_1$ where $U = -\int_0^y W\, dy$, $T_2 - T_1 = \dfrac{1}{2}\dfrac{W}{g}(v_2^2 - v_1^2)$. Then

$$-Wy = \frac{W}{2g}(v_2^2 - v_1^2)$$

from which for $y = 0$, $v_2 = v_1$ (note v_1 in this problem equals v_0 in Problem 2.6).

2.35 A steel chain of weight mg and length $l = l_1 + l_2$ is placed as shown in Fig. P-2.35.   Neglecting friction, determine the velocity with which it will begin its free fall after slipping over the corner of the concrete wall.

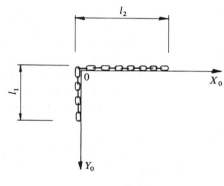

Fig. P-2.35

By (2-18a),

$$U = T_2 - T_1 \qquad (1)$$

where

$$U = \int_0^{l_2} (l_1 + y)(mg/l)\, dy = \left[(mg/l)(l_1 y + y^2/2) \right]_0^{l_2}$$

$$= (mg/l)(l_1 l_2 + l_2^2/2) = (mg/l)(l^2 - l_1^2)/2 \qquad (2)$$

In terms of the final velocity v_2 and the initial velocity $v_1 = 0$,

$$T_2 - T_1 = \tfrac{1}{2}mv_2^2 \qquad (3)$$

Then (1) in terms of (2) and (3) is $(mg/l)(l^2 - l_1^2)/2 = \tfrac{1}{2}mv_2^2$ from which $v_2 = \sqrt{g(l^2 - l_1^2)/l}$.

POTENTIAL ENERGY

2.36 Show that a necessary and sufficient condition for $\mathbf{F} \cdot d\mathbf{r}$ to be an exact differential is $\mathbf{V} \times \mathbf{F}$. Given: $\mathbf{F} = F_x \mathbf{i} + F_y \mathbf{j}$, $\mathbf{r} = x\mathbf{i} + y\mathbf{j}$.

By definition, the exact differential is

$$dV(x,y) = \frac{\partial V(x,y)}{\partial x}\, dx + \frac{\partial V(x,y)}{\partial y}\, dy \qquad (1)$$

and in this case

$$\mathbf{F} \cdot d\mathbf{r} = \frac{\partial V(x,y)}{\partial x}\, dx + \frac{\partial V(x,y)}{\partial y}\, dy \qquad (2)$$

where

$$\mathbf{F} = \frac{\partial V(x,y)}{\partial x}\, \mathbf{i} + \frac{\partial V(x,y)}{\partial y}\, \mathbf{j} = \mathbf{V}V(x,y), \qquad d\mathbf{r} = dx\, \mathbf{i} + dy\, \mathbf{j} \qquad (3), (4)$$

and $\mathbf{V}$ is a differential operator called the gradient.   If (2) is satisfied, then from (3), $F_x = \partial V(x,y)/\partial x$, $F_y = \partial V(x,y)/\partial y$ and

$$\mathbf{V} \times \mathbf{F} = \begin{vmatrix} \mathbf{i} & \mathbf{j} & \mathbf{k} \\ \dfrac{\partial}{\partial x} & \dfrac{\partial}{\partial y} & \dfrac{\partial}{\partial z} \\ F_x & F_y & 0 \end{vmatrix} = \left(\frac{\partial F_y}{\partial x} - \frac{\partial F_x}{\partial y} \right) \mathbf{k} = \left(\frac{\partial^2 V(x,y)}{\partial y \partial x} - \frac{\partial^2 V(x,y)}{\partial y \partial x} \right) \mathbf{k} = 0 \qquad (5)$$

where $\mathbf{V} \times \mathbf{F}$ is called the curl of $\mathbf{F}$ (rot of $\mathbf{F}$).

Thus the necessary and sufficient condition for $\mathbf{F} \cdot d\mathbf{r}$ to be an exact differential is (2), (3), or (5). The latter can be used directly if $\mathbf{F}$ is known; (3) and (4) require a knowledge of $V(x,y)$.

The function $V(x,y)$ is called a potential function and $-V(x,y)$ is called the potential energy measured with respect to an arbitrary datum.

Two typical potential functions are:

(a) Gravitational potential, $V(x,y) = -mgy$
(b) Linear spring potential, $V(x,y) = -kx^2/2, \quad V(x,y) = -ky^2/2$

2.37 The necessary and sufficient condition for a force field to be conservative is $\nabla \times \mathbf{F} = 0$.   Check if the force field defined by $\mathbf{F} = -2\lambda(x\mathbf{i} + y\mathbf{j})(x^2 + y^2)^{-2}$ is a conservative field. λ is a constant.

$$\nabla \times \mathbf{F} = \begin{vmatrix} \mathbf{i} & \mathbf{j} & \mathbf{k} \\ \dfrac{\partial}{\partial x} & \dfrac{\partial}{\partial y} & \dfrac{\partial}{\partial z} \\ F_x & F_y & 0 \end{vmatrix} = \left(\dfrac{\partial F_y}{\partial x} - \dfrac{\partial F_x}{\partial y} \right) \mathbf{k}$$

$$= \left\{ \dfrac{\partial[-2\lambda y/(x^2 + y^2)^2]}{\partial x} - \dfrac{\partial[-2\lambda x/(x^2 + y^2)^2]}{\partial y} \right\} \mathbf{k} = \left(\dfrac{8\lambda xy}{(x^2 + y^2)^3} - \dfrac{8\lambda xy}{(x^2 + y^2)^3} \right) \mathbf{k} = 0$$

which shows the field is conservative.

2.38 Show that the mechanical work done by a block of weight W on an inclined plane of angle α and length l is independent of path (Fig. P-2.38).

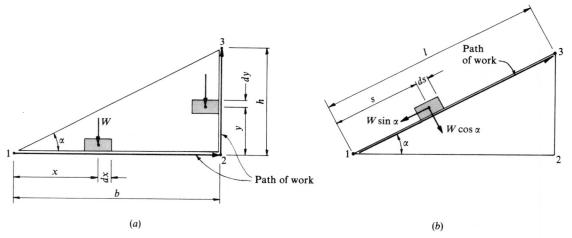

(a)   (b)

Fig. P-2.38

(a) Referring to Fig. P-2.38a,

$$\mathbf{F} = -W\mathbf{j}, \qquad \mathbf{r} = x\mathbf{i} + y\mathbf{j}$$

$$U = \int_1^3 \mathbf{F} \cdot d\mathbf{r} = \int_0^b 0 \, dx + \int_0^h -W \, dy = -Wh$$

(b) Referring to Fig. P-2.38b,

$$\mathbf{F} = (-W \sin \alpha)\mathbf{e}_s, \qquad \mathbf{r} = s\mathbf{e}_s$$

$$U = \int_1^3 \mathbf{F} \cdot d\mathbf{r} = \int_0^l (-W \sin \alpha)\, ds = -Wl \sin \alpha = -Wh$$

Also note (Problem 2.36) that

$$V(x,y) = -Wy, \qquad \frac{\partial V(x,y)}{\partial x} = 0, \qquad \frac{\partial V(x,y)}{\partial y} = -W, \qquad \mathbf{F} = \nabla V(x,y)$$

and

$$\nabla \times \mathbf{F} = \begin{vmatrix} \mathbf{i} & \mathbf{j} & \mathbf{k} \\ \dfrac{\partial}{\partial x} & \dfrac{\partial}{\partial y} & \dfrac{\partial}{\partial z} \\ -W & 0 & 0 \end{vmatrix} = 0$$

CONSERVATION OF ENERGY

2.39   Refer to Fig. P-2.39.   Using the principle of conservation of energy, determine the deflection of the spring produced by the ball of mass m dropped on it from the distance h.   Given: m, g, h, and k = spring constant.

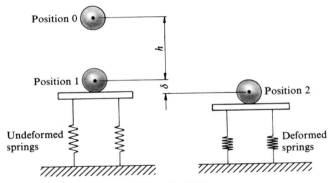

Position 0

Position 1

Position 2

Undeformed springs

Deformed springs

Fig. P-2.39

By (2-20), $T_1 + V_1 = T_2 + V_2$ where at the first contact $T_1 = \frac{1}{2}mv_1^2$, $V_1 = mg\delta$ and at final rest $T_2 = 0$, $V_2 = k\delta^2/2$.   Thus

$$\tfrac{1}{2}mv_1^2 + mg\delta = k\delta^2/2$$

From the free fall equation, $v_1 = \sqrt{2gh}$ and so

$$\delta^2 - \frac{2mg}{k}\delta - \frac{2mgh}{k} = 0$$

from which

$$\delta = \underbrace{\frac{mg}{k}}_{\delta_{\text{static}}} + \underbrace{\sqrt{\left(\frac{mg}{k}\right)^2 + \frac{2mgh}{k}}}_{\delta_{\text{dynamic}}} = \frac{mg}{k}\left(1 + \sqrt{1 + \frac{2kh}{mg}}\right)$$

where δ_{static} is the static deflection of the spring and δ_{dynamic} is the deflection due to the motion of mg.   For $h = 0$ we have $\delta = 2mg/k$, which is twice the value of δ_{static}.

2.40 A ball of weight mg is ejected at 1 by releasing a linear spring of initial compression δ and hits a target 2 as shown in Fig. P-2.40.   If the friction and air resistance are neglected, what is the impact velocity v_2?   Given: α, mg, h, and k = spring constant.

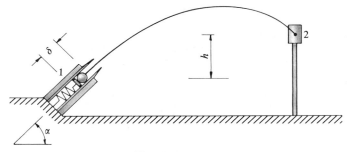

Fig. P-2.40

By (2-20), $T_1 + V_1 = T_2 + V_2$ where $T_1 = 0$, $V_1 = k\delta^2/2$, $T_2 = \frac{1}{2}mv_2^2$, $V_2 = mg(h + \delta \sin x)$.
Hence

$$k\delta^2/2 = \tfrac{1}{2}mv_2^2 + mg(h + \delta \sin \alpha) \qquad \text{and} \qquad v_2 = \sqrt{k\delta^2/m - 2g\delta \sin \alpha - 2gh}$$

If $v_2 = 0$, then

$$\delta^2 - \frac{2\delta mg \sin \alpha}{k} - \frac{2mgh}{k} = 0$$

from which

$$\delta = \frac{mg \sin \alpha}{k} + \sqrt{\left(\frac{mg \sin \alpha}{k}\right)^2 + \frac{2mgh}{k}} = \frac{mg \sin \alpha}{k}\left(1 + \sqrt{1 + \frac{2kh}{mg \sin^2 \alpha}}\right)$$

Problems

EQUATIONS OF MOTION

2.41 A particle of mass 3 slugs, acted upon by an unknown force, moves along a path given by $\mathbf{r} = 6t^2\mathbf{i} + (10t^2 + 2)\mathbf{j}$ ft.   Find the force required to produce and sustain this motion.

2.42 A particle of mass of 1000 kg, acted upon by an unknown force, moves along a circular path of radius $R = 100$ m given by $\mathbf{r} = R[(\cos \pi t/10)\mathbf{i} + (\sin \pi t/10)\mathbf{j}]$ m.   Find the force vector required to produce and sustain this motion.

2.43 Consider a particle of mass m acted upon by a force $\mathbf{F} = (10\mathbf{i} + 20\mathbf{j})$ kg in the XY plane.   Derive the vector equations of motion of this particle.   Given: $\mathbf{r}_0 = (30\mathbf{i} + 30\mathbf{j})$ m, $\dot{\mathbf{r}}_0 = (10\mathbf{i} + 40\mathbf{j})$ m/sec and $g = 9.8$ m/sec^2.

2.44 Compute the time required for the particle of Problem 2.41 to attain a velocity $\dot{\mathbf{r}}_1 = (120\mathbf{i} + 200\mathbf{j})$ m/sec.

2.45 A particle of mass $m = 10$ slugs is acted upon by a force $F = (100t + 500)$ lb.   If the initial speed is $v = 10$ ft/sec, find its velocity and distance traveled after 10 sec.

2.46   A block of mass $m = 1000\ \text{kg}_m$ is acted upon by a force vector

$$\mathbf{F} = -100[(50 \cos \pi t/10)\mathbf{i} + (20 \sin \pi t/10)\mathbf{j}]\ \text{kg}$$

Derive the vector equations of motion.   Given: $\mathbf{r}_0 = (50\mathbf{i})\ \text{m}$, $\dot{\mathbf{r}}_0 = (2\pi\mathbf{j})\ \text{m/sec}$.

2.47   Derive the equations of motion for a block of weight $W = 1000\ \text{kg}$ sliding down freely on a frictionless inclined plane of base $b = 100\ \text{m}$ and height $h = 20\ \text{m}$.

2.48   A particle of mass $m = 5$ slugs moves under the influence of $\mathbf{F} = (100x^{3/2}\mathbf{i})\ \text{lb}$.   Investigate the motion. Given: $\mathbf{r}_0 = 0$, $\dot{\mathbf{r}}_0 = 0$.

2.49   A particle of mass m is ejected with the velocity v_0 upward in a medium of resistance linearly proportional to the speed (kv).   Determine the time for the particle to come to rest.

2.50   A stone is dropped in the shaft of a deep well and the splash is heard t_1 seconds after the drop.   Compute the depth of the well (to the water table) in terms of g, t, and the speed of sound e.

2.51   Include the effect of kinetic friction of coefficient μ_k in Problem 2.47.

2.52   Determine the maximum acceleration that can be attained by the rear wheel drive vehicle of Fig. P-2.52 on a level highway.   Given: W, a, b, c, μ_k.

2.53   Include the effect of a 2% grade in Problem 2.52.

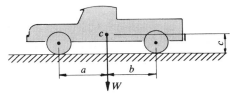

Fig. P-2.52

MOMENTUM AND IMPULSE

2.54   A jet airplane of mass $20{,}000\ \text{kg}_m$ moves on a straight line from speed 500 km/hr to 800 km/hr in 3 minutes. Compute its linear momentum at each speed, and the impulse developed during these 3 minutes.

2.55   A body is acted upon by a force of 1000 lb.   Find its linear momentum after 10 sec of motion from rest.

2.56   Compute the linear momenta and impulse in Problem 2.46.   Given: $t_1 = 10\ \text{sec}$, $t_2 = 20\ \text{sec}$.

2.57   The position vector of a particle of mass $m = 30$ slugs is $\mathbf{r} = (10t\mathbf{i} + 20t\mathbf{j})\ \text{ft}$ and its velocity vector is $\dot{\mathbf{r}} = (10\mathbf{i} + 20\mathbf{j})\ \text{ft/sec}$.   Compute its angular momenta at $t_1 = 8\ \text{sec}$ and $t_2 = 12\ \text{sec}$, and the corresponding angular impulse.

2.58   A mass of 100 kg moves in a circle of radius $R = 10\ \text{m}$ around a fixed center with a constant angular velocity $\dot{\theta} = 2\ \text{rad/sec}$.   Compute its angular momentum.

2.59   In Problem 2.58, find the moment required to produce the motion from rest in 2 sec.

WORK AND KINETIC ENERGY

2.60   Compute the work done by the force $\mathbf{F} = (200t\mathbf{i} + 400t\mathbf{j})\ \text{lb}$ moving along a path given by $\mathbf{r} = [(2 + 5t)\mathbf{i} + (7 + 3t^2)\mathbf{j}]\ \text{ft}$ in the interval $t_1 = 10\ \text{sec}$, $t_2 = 20\ \text{sec}$.

2.61   Compute the work done by the ball of weight W moving along the circular path shown in Fig. P-2.61.   Given: $R = 100\ \text{ft}$, $W = 1000\ \text{lb}$, $\theta_1 = 0$, $\theta_2 = \pi$, $P = 0$.

2.62   Compute the normal reaction N produced by the motion of W on the path of motion in Problem 2.61.

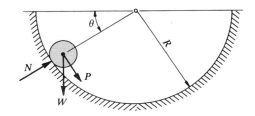

Fig. P-2.61

2.63   A block of $W = 1000\,\text{lb}$ is acted upon by a force $P = 2000\,\text{lb}$ as shown in Fig. P-2.61.   If the coefficient of kinetic friction is $\mu_k = 0.2$, determine the work required to move this block 100 ft.

2.64   Determine the time required for the chain of Problem 2.35 to begin its free fall.

POTENTIAL ENERGY

2.65   Determine if the force

$$\mathbf{F} = \frac{y}{x^2 + y^2}\,\mathbf{i} - \frac{x}{x^2 + y^2}\,\mathbf{j}$$

is conservative and if so, find its potential function.

2.66   Find the work done by a particle moving in the force field of Problem 2.65 from $1(-2, 4)$ to $2(3, 5)$ as shown in Fig. P-2.66.

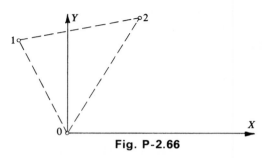

Fig. P-2.66

2.67   Show numerically that the work done by a particle moving in the force field of Problem 2.65 from $1(-2, 4)$ to $0(0, 0)$ and then to $2(3, 5)$, is the same as in Problem 2.66.

2.68   Show numerically that the work done by the particle of Problem 2.67 is zero for the closed path $\overline{1021}$.

Chapter 3

Kinematics of Particles, Space Motion

3.1 GEOMETRY OF SPACE PATH

Coordinate Equations

If the path of motion is a space (nonplanar) curve, the motion is said to be a *space (general) motion*. Two analytical forms are used for the definition of this path.

(a) *Intersection form*, given by two equations,

$$\Phi_1(x,y,z) = 0, \qquad \Phi_2(x,y,z) = 0 \tag{3-1}$$

where Φ_1, Φ_2 are implicit functions which have continuous partial derivatives of (at least) the first order in a given interval, and which represent two surfaces whose intersection is the path of motion.

(b) *Parametric form*, given by three equations,

$$x = x(s), \qquad y = y(s), \qquad z = z(s) \tag{3-2}$$

where $x(s)$, $y(s)$, $z(s)$ are continuous functions of the curvilinear coordinate s measured along the curve and which have continuous derivatives of at least first order with respect to s.

Both sets of equations (3-1) and (3-2) can be expressed in the cartesian system or in any other system of coordinates, chosen as desired.

The *positive direction* of the curve given by (3-1) and (3-2) is that in which the particle moves when the time t increases.

Vector Equations

An alternative and more compact form of (3-2) is the vector form (Fig. 3-1) written as

$$\mathbf{r} = \mathbf{r}(s) = x(s)\mathbf{i} + y(s)\mathbf{j} + z(s)\mathbf{k} = r\mathbf{e}_r \tag{3-3}$$

where $\mathbf{r}$ is the *position vector* (radius vector), r is the *radius*, $\mathbf{e}_r$ is the *unit radial vector*, and $\mathbf{i}$, $\mathbf{j}$, $\mathbf{k}$ are the cartesian unit vectors.

The *magnitude* of $\mathbf{r}$ is

$$r = \sqrt{x^2 + y^2 + z^2} \tag{3-4}$$

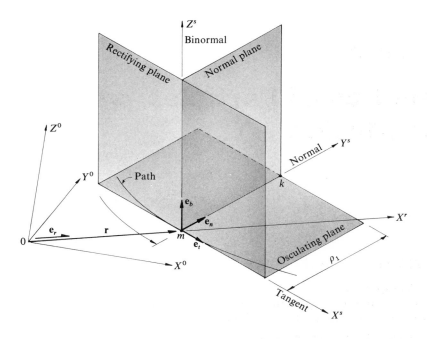

Fig. 3-1

and

$$\mathbf{e}_r = (x/r)\mathbf{i} + (y/r)\mathbf{j} + (z/r)\mathbf{k} = \alpha_r\mathbf{i} + \beta_r\mathbf{j} + \gamma_r\mathbf{k} \qquad (3\text{-}5)$$

where $\alpha_r = \cos(X^r, X^0)$, $\beta_r = \cos(X^r, Y^0)$, $\gamma_r = \cos(X^r, Y^0)$ are the direction cosines of $\mathbf{e}_r$.

Path Derivatives

The *first and second derivatives* of $\mathbf{r}$ with respect to s (path derivatives) are

$$\mathbf{r}' = \frac{d\mathbf{r}(s)}{ds} = x'\mathbf{i} + y'\mathbf{j} + z'\mathbf{k} = r'\mathbf{e}_t = \mathbf{e}_t$$

$$\mathbf{r}'' = \frac{d^2\mathbf{r}(s)}{ds^2} = x''\mathbf{i} + y''\mathbf{j} + z''\mathbf{k} = r''\mathbf{e}_n = \kappa_1\mathbf{e}_n \qquad (3\text{-}6)$$

where $x' = dx/ds$, $x'' = d^2x/ds^2$, ..., r', r'' are magnitudes of $\mathbf{r}'$, $\mathbf{r}''$ respectively; κ_1 is the curvature defined by (3-10); $\mathbf{e}_t$, $\mathbf{e}_n$ are the *unit tangent* and *unit normal* (*principal normal*) *vectors* respectively, and the elemental length ds is

$$ds = \sqrt{dx^2 + dy^2 + dz^2} \qquad (3\text{-}7)$$

The *magnitude* of $\mathbf{r}'$ is

$$r' = \sqrt{x'^2 + y'^2 + z'^2} = 1 \qquad (3\text{-}8)$$

and

$$\mathbf{e}_t = x'\mathbf{i} + y'\mathbf{j} + z'\mathbf{k} = \alpha_t\mathbf{i} + \beta_t\mathbf{j} + \gamma_t\mathbf{k} \tag{3-9}$$

where $\alpha_t = \cos(X^s, X^0)$, $\beta_t = \cos(X^s, Y^0)$, $\gamma_t = \cos(X^s, Z^0)$ are the direction cosines of $\mathbf{e}_t$.
  The *magnitude* of $\mathbf{r}''$ is

$$r'' = \sqrt{x''^2 + y''^2 + z''^2} = \kappa_1 = \text{curvature} \tag{3-10}$$

and

$$\mathbf{e}_n = (x''/r'')\mathbf{i} + (y''/r'')\mathbf{j} + (z''/r'')\mathbf{k} = \alpha_n\mathbf{i} + \beta_n\mathbf{j} + \gamma_n\mathbf{k} \tag{3-11}$$

where $\alpha_n = \cos(Y^s, X^0)$, $\beta_n = \cos(Y^s, Y^0)$, $\gamma_n = \cos(Y^s, Z^0)$ are the direction cosines of $\mathbf{e}_n$.

Moving Trihedral

The plane determined at each point of the path by the unit vectors $\mathbf{e}_t$ and $\mathbf{e}_n$ is called the *osculating plane* (curvature plane). As $\mathbf{e}_t \cdot \mathbf{e}_n = 0$, they are normal and the vector normal to their plane, called the *unit binormal vector* $\mathbf{e}_b$, is

$$\mathbf{e}_b = \mathbf{e}_t \times \mathbf{e}_n = \frac{1}{\kappa_1}\begin{vmatrix} \mathbf{i} & \mathbf{j} & \mathbf{k} \\ x' & y' & z' \\ x'' & y'' & z'' \end{vmatrix} = \alpha_b\mathbf{i} + \beta_b\mathbf{j} + \gamma_b\mathbf{k} \tag{3-12}$$

where $\alpha_b = \cos(Z^s, X^0)$, $\beta_b = \cos(Z^s, Y^0)$, $\gamma_b = \cos(Z^s, Z^0)$ are the direction cosines of $\mathbf{e}_b$.
  By definition of cross product of *orthogonal vectors*,

$$\mathbf{e}_t = \mathbf{e}_n \times \mathbf{e}_b, \qquad \mathbf{e}_n = \mathbf{e}_b \times \mathbf{e}_t, \qquad \mathbf{e}_b = \mathbf{e}_t \times \mathbf{e}_n \tag{3-13}$$

which follows the cycle diagram of Fig. 3-2.
  These three orthogonal unit vectors define at every point of the path a *moving trihedral* (Fig. 3-1), the planes of which are the *osculating plane* X^sY^s, the *normal plane* Y^sZ^s, and the *rectifying plane* Z^sX^s. The intersections of these planes are the *tangent* X^s, the *principal normal* Y^s, and the *binormal* Z^s.

Fig. 3-2 Unit vector's cycle.

Serret-Frenet Formulas

The relationship between the moving trihedral unit vectors $\mathbf{e}_t$, $\mathbf{e}_n$, $\mathbf{e}_b$ and the stationary cartesian unit vectors $\mathbf{i}$, $\mathbf{j}$, $\mathbf{k}$ in terms of (3-9), (3-11), (3-12) are

$$\underbrace{\begin{bmatrix} \mathbf{e}_t \\ \mathbf{e}_n \\ \mathbf{e}_n \end{bmatrix}}_{[\mathbf{e}^s]} = \underbrace{\begin{bmatrix} \alpha_t & \beta_t & \gamma_t \\ \alpha_n & \beta_n & \gamma_n \\ \alpha_b & \beta_b & \gamma_b \end{bmatrix}}_{[\pi^{s0}]} \underbrace{\begin{bmatrix} \mathbf{i} \\ \mathbf{j} \\ \mathbf{k} \end{bmatrix}}_{[\mathbf{e}^0]}, \qquad \underbrace{\begin{bmatrix} \mathbf{i} \\ \mathbf{j} \\ \mathbf{k} \end{bmatrix}}_{[\mathbf{e}^0]} = \underbrace{\begin{bmatrix} \alpha_t & \alpha_n & \alpha_b \\ \beta_t & \beta_n & \beta_b \\ \gamma_t & \gamma_n & \gamma_b \end{bmatrix}}_{[\pi^{0s}]} \underbrace{\begin{bmatrix} \mathbf{e}_t \\ \mathbf{e}_n \\ \mathbf{e}_b \end{bmatrix}}_{[\mathbf{e}^s]} \tag{3-14), (3-15}$$

where $[\mathbf{e}^0]$ is the column matrix of the *cartesian unit vectors*, $[\mathbf{e}^s]$ is the column matrix of the *moving trihedral unit vectors*, and $[\pi^{0s}]$, $[\pi^{s0}]$ are their angular transformation matrices.

The matrix equations (*3-14*) and (*3-15*) provide a convenient vehicle for the development of path derivatives of the moving trihedral unit vectors, known as the *Serret-Frenet formulas*. In matrix form, they are

$$\begin{bmatrix} d\mathbf{e}_t/ds \\ d\mathbf{e}_n/ds \\ d\mathbf{e}_b/ds \end{bmatrix} = \begin{bmatrix} 0 & \kappa_1 & 0 \\ -\kappa_1 & 0 & \kappa_2 \\ 0 & -\kappa_2 & 0 \end{bmatrix} \begin{bmatrix} \mathbf{e}_t \\ \mathbf{e}_n \\ \mathbf{e}_b \end{bmatrix} \qquad (3\text{-}16)$$

where

$$\kappa_1 = 1/\rho_1 = r'' \qquad (3\text{-}17)$$

is the *curvature of path*, and ρ_1 is the *radius of curvature*.

$$\kappa_2 = 1/\rho_2 = [\mathbf{r}' \cdot \mathbf{r}'' \times \mathbf{r}''']/(r'')^2 \qquad (3\text{-}18)$$

is the *torsion of path* and ρ_2 is the *radius of torsion*.

The position vector of the *center of curvature* $\mathbf{r}_1$ and of the *center of torsion* $\mathbf{r}_2$ are respectively

$$\mathbf{r}_1 = (x + \rho_1\alpha_n)\mathbf{i} + (y + \rho_1\beta_n)\mathbf{j} + (z + \rho_1\gamma_n)\mathbf{k} = \mathbf{r} + \rho_1\mathbf{e}_n \qquad (3\text{-}19)$$

$$\mathbf{r}_2 = (x + \rho_2\alpha_b)\mathbf{i} + (y + \rho_2\beta_b)\mathbf{j} + (z + \rho_2\gamma_b)\mathbf{k} = \mathbf{r} + \rho_2\mathbf{e}_b \qquad (3\text{-}20)$$

where $\alpha_n, \beta_n, \gamma_n$ = direction cosines of $\mathbf{e}_n$, (*3-11*),
$\quad\quad\quad \alpha_b, \beta_b, \gamma_b$ = direction cosines of $\mathbf{e}_b$, (*3-12*),
$\quad\quad\quad \mathbf{r}$ = position vector of path, (*3-3*).

3.2   ABSOLUTE CURVILINEAR MOTION

Coordinate Systems

For the study of space motion, four different coordinate systems are presented in this section: the *cartesian, cylindrical, spherical,* and *curvilinear* coordinate systems.

Cartesian Coordinates

In cartesian coordinates $x = x(t)$, $y = y(t)$, $z = z(t)$ (Fig. 3-3), the *equations of motion* (*1-1*), (*1-2*) and (*1-3*) are

$$\mathbf{r} = x\mathbf{i} + y\mathbf{j} + z\mathbf{k} = r\mathbf{e}_r$$
$$\mathbf{v} = \dot{\mathbf{r}} = \dot{x}\mathbf{i} + \dot{y}\mathbf{j} + \dot{z}\mathbf{k} = v\mathbf{e}_v \qquad (3\text{-}21)$$
$$\mathbf{a} = \dot{\mathbf{v}} = \ddot{\mathbf{r}} = \ddot{x}\mathbf{i} + \ddot{y}\mathbf{j} + \ddot{z}\mathbf{k} = a\mathbf{e}_a$$

where $r = \sqrt{x^2 + y^2 + z^2}$,

$$v = \sqrt{\dot{x}^2 + \dot{y}^2 + \dot{z}^2},$$

$$a = \sqrt{\ddot{x}^2 + \ddot{y}^2 + \ddot{z}^2}$$

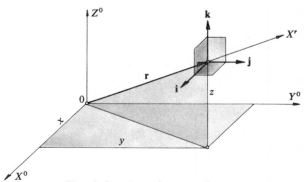

Fig. 3-3   Cartesian coordinates.

are the respective magnitudes and $\mathbf{e}_r$, $\mathbf{e}_v$, $\mathbf{e}_a$ are the respective unit vectors.

Again, as in *(1-17)*, the time derivatives of **i, j, k** must be zero, since their directions are constant (independent of time).

Cylindrical Coordinates

In cylindrical coordinates $c = c(t)$, $\theta = \theta(t)$, $z = z(t)$ (Fig. 3-4), the *equations of motion (1-1)*, *(1-2)* and *(1-3)* are

$$\mathbf{r} = c\mathbf{e}_c + z\mathbf{e}_z$$
$$\mathbf{v} = \dot{\mathbf{r}} = \dot{c}\mathbf{e}_c + c\dot{\theta}\mathbf{e}_\theta + \dot{z}\mathbf{e}_z = v_c\mathbf{e}_c + v_\theta\mathbf{e}_\theta + v_z\mathbf{e}_z \qquad (3\text{-}22)$$
$$\mathbf{a} = \dot{\mathbf{v}} = \ddot{\mathbf{r}} = (\ddot{c} - c\dot{\theta}^2)\mathbf{e}_c + (c\ddot{\theta} + 2\dot{c}\dot{\theta})\mathbf{e}_\theta + \ddot{z}\mathbf{e} = a_c\mathbf{e}_c + a_\theta\mathbf{e}_\theta + a_z\mathbf{e}_z$$

where v_c, v_θ, v_z are the scalar components of **v**; a_c, a_θ, a_z are the scalar components of **a**; and $\mathbf{e}_c$, $\mathbf{e}_\theta$, $\mathbf{e}_z$ are the respective unit vectors.

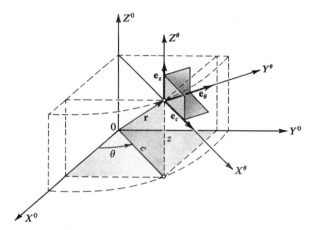

Fig. 3-4 Cylindrical coordinates.

The *time derivatives* of these unit vectors are

$$\dot{\mathbf{e}}_c = \dot{\theta}\mathbf{e}_\theta, \qquad \dot{\mathbf{e}}_\theta = -\dot{\theta}\mathbf{e}_c, \qquad \dot{\mathbf{e}}_z = 0 \qquad (3\text{-}23)$$

as shown in Problem 3.13.

Spherical Coordinates

In spherical coordinates $\phi = \phi(t)$, $\theta = \theta(t)$, $r = r(t)$ (Fig. 3-5), the *equations of motion (1-1)*, *(1-2)* and *(1-3)* are

$$\left.\begin{aligned}
\mathbf{r} &= r\mathbf{e}_r \\
\mathbf{v} = \dot{\mathbf{r}} &= r\dot{\phi}\mathbf{e}_\phi + (r\dot{\theta}\sin\phi)\mathbf{e}_\theta + \dot{r}\mathbf{e}_r = v_\phi\mathbf{e}_\phi + v_\theta\mathbf{e}_\theta + v_r\mathbf{e}_r \\
\mathbf{a} = \dot{\mathbf{v}} = \ddot{\mathbf{r}} &= (2\dot{r}\dot{\phi} + r\ddot{\phi} - r\dot{\theta}^2\sin\phi\cos\phi)\mathbf{e}_\phi \\
&\quad + (2\dot{r}\dot{\theta}\sin\phi + r\ddot{\theta}\sin\phi + 2r\dot{\phi}\dot{\theta}\cos\phi)\mathbf{e}_\theta + (\ddot{r} - r\dot{\phi}^2 - r\dot{\theta}^2\sin^2\phi)\mathbf{e}_r \\
&= \alpha_\phi\mathbf{e}_\phi + \alpha_\theta\mathbf{e}_\theta + a_r\mathbf{e}_r
\end{aligned}\right\} \qquad (3\text{-}24)$$

where v_ϕ, v_θ, v_r are the scalar components of **v**; a_ϕ, a_θ, a_v are the scalar components of **a**; and $\mathbf{e}_\phi$, $\mathbf{e}_\theta$, $\mathbf{e}_r$ are the respective unit vectors (Problem 3.22).

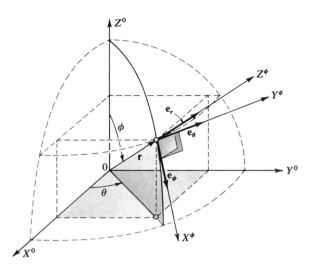

Fig. 3-5 Spherical coordinates.

The *time derivatives* of these unit vectors are

$$\dot{\mathbf{e}}_\phi = (\dot{\theta}\cos\phi)\mathbf{e}_\theta - \dot{\phi}\mathbf{e}_r, \qquad \dot{\mathbf{e}}_\theta = (-\dot{\theta}\cos\phi)\mathbf{e}_\phi - (\dot{\theta}\sin\phi)\mathbf{e}_r, \qquad \dot{\mathbf{e}}_r = \dot{\phi}\mathbf{e}_\phi + (\dot{\theta}\sin\phi)\mathbf{e}_\theta \qquad (3\text{-}25)$$

as shown in Problem 3.21.

Curvilinear Coordinates

As in Section 1.4, an alternate form of the equations of motion is in terms of the *tangent unit vector* $\mathbf{e}_t$, the *normal unit vector* $\mathbf{e}_n$, and the curvilinear coordinate $s = s(t)$ (Fig. 3-1).

Analytically these equations are formally identical to (*1-21*) but the position vector $\mathbf{r}$ and the unit vectors $\mathbf{e}_t$ and $\mathbf{e}_n$ are three-dimensional vectors and the radius of curvature ρ_1 is in this case given by (*3-18*).

If $\mathbf{r}$ is a function of t and if the curvilinear coordinate $s = s(t)$ is not given, the *path derivatives* must be found by chain differentiation as follows:

$$\frac{d\mathbf{r}(t)}{ds} = \frac{d\mathbf{r}}{dt}\frac{dt}{ds} = \frac{d\mathbf{r}/dt}{ds/dt} = \frac{\dot{\mathbf{r}}}{\dot{r}} = \mathbf{e}_t$$

$$\frac{d^2\mathbf{r}(t)}{ds^2} = \frac{d\left[\dfrac{d\mathbf{r}/dt}{ds/dt}\right]}{dt}\frac{dt}{ds} = \frac{\dot{r}\ddot{\mathbf{r}} - \ddot{r}\dot{\mathbf{r}}}{\dot{r}^3} = \kappa_1\mathbf{e}_n \qquad (3\text{-}26)$$

which are the equivalents of (*3-6*).

3.3   TRANSFORMATION MATRICES

Concept

Although the transformation relations between the kinematic vectors given in Section 3.2 in four different coordinate systems can always be obtained by scalar vector multiplication, the matrix transformations offer many advantages and are used consistently in this chapter.

For this purpose, the respective *kinematic vectors* (radius, velocity, acceleration, etc.) are assembled in column matrices designated symbolically as

$$[V^0] = \text{kinematic vector in cartesian system,}$$
$$[V^\theta] = \text{kinematic vector in cylindrical system,}$$
$$[V^\phi] = \text{kinematic vector in spherical system,}$$
$$[V^s] = \text{kinematic vector in curvilinear system,}$$

and related as follows:

$$
\left.
\begin{aligned}
[V^0] &= [\pi^{00}][V^0]; & [V^0] &= [\pi^{0\theta}][V^\theta]; & [V^0] &= [\pi^{0\phi}][V^\phi]; & [V^0] &= [\pi^{0s}][V^s] \\
[V^\theta] &= [\pi^{\theta 0}][V^0]; & [V^\theta] &= [\pi^{\theta\theta}][V^\theta]; & [V^\theta] &= [\pi^{\theta\phi}][V^\phi]; & [V^\theta] &= [\pi^{\theta s}][V^s] \\
[V^\phi] &= [\pi^{\phi 0}][V^0]; & [V^\phi] &= [\pi^{\phi\theta}][V^\theta]; & [V^\phi] &= [\pi^{\phi\phi}][V^\phi]; & [V^\phi] &= [\pi^{\phi s}][V^s] \\
[V^s] &= [\pi^{s0}][V^0]; & [V^s] &= [\pi^{s\theta}][V^\theta]; & [V^s] &= [\pi^{s\phi}][V^\phi]; & [V^s] &= [\pi^{ss}][V^s]
\end{aligned}
\right\} \quad (3\text{-}27)
$$

where by inspection

$$[\pi^{00}] = [\pi^{\theta\theta}] = [\pi^{\phi\phi}] = [\pi^{ss}] = [I] = \begin{bmatrix} 1 & 0 & 0 \\ 0 & 1 & 0 \\ 0 & 0 & 1 \end{bmatrix} \qquad (3\text{-}28)$$

The remaining π-matrices are the *angular transformation matrices*, the elements of which are the respective direction cosines.

Cartesian-Cylindrical Transformation, $[\pi^{0\theta}]$, $[\pi^{\theta 0}]$

From Figs. (3-3) and (3-4),

$$
\underbrace{\begin{bmatrix} V_x \\ V_y \\ V_z \end{bmatrix}}_{[V^0]} = \underbrace{\begin{bmatrix} \cos\theta & -\sin\theta & 0 \\ \sin\theta & \cos\theta & 0 \\ 0 & 0 & 1 \end{bmatrix}}_{[\pi^{0\theta}]} \underbrace{\begin{bmatrix} V_c \\ V_\theta \\ V_z \end{bmatrix}}_{[V^\theta]}, \qquad
\underbrace{\begin{bmatrix} V_c \\ V_\theta \\ V_z \end{bmatrix}}_{[V^\theta]} = \underbrace{\begin{bmatrix} \cos\theta & \sin\theta & 0 \\ -\sin\theta & \cos\theta & 0 \\ 0 & 0 & 1 \end{bmatrix}}_{[\pi^{\theta 0}]} \underbrace{\begin{bmatrix} V_x \\ V_y \\ V_z \end{bmatrix}}_{[V^0]} \qquad (3\text{-}29),\ (3\text{-}30)
$$

where $[V^0]$ represents $V_x\mathbf{i} + V_y\mathbf{j} + V_z\mathbf{k}$, $[V^\theta]$ represents $V_c\mathbf{e}_c + V_\theta\mathbf{e}_\theta + V_z\mathbf{e}_z$, and

$$[\pi^{0\theta}] = [\pi^{\theta 0}]^T, \qquad [\pi^{\theta 0}] = [\pi^{0\theta}]^T, \qquad [\pi^{0\theta}][\pi^{\theta 0}] = [I] \qquad (3\text{-}31)$$

Cartesian-Spherical Transformations, $[\pi^{0\phi}]$, $[\pi^{\phi 0}]$

From Figs. (3-3) and (3-5),

$$
\underbrace{\begin{bmatrix} V_x \\ V_y \\ V_z \end{bmatrix}}_{[V^0]} = \underbrace{\begin{bmatrix} \cos\theta\cos\phi & -\sin\theta & \cos\theta\sin\phi \\ \sin\theta\cos\phi & \cos\theta & \sin\theta\sin\phi \\ -\sin\phi & 0 & \cos\phi \end{bmatrix}}_{[\pi^{0\phi}]} \underbrace{\begin{bmatrix} V_\phi \\ V_\theta \\ V_r \end{bmatrix}}_{[V^\phi]} \qquad (3\text{-}32)
$$

$$\begin{bmatrix} V_\phi \\ V_\theta \\ V_r \end{bmatrix} = \begin{bmatrix} \cos\theta\cos\phi & \sin\theta\cos\phi & -\sin\phi \\ -\sin\theta & \cos\theta & 0 \\ \cos\theta\sin\phi & \sin\theta\sin\phi & \cos\phi \end{bmatrix} \begin{bmatrix} V_x \\ V_y \\ V_z \end{bmatrix} \qquad (3\text{-}33)$$

$$\underbrace{}_{[V^\phi]} \qquad \underbrace{}_{[\pi^{\phi 0}]} \qquad \underbrace{}_{[V^0]}$$

where $[V^\phi]$ represents $V_\phi \mathbf{e}_\phi + V_\theta \mathbf{e}_\theta + V_r \mathbf{e}_r$ and

$$[\pi^{0\phi}] = [\pi^{\phi 0}]^T, \qquad [\pi^{\phi 0}] = [\pi^{0\phi}]^T, \qquad [\pi^{0\phi}][\pi^{\phi 0}] = [I] \qquad (3\text{-}34)$$

Cartesian-Curvilinear Transformations, $[\pi^{0s}]$, $[\pi^{s0}]$

From Figs. (3-1) and (3-3),

$$\begin{bmatrix} V_x \\ V_y \\ V_z \end{bmatrix} = \begin{bmatrix} \alpha_t & \alpha_n & \alpha_b \\ \beta_t & \beta_n & \beta_b \\ \gamma_t & \gamma_n & \gamma_b \end{bmatrix} \begin{bmatrix} V_t \\ V_n \\ V_b \end{bmatrix}, \qquad \begin{bmatrix} V_t \\ V_n \\ V_b \end{bmatrix} = \begin{bmatrix} \alpha_t & \beta_t & \gamma_t \\ \alpha_n & \beta_n & \gamma_n \\ \alpha_b & \beta_b & \gamma_b \end{bmatrix} \begin{bmatrix} V_x \\ V_y \\ V_z \end{bmatrix} \qquad (3\text{-}35), (3\text{-}36)$$

$$\underbrace{}_{[V^0]} \quad \underbrace{}_{[\pi^{0s}]} \quad \underbrace{}_{[V^s]} \qquad \underbrace{}_{[V^s]} \quad \underbrace{}_{[\pi^{s0}]} \quad \underbrace{}_{[V^0]}$$

where $[V^s]$ represents $V_t \mathbf{e}_t + V_n \mathbf{e}_n + V_b \mathbf{e}_b$, and

$$[\pi^{0s}] = [\pi^{s0}]^T, \qquad [\pi^{s0}] = [\pi^{0s}]^T, \qquad [\pi^{0s}][\pi^{s0}] = [I] \qquad (3\text{-}37)$$

The direction cosines $\alpha_t, \beta_t, \ldots, \beta_b, \gamma_b$ are given analytically in (3-9), (3-11) and (3-12).

Cylindrical-Spherical Transformations, $[\pi^{\theta\phi}]$, $[\pi^{\phi\theta}]$

From Figs. (3-4) and (3-5),

$$\begin{bmatrix} V_c \\ V_\theta \\ V_z \end{bmatrix} = \begin{bmatrix} \cos\phi & 0 & \sin\phi \\ 0 & 1 & 0 \\ -\sin\phi & 0 & \cos\phi \end{bmatrix} \begin{bmatrix} V_\phi \\ V_\theta \\ V_r \end{bmatrix}, \qquad \begin{bmatrix} V_\phi \\ V_\theta \\ V_r \end{bmatrix} = \begin{bmatrix} \cos\phi & 0 & -\sin\phi \\ 0 & 1 & 0 \\ \sin\phi & 0 & \cos\phi \end{bmatrix} \begin{bmatrix} V_c \\ V_\theta \\ V_z \end{bmatrix} \qquad (3\text{-}38), (3\text{-}39)$$

$$\underbrace{}_{[V^\theta]} \quad \underbrace{}_{[\pi^{\theta\phi}]} \quad \underbrace{}_{[V^\phi]} \qquad \underbrace{}_{[V^\phi]} \quad \underbrace{}_{[\pi^{\phi\theta}]} \quad \underbrace{}_{[V^\theta]}$$

where $[V^\phi]$ represents $V_\phi \mathbf{e}_\phi + V_\theta \mathbf{e}_\theta + V_r \mathbf{e}_r$, and

$$[\pi^{\theta\phi}] = [\pi^{\phi\theta}]^T, \qquad [\pi^{\phi\theta}] = [\pi^{\theta\phi}]^T, \qquad [\pi^{\theta\phi}][\pi^{\phi\theta}] = [I] \qquad (3\text{-}40)$$

Transformation Chains

The remaining angular transformation matrices in (3-27) can be constructed in terms of (3-29), (3-30), (3-32), (3-33), (3-35), (3-36), (3-38) and (3-39) by matrix multiplication, i.e.

$$[\pi^{\theta s}] = [\pi^{\theta 0}][\pi^{0s}], \qquad [\pi^{s\theta}] = [\pi^{s0}][\pi^{0\theta}] \qquad (3\text{-}41)$$

$$[\pi^{\phi s}] = [\pi^{\phi 0}][\pi^{0s}], \qquad [\pi^{s\phi}] = [\pi^{s0}][\pi^{0\phi}] \qquad (3\text{-}42)$$

where

$$[\pi^{\theta s}] = [\pi^{s\theta}]^T, \qquad [\pi^{s\theta}] = [\pi^{\theta s}]^T, \qquad [\pi^{\theta s}][\pi^{s\theta}] = [I] \qquad (3\text{-}43)$$

$$[\pi^{\phi s}] = [\pi^{s\phi}]^T, \qquad [\pi^{s\phi}] = [\pi^{\phi s}]^T, \qquad [\pi^{\phi s}][\pi^{s\phi}] = [I] \qquad (3\text{-}44)$$

The complete *correspondence of superscripts* (systems) provides a continuous check of matrix operations and facilitates the visual control of calculation.

Illustrative Problems

GEOMETRY OF SPACE PATH

3.1 Given: $\mathbf{r} = 2t\mathbf{i} + t^2\mathbf{j} + t\mathbf{k}$, where t is the curvilinear coordinate.   Find the first and second path derivatives of $\mathbf{r}$, the unit vectors $\mathbf{e}_t$, $\mathbf{e}_n$, and the curvature κ_1.

Parametric equations of position are $x = 2t$, $y = t^2$, $z = t$ and

$$dx = 2\,dt, \qquad dy = 2t\,dt, \qquad dz = dt$$

$$ds = \sqrt{(dx)^2 + (dy)^2 + (dz)^2} = \sqrt{5 + 4t^2}\,dt$$

First path derivatives are

$$dx/ds = 2/\sqrt{5 + 4t^2}, \qquad dy/ds = 2t/\sqrt{5 + 4t^2}, \qquad dz/ds = 1/\sqrt{5 + 4t^2}$$

By (3-6),

$$\mathbf{r}' = x'\mathbf{i} + y'\mathbf{j} + z'\mathbf{k} = (5 + 4t^2)^{-1/2}(2\mathbf{i} + 2t\mathbf{j} + \mathbf{k}) = r'\mathbf{e}_t$$

$$r' = \sqrt{(4 + 4t^2 + 1)/(5 + 4t^2)} = 1$$

and the unit tangent vector $\mathbf{e}_t = \mathbf{r}'$.
Differentials of x', y', z' are

$$dx' = -8t(5 + 4t^2)^{-3/2}\,dt, \qquad dy' = 10(5 + 4t^2)^{-3/2}\,dt, \qquad dz' = -4t(5 + 4t^2)^{-3/2}\,dt$$

Second path derivatives $(dx'/ds = d^2x/ds^2, \ldots)$ are

$$d^2x/ds^2 = -8t/(5 + 4t^2)^2, \qquad d^2y/ds^2 = 10/(5 + 4t^2)^2, \qquad d^2z/ds^2 = -4t/(5 + 4t^2)^2$$

By (3-6),

$$\mathbf{r}'' = x''\mathbf{i} + y''\mathbf{j} + z''\mathbf{k} = (5 + 4s^2)^{-2}(-8t\mathbf{i} + 10\mathbf{j} - 4t\mathbf{k}) = r''\mathbf{e}_n$$

$$r'' = \sqrt{(x'')^2 + (y'')^2 + (z'')^2} = \sqrt{100 + 80t^2}/(5 + 4t)^2 = \kappa_1$$

and the unit normal vector is

$$\mathbf{e}_n = (100 + 80t^2)^{-1/2}(-8t\mathbf{i} + 10\mathbf{j} - 4t\mathbf{k})$$

3.2 Using the results of Problem 3.1, find the moving trihedral unit vectors at $s = 1$.

From Problem 3.1, for $t = 1$,

$$(5 + 4t^2)^{-1/2} = 0.33333, \qquad e_t = 0.66666i + 0.66666j + 0.33333k$$

$$(100 + 80t^2)^{-1/2} = 0.07453, \qquad e_n = -0.59624i + 0.74530j - 0.29812k$$

By (3-13),

$$e_b = e_t \times e_n = \begin{vmatrix} i & j & k \\ 0.66666 & 0.66666 & 0.33333 \\ -0.59624 & 0.74530 & -0.29812 \end{vmatrix} = 0.44717i + 0.89435k$$

This result must satisfy

$$e_t = e_n \times e_b = \begin{vmatrix} i & j & k \\ -0.59624 & 0.74530 & -0.29812 \\ -0.44717 & 0 & 0.89435 \end{vmatrix} = 0.66655i + 0.66655j + 0.33327k$$

and also

$$e_n = e_b \times e_t = \begin{vmatrix} i & j & k \\ -0.44717 & 0 & 0.89435 \\ 0.66666 & 0.66666 & 0.33333 \end{vmatrix} = -0.59622i + 0.74527j - 0.29810k$$

3.3 Using the results of Problems 3.1 and 3.2, construct $[\pi^{0s}]$ and $[\pi^{s0}]$ matrices at $t = 1$.

The scalar components of e_t, e_n, e_b are the respective direction cosines of these matrices (3-14 and 3-15),

$$[\pi^{s0}] = \begin{bmatrix} \alpha_t & \beta_t & \gamma_t \\ \alpha_n & \beta_n & \gamma_n \\ \alpha_b & \beta_b & \gamma_b \end{bmatrix} = \begin{bmatrix} 0.66666 & 0.66666 & 0.33333 \\ -0.59624 & 0.74530 & -0.29812 \\ -0.44717 & 0 & 0.89435 \end{bmatrix}$$

$$[\pi^{0s}] = \begin{bmatrix} \alpha_t & \alpha_n & \alpha_b \\ \beta_t & \beta_n & \beta_b \\ \gamma_t & \gamma_n & \gamma_b \end{bmatrix} = \begin{bmatrix} 0.66666 & -0.59624 & -0.44717 \\ 0.66666 & 0.74530 & 0 \\ 0.33333 & -0.29812 & 0.89435 \end{bmatrix}$$

Since these matrices are orthogonal, their determinants must equal $+1$.

$$| \pi^{s0} | = | \pi^{0s} | = 0.99980$$

3.4 Using the transformation matrix equation (3-15), derive the Serret-Frenet formulas (3-16).

The path derivative of (3-15) is

$$[de^0/ds] = [d\pi^{0s}/ds][e^s] + [\pi^{0s}][de^s/ds] \tag{1}$$

where the derivative of a matrix product is obtained as a derivative of the product of two functions, and $[de^0/ds] = 0$.

From (1),

$$[de^s/ds] = -[\pi^{s0}][d\pi^{0s}/ds][e^s] \qquad (2)$$

where by (3-14), (3-15) and (3-9), (3-11), (3-12),

$$\underbrace{\begin{bmatrix} \alpha_t & \beta_t & \gamma_t \\ \alpha_n & \beta_n & \gamma_n \\ \alpha_b & \beta_b & \gamma_b \end{bmatrix}}_{[\pi^{s0}]} \underbrace{\begin{bmatrix} \alpha'_t & \alpha'_n & \alpha'_b \\ \beta'_t & \beta'_n & \beta'_b \\ \gamma'_t & \gamma'_n & \gamma'_b \end{bmatrix}}_{[d\pi^{0s}/ds]} = \begin{bmatrix} e_t \\ e_n \\ e_b \end{bmatrix} \begin{bmatrix} e'_t & e'_n & e'_b \end{bmatrix} = \begin{bmatrix} e_t \cdot e'_t & e_t \cdot e'_n & e_t \cdot e'_b \\ e_n \cdot e'_t & e_n \cdot e'_n & e_n \cdot e'_b \\ e_b \cdot e'_t & e_b \cdot e'_n & e_b \cdot e'_b \end{bmatrix} \qquad (3)$$

By inspection,

$$e_t \cdot e'_t = e_n \cdot e'_n = e_b \cdot e'_b = 0 \quad \text{(normal vectors)} \qquad (4)$$

Since $e_t \cdot e_b = 0$ (normal vectors), the path derivative

$$d[e_t \cdot e_b]/ds = e_t \cdot e'_b + e'_t \cdot e_b = 0$$

where

$$e'_t \cdot e_b = \underbrace{\kappa_1 e_n \cdot e_b}_{0} = 0 \quad \text{(normal vectors)} \qquad (5)$$

and therefore, $e_t \cdot e'_b = e'_t \cdot e_b = 0$.

Finally,

$$\underbrace{d[e_t \cdot e_n]/ds}_{\substack{\text{Normal} \\ \text{vectors}}} = e_t \cdot e'_n + \underbrace{e'_t \cdot e_n}_{\kappa_1} = 0, \qquad e_t \cdot e'_n = -\kappa_1, \qquad e'_t \cdot e_n = \kappa_1 \qquad (6)$$

$$\underbrace{d[e_n \cdot e_b]/ds}_{\substack{\text{Normal} \\ \text{vectors}}} = e_n \cdot e'_b + \underbrace{e'_n \cdot e_b}_{\kappa_2} = 0, \qquad e_n \cdot e'_b = -\kappa_2, \qquad e'_n \cdot e_b = \kappa_2 \qquad (7)$$

where κ_1, κ_2 are respectively the curvature and torsion derived in Problem 3.5.

With (4)-(7), equation (3) inserted in (2) yields

$$\underbrace{\begin{bmatrix} de_t/ds \\ de_n/ds \\ de_b/ds \end{bmatrix}}_{[de^s/ds]} = \underbrace{\begin{bmatrix} 0 & \kappa_1 & 0 \\ -\kappa_1 & 0 & \kappa_2 \\ 0 & -\kappa_2 & 0 \end{bmatrix}}_{-[\pi^{s0}][d\pi^{0s}/ds]} \underbrace{\begin{bmatrix} e_t \\ e_n \\ e_b \end{bmatrix}}_{[e^s]} \qquad (8)$$

which is the desired matrix equation (3-16).

It should be noted that $[de^s/ds]$ can be computed directly in the cartesian system from (3-14) as

$$\begin{bmatrix} de_t/ds \\ de_n/ds \\ de_b/ds \end{bmatrix} = \begin{bmatrix} d\alpha_t/ds & d\beta_t/ds & d\gamma_t/ds \\ d\alpha_n/ds & d\beta_n/ds & d\gamma_n/ds \\ d\alpha_b/ds & d\beta_b/ds & d\gamma_b/ds \end{bmatrix} \begin{bmatrix} i \\ j \\ k \end{bmatrix}$$

where the path derivatives of the direction cosines are frequently simple expressions.

3.5   Using the cross products *(3-13)* derive the expressions for curvature κ_1 and torsion κ_2.

From the orthogonality condition *(3-13)*,

$$\mathbf{e}_t = \mathbf{e}_n \times \mathbf{e}_b, \qquad \mathbf{e}_n = \mathbf{e}_b \times \mathbf{e}_t, \qquad \mathbf{e}_b = \mathbf{e}_t \times \mathbf{e}_n \qquad\qquad (1), (2), (3)$$

The path derivative of $\mathbf{e}_t$ [equation *(3-6)*] is

$$\mathbf{e}_t' = \kappa_1 \mathbf{e}_n \qquad\qquad (4)$$

and

$$\kappa_1 = \lim_{\Delta s \to 0} \left| \frac{\Delta \mathbf{e}_t}{\Delta s} \right| = \left| \frac{d \mathbf{e}_t}{ds} \right| = \sqrt{(x'')^2 + (y'')^2 + (z'')^2}$$

where $\Delta \mathbf{e}_t$ and Δs are defined in Fig. P-3.5a.

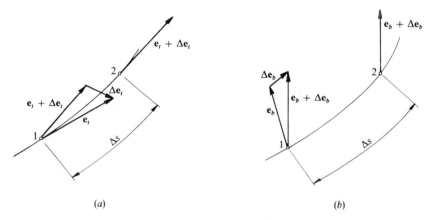

(a)   (b)

Fig. P-3.5

From *(2)*,

$$\mathbf{e}_n' = \mathbf{e}_b \times \mathbf{e}_t' + \mathbf{e}_b' \times \mathbf{e}_t = \mathbf{e}_b \times \kappa_1 \mathbf{e}_n + \mathbf{e}_b' \times \mathbf{e}_t = -\kappa_1 \mathbf{e}_t + \mathbf{e}_b' \times \mathbf{e}_t \qquad\qquad (5)$$

where $\mathbf{e}_b'$ remains to be determined.

Since $\mathbf{e}_b \cdot \mathbf{e}_b = 1$, $d(\mathbf{e}_b \cdot \mathbf{e}_b)/ds = 0$, $\mathbf{e}_b \cdot \mathbf{e}_b' = 0$, and so $\mathbf{e}_b$ and $\mathbf{e}_b'$ are normal.
From *(3)*,

$$\mathbf{e}_b' = \mathbf{e}_t \times \mathbf{e}_n' + \mathbf{e}_t' \times \mathbf{e}_n = \mathbf{e}_t \times \mathbf{e}_n' + \underbrace{\kappa_1 \mathbf{e}_n \times \mathbf{e}_n}_{0}$$

Since $\mathbf{e}_t \cdot \mathbf{e}_b' = \underbrace{\mathbf{e}_t \cdot \mathbf{e}_t}_{0} \times \mathbf{e}_n' = 0$, $\mathbf{e}_t$ and $\mathbf{e}_b'$ are also normal.   Then it can be concluded that $\mathbf{e}_b'$ is

normal to $\mathbf{e}_t$ and $\mathbf{e}_b$, and must be a linear function of $\mathbf{e}_n$.   Hence

$$\mathbf{e}_b' = \lambda \mathbf{e}_n$$

where

$$\lambda = \lim_{\Delta s \to 0} \left| \frac{\Delta \mathbf{e}_b}{\Delta s} \right| = \left| \frac{d\mathbf{e}_b}{ds} \right| = -\frac{1}{\kappa_1^2} \begin{vmatrix} x' & y' & z' \\ x'' & y'' & z'' \\ x''' & y''' & z''' \end{vmatrix} = -[\mathbf{r}' \cdot \mathbf{r}'' \times \mathbf{r}''']/(r'')^2 = -\kappa_2$$

and κ_2 is called the torsion and defined by Fig. P-3.5b, where $\Delta \mathbf{e}_b$ and Δs are shown. Alternatively,

$$\kappa_2 = -\mathbf{e}_n \cdot \mathbf{e}_b' = \mathbf{e}_b \cdot \mathbf{e}_n' = \alpha_b \alpha_n' + \beta_b \beta_n' + \gamma_b \gamma_n'$$

where α_b, β_b, γ_b are given by (3-12) and α_n', β_n', γ_n' are the path derivatives of the direction cosines in (3-11).

The curvature κ_1 defines the deviation of the curve from a straight line (Fig. P-3.5a) and the torsion κ_2 defines the deviation of the curve from a plane (Fig. P-3.5b). The radius of curvature ρ_1 measured along $\mathbf{e}_n$ and the radius of torsion ρ_2 measured along $\mathbf{e}_b$ are respectively

$$\rho_1 = 1/\kappa_1 \qquad \text{and} \qquad \rho_2 = 1/\kappa_2$$

3.6   For the circular helix given by

$$x = R \cos \frac{s}{\sqrt{R^2 + h^2}}, \qquad y = R \sin \frac{s}{\sqrt{R^2 + h^2}}, \qquad z = \frac{hs}{\sqrt{R^2 + h^2}}$$

find $\mathbf{e}_t$, $\mathbf{e}_n$, $\mathbf{e}_b$, $\mathbf{e}_t'$, $\mathbf{e}_n'$, $\mathbf{e}_b'$, κ_1, κ_2, ρ_1, ρ_2.   Given: R, h and $c = \sqrt{R^2 + h^2}$ (Fig. P-3.6).

In (3-9) and (3-11),

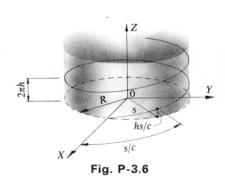

$$x' = -\frac{R}{c} \sin \frac{s}{c}, \qquad y' = \frac{R}{c} \cos \frac{s}{c}, \qquad z' = \frac{h}{c}$$

$$\mathbf{e}_t = \frac{R}{c} \left[\left(-\sin \frac{s}{c} \right) \mathbf{i} + \left(\cos \frac{s}{c} \right) \mathbf{j} \right] + \frac{h}{c} \mathbf{k}$$

$$x'' = -\frac{R}{c^2} \cos \frac{s}{c}, \qquad y'' = -\frac{R}{c^2} \sin \frac{s}{c}, \qquad z'' = 0$$

$$\mathbf{e}_n = -\left[\left(\cos \frac{s}{c} \right) \mathbf{i} + \left(\sin \frac{s}{c} \right) \mathbf{j} \right], \qquad \kappa_1 = \frac{R}{c^2}, \qquad \rho_1 = \frac{c^2}{R}$$

Fig. P-3.6

By (3-12),

$$\mathbf{e}_b = \mathbf{e}_t \times \mathbf{e}_n = \begin{vmatrix} \mathbf{i} & \mathbf{j} & \mathbf{k} \\ -\frac{R}{c} \sin \frac{s}{c} & \frac{R}{c} \cos \frac{s}{c} & \frac{h}{c} \\ -\cos \frac{s}{c} & -\sin \frac{s}{c} & 0 \end{vmatrix} = \left(\frac{h}{c} \sin \frac{s}{c} \right) \mathbf{i} - \left(\frac{h}{c} \cos \frac{s}{c} \right) \mathbf{j} + \frac{R}{c} \mathbf{k}$$

$$\mathbf{e}_b' = \left(\frac{h}{c^2} \cos \frac{s}{c} \right) \mathbf{i} + \left(\frac{h}{c^2} \sin \frac{s}{c} \right) \mathbf{j} = -\frac{h}{c^2} \mathbf{e}_n, \qquad \kappa_2 = \frac{h}{c^2}, \qquad \rho_2 = \frac{c^2}{h}$$

3.7   Construct the angular transformation matrix *(3-14)* for the helix of Problem 3.6 and show its relationship to the Sarre-Frenet matrix *(3-16)*.

By *(3-14)*, and in terms of results of Problem 3.6,

$$
\begin{bmatrix} \mathbf{e}_t \\[6pt] \mathbf{e}_n \\[6pt] \mathbf{e}_b \end{bmatrix}
=
\begin{bmatrix}
-\dfrac{R}{c}\sin\dfrac{s}{c} & \dfrac{R}{c}\cos\dfrac{s}{c} & \dfrac{h}{c} \\[8pt]
-\cos\dfrac{s}{c} & -\sin\dfrac{s}{c} & 0 \\[8pt]
\dfrac{h}{c}\sin\dfrac{s}{c} & \dfrac{h}{c}\cos\dfrac{s}{c} & \dfrac{r}{c}
\end{bmatrix}
\begin{bmatrix} \mathbf{i} \\[6pt] \mathbf{j} \\[6pt] \mathbf{k} \end{bmatrix}
$$

$$\underbrace{}_{[\mathbf{e}^s]} \qquad \underbrace{}_{[\pi^{s0}]} \qquad \underbrace{}_{[\mathbf{e}^0]}$$

By direct differentiation and in terms of κ_1, κ_2 of Problem 3.6,

$$
\begin{bmatrix} \mathbf{e}'_t \\[6pt] \mathbf{e}'_n \\[6pt] \mathbf{e}'_b \end{bmatrix}
=
\begin{bmatrix}
-\dfrac{R}{c^2}\cos\dfrac{s}{c} & -\dfrac{R}{c^2}\sin\dfrac{s}{c} & 0 \\[8pt]
\dfrac{1}{c}\sin\dfrac{s}{c} & -\dfrac{1}{c}\cos\dfrac{s}{c} & 0 \\[8pt]
\dfrac{h}{c^2}\cos\dfrac{s}{c} & +\dfrac{h}{c^2}\sin\dfrac{s}{c} & 0
\end{bmatrix}
\begin{bmatrix} \mathbf{i} \\[6pt] \mathbf{j} \\[6pt] \mathbf{k} \end{bmatrix}
=
\begin{bmatrix}
0 & \dfrac{R}{c^2} & 0 \\[8pt]
-\dfrac{R}{c^2} & 0 & \dfrac{h}{c^2} \\[8pt]
0 & -\dfrac{h}{c^2} & 0
\end{bmatrix}
\begin{bmatrix} \mathbf{e}_t \\[6pt] \mathbf{e}_n \\[6pt] \mathbf{e}_b \end{bmatrix}
$$

$$\underbrace{}_{[d\mathbf{e}^s/ds]} \quad \underbrace{}_{[d\pi^{s0}/ds]} \quad \underbrace{}_{[\mathbf{e}^0]} \qquad \underbrace{}_{[d\pi^{s0}/ds]\,[\pi^{0s}]} \quad \underbrace{}_{[\mathbf{e}^s]}$$

where by *(3-37)*,

$$[\pi^{0s}] = [\pi^{s0}]^T$$

which shows the simplicity of the matrix derivation of the Serret–Frenet formulas.

3.8   Find the center of curvature and of torsion of the helix of Problem 3.6 at $s = c\pi$.

By *(3-19)*, and in terms of results of Problems 3.6 and 3.7,

$$
\mathbf{r}_1 = \mathbf{r} + \rho_1 \mathbf{e}_n = \left(R\cos\dfrac{s}{c}\right)\mathbf{i} + \left(R\sin\dfrac{s}{c}\right)\mathbf{j} + \dfrac{hs}{c}\mathbf{k} + \dfrac{c^2}{R}\left[\left(-\cos\dfrac{s}{c}\right)\mathbf{i} - \left(\sin\dfrac{s}{c}\right)\mathbf{j}\right]
$$

$$
= -\dfrac{h^2}{R}\left[\left(\cos\dfrac{s}{c}\right)\mathbf{i} + \left(\sin\dfrac{s}{c}\right)\mathbf{j}\right] + \dfrac{hs}{c}\mathbf{k}
$$

By *(3-20)*, and in terms of results of Problems 3.6 and 3.7,

$$
\mathbf{r}_2 = \mathbf{r} + \rho_2 \mathbf{e}_b = \left(R\cos\dfrac{s}{c}\right)\mathbf{i} + \left(R\sin\dfrac{s}{c}\right)\mathbf{j} + \dfrac{hs}{c}\mathbf{k} + \dfrac{c^2}{h}\left[\left(\dfrac{h}{c}\sin\dfrac{s}{c}\right)\mathbf{i} - \left(\dfrac{h}{c}\cos\dfrac{s}{c}\right)\mathbf{j} + \dfrac{R}{c}\mathbf{k}\right]
$$

$$
= \left(R\cos\dfrac{s}{c} + c\sin\dfrac{s}{c}\right)\mathbf{i} + \left(R\sin\dfrac{s}{c} - c\cos\dfrac{s}{c}\right)\mathbf{j} + \left(\dfrac{Rc}{h} + \dfrac{hs}{c}\right)\mathbf{k}
$$

At $s = c\pi$,

$$\mathbf{r}_1 = \frac{h^2}{R}\mathbf{i} + h\pi\mathbf{k}, \qquad \mathbf{r}_2 = -R\mathbf{i} + c\mathbf{j} + \left(\frac{Rc}{h} + h\pi\right)\mathbf{k}$$

EQUATIONS OF MOTION, CARTESIAN SYSTEM

3.9 The path of a moving particle is given by $\mathbf{r} = 2t\mathbf{i} + t^2\mathbf{j} + t\mathbf{k}$ where t is time. Find the equations of motion.

By (*3-21*), the velocity vector is

$$\mathbf{v} = \dot{\mathbf{r}} = d\mathbf{r}/dt = 2\mathbf{i} + 2t\mathbf{j} + \mathbf{k}$$

and the acceleration vector is

$$\mathbf{a} = \dot{\mathbf{v}} = \ddot{\mathbf{r}} = d^2\mathbf{r}/dt^2 = 2\mathbf{j}$$

The respective magnitudes are

$$r = \sqrt{(2t)^2 + (t^2)^2 + t^2} = t\sqrt{5 + t^2}, \qquad v = \sqrt{2^2 + (2t)^2 + 1^2} = \sqrt{5 + 4t^2}, \qquad a = 2$$

The unit vectors are

$$\mathbf{e}_r = (2/\sqrt{5 + t^2})\mathbf{i} + (t/\sqrt{5 + t^2})\mathbf{j} + (1/\sqrt{5 + t^2})\mathbf{k}$$

$$\mathbf{e}_v = (2/\sqrt{5 + 4t^2})\mathbf{i} + (2t/\sqrt{5 + 4t^2})\mathbf{j} + (1/\sqrt{5 + 4t^2})\mathbf{k}, \qquad \mathbf{e}_a = \mathbf{j}$$

The initial vectors (at $t = 0$) are $\mathbf{r}_0 = 0$, $\mathbf{v}_0 = 2\mathbf{i} + \mathbf{k}$, $\mathbf{a}_0 = 2\mathbf{j}$, and the motion is uniformly accelerated.

3.10 The velocity vector of a moving particle is

$$\mathbf{v} = R(\cos t - t \sin t)\mathbf{i} + R(\sin t + t \cos t)\mathbf{j} + h\mathbf{k}$$

where R, h are constants and t is time (Fig. P-3.10). Find the path of motion. Given: R, h, $x(0) = 0$, $y(0) = 0$, $z(0) = 0$.

By definition,

$$\mathbf{r} = \mathbf{i}R\int_0^t (\cos t - t \sin t)\, dt \; + \; \mathbf{i}C_1$$

$$+ \; \mathbf{j}R\int_0^t (\sin t - t \cos t)\, dt \; + \; \mathbf{j}C_2$$

$$+ \; \mathbf{k}h\int_0^t dt \; + \; \mathbf{k}C_3$$

$$= \mathbf{i}(Rt \cos t + C_1) \; + \; \mathbf{j}(Rt \sin t + C_2)$$

$$+ \; \mathbf{k}(ht + C_3)$$

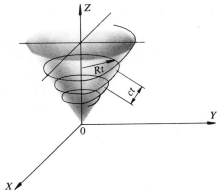

Fig. P-3.10

Since at $t = 0$, $\mathbf{r} = 0$, $C_1 = C_2 = C_3 = 0$ and so

$$\mathbf{r} = \mathbf{i}(Rt \cos t) + \mathbf{j}(Rt \sin t) + \mathbf{k}(ht)$$

where $r = t\sqrt{R^2 + h^2} = tc$.

By inspection, the path is a conical helix of normal radius Rt, surface radius $t\sqrt{R^2 + h^2} = tc$, and surface slope $\tan \delta = h/R$ (Fig. P-3.10).

EQUATIONS OF MOTION, CYLINDRICAL COORDINATES

3.11 Derive the transformation relations between the cartesian coordinates $x = x(t)$, $y = y(t)$, $z = z(t)$ and the cylindrical coordinates $c = c(t)$, $\theta = \theta(t)$, $z = z(t)$, and vice versa.

Referring to Figs. 3-3, page 54, and 3-4, page 55,

$$x = c \cos \theta, \qquad y = c \sin \theta, \qquad z = z \tag{1}$$

$$c = \sqrt{x^2 + y^2}, \qquad \theta = \tan^{-1}\frac{y}{x}, \qquad z = z \tag{2}$$

3.12 Derive the transformation relations between the cartesian unit vectors $\mathbf{i}$, $\mathbf{j}$, $\mathbf{k}$ and the cylindrical unit vectors $\mathbf{e}_c$, $\mathbf{e}_\theta$, $\mathbf{e}_z$, and vice versa.

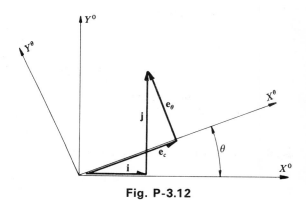

Fig. P-3.12

Referring to Fig. P-3.12,

$$\left.\begin{aligned} \mathbf{i} &= \mathbf{e}_c \cos \theta - \mathbf{e}_\theta \sin \theta \\ \mathbf{j} &= \mathbf{e}_c \sin \theta + \mathbf{e}_\theta \cos \theta \\ \mathbf{k} &= \mathbf{e}_z \end{aligned}\right\} \tag{1}$$

$$\left.\begin{aligned} \mathbf{e}_c &= \mathbf{i} \cos \theta + \mathbf{j} \sin \theta \\ \mathbf{e}_\theta &= -\mathbf{i} \sin \theta + \mathbf{j} \cos \theta \\ \mathbf{e}_z &= \mathbf{k} \end{aligned}\right\} \tag{2}$$

3.13 Using the relations (1), (2) of Problem 3.12, derive the time derivatives of $\mathbf{e}_c$, $\mathbf{e}_\theta$, $\mathbf{e}_z$.

Since $\mathbf{i}$, $\mathbf{j}$, $\mathbf{k}$ are independent of time, by (1) of Problem 3.12,

$$\begin{aligned} d\mathbf{i}/dt &= \dot{\mathbf{e}}_c \cos \theta - \mathbf{e}_c \dot{\theta} \sin \theta - \dot{\mathbf{e}}_\theta \sin \theta - \mathbf{e}_\theta \dot{\theta} \cos \theta = 0 \\ d\mathbf{j}/dt &= \dot{\mathbf{e}}_c \sin \theta + \mathbf{e}_c \dot{\theta} \cos \theta + \dot{\mathbf{e}} \cos \theta - \mathbf{e}_\theta \dot{\theta} \sin \theta = 0 \\ d\mathbf{k}/dt &= \dot{\mathbf{e}}_z = 0 \end{aligned} \tag{1}$$

Since $\mathbf{e}_c$, $\mathbf{e}_\theta$, $\mathbf{e}_z$ are functions of time, by (2) of Problem 3.12,

$$\begin{aligned} d\mathbf{e}_c/dt &= -\mathbf{i}\dot{\theta} \sin \theta + \mathbf{j}\dot{\theta} \cos \theta = \dot{\mathbf{e}}_c \\ d\mathbf{e}_\theta/dt &= -\mathbf{i}\dot{\theta} \cos \theta - \mathbf{j}\dot{\theta} \sin \theta = \dot{\mathbf{e}}_\theta \\ d\mathbf{e}_z/dt &= 0 = \dot{\mathbf{e}}_z \end{aligned} \tag{2}$$

and in terms of (2) of Problem 3.12,

$$\dot{\mathbf{e}}_c = \dot{\theta}\mathbf{e}_\theta, \qquad \dot{\mathbf{e}}_\theta = -\dot{\theta}\mathbf{e}_c, \qquad \dot{\mathbf{e}}_z = 0 \qquad\qquad (3)$$

which are (3-23).

The second time derivatives, obtained by differentiating (3) and using (2) of Problem 3.12, are

$$\ddot{\mathbf{e}}_c = \ddot{\theta}\mathbf{e}_\theta + \dot{\theta}\dot{\mathbf{e}}_\theta = \ddot{\theta}\mathbf{e}_\theta - \dot{\theta}^2\mathbf{e}_c, \qquad \ddot{\mathbf{e}}_\theta = -\ddot{\theta}\mathbf{e}_c - \dot{\theta}\dot{\mathbf{e}}_c = -\ddot{\theta}\mathbf{e}_c - \dot{\theta}^2\mathbf{e}_\theta, \qquad \ddot{\mathbf{e}}_z = 0 \qquad (4)$$

3.14 Derive the equations of space motion in cylindrical coordinates, (3-22).   Given: cylindrical coordinates $c = \theta c(t)$, $\theta = \theta(t)$, $z = z(t)$.

Referring to Fig. 3-4, page 55,

$$\mathbf{r} = c\mathbf{e}_c + z\mathbf{e}_z \qquad\qquad (1)$$

In terms of the time derivatives (3), (4) of Problem 3.13,

$$\mathbf{v} = \dot{\mathbf{r}} = \dot{c}\mathbf{e}_c + c\dot{\mathbf{e}}_c + \dot{z}\mathbf{e}_z + z\overset{0}{\cancel{\dot{\mathbf{e}}_z}} = \dot{c}\mathbf{e}_c + c\dot{\theta}\mathbf{e}_\theta + \dot{z}\mathbf{e}_z = v_c\theta_c + v_\theta\mathbf{e}_\theta + v_z\mathbf{e}_z$$

$$\mathbf{a} = \dot{\mathbf{v}} = \ddot{\mathbf{r}} = \ddot{c}\mathbf{e}_c + \dot{c}\dot{\mathbf{e}}_c + \dot{c}\dot{\mathbf{e}}_c + c\ddot{\mathbf{e}}_c + \ddot{z}\mathbf{e}_z + z\overset{0}{\cancel{\ddot{\mathbf{e}}_z}}$$
$$= \ddot{c}\mathbf{e}_c + 2\dot{c}\dot{\theta}\mathbf{e} + c\ddot{\theta}\mathbf{e}_\theta - c\dot{\theta}^2\mathbf{e}_c + \ddot{z}\mathbf{e}_z$$
$$= (\ddot{c} - c\dot{\theta}^2)\mathbf{e}_c + (c\ddot{\theta} + 2\dot{c}\dot{\theta})\mathbf{e}_\theta + \ddot{z}\mathbf{e}_z = a_c\mathbf{e}_c + a_\theta\mathbf{e}_\theta + a_z\mathbf{e}_z$$

3.15 The path of a moving particle is given parametrically by $c = R$, $\theta = t$, $z = ht$.   Find the equations of motion and describe the path.   Given: $R, h = $ constants.

By (3-22) and (3-23),

$$\mathbf{r} = R\mathbf{e}_c + ht\mathbf{e}_z$$

$$\mathbf{v} = \dot{\mathbf{r}} = \overset{0}{\cancel{\dot{R}\mathbf{e}_c}} + R\dot{\theta}\mathbf{e}_\theta + \dot{z}\mathbf{e}_z = R\mathbf{e}_\theta + h\mathbf{e}_z$$

$$\mathbf{a} = \ddot{\mathbf{r}} = (\overset{0}{\cancel{\ddot{R}}} - R\dot{\theta}^2)\mathbf{e}_c + (\overset{0}{\cancel{R\ddot{\theta}}} + 2\overset{0}{\cancel{\dot{R}\dot{\theta}}})\mathbf{e}_\theta + \overset{0}{\cancel{\ddot{z}\mathbf{e}_z}} = -R\mathbf{e}_c$$

Note: The path is a circular helix of cartesian equation $\mathbf{r} = (R\cos t)\mathbf{i} + (R\sin t)\mathbf{j} + ht\mathbf{k}$.

3.16 Solve Problem 3.15 in the cartesian system and compare both solutions.

By (3-21), in the cartesian system,

$$\dot{\mathbf{r}} = \underbrace{(-R\sin t)\mathbf{i} + (R\cos t)\mathbf{j}}_{R\mathbf{e}_\theta} + \underbrace{h\mathbf{k}}_{h\mathbf{e}_z}$$

$$\ddot{\mathbf{r}} = \underbrace{(-R\cos t)\mathbf{i} + (-R\sin t)\mathbf{j}}_{-R\mathbf{e}_c}$$

Note the simplicity of the formulation in the cylindrical coordinate system.   Also note that from the solution of Problem 3.15 it is immediately apparent that $\mathbf{r}$ varies linearly with time and that $\mathbf{v}, \mathbf{a}$ are constants.

The velocity vector is tangent to the path,

$$\tan \psi_r = \tan \psi_v = h/R$$

and the acceleration vector is normal to the cylindrical surface and directed toward the Z axis.

EQUATIONS OF MOTION, SPHERICAL COORDINATES

3.17 Derive the transformation relationships between the cylindrical coordinates $c = c(t)$, $\theta = (t)$, $z = z(t)$ and the spherical coordinates $\phi = (t)$, $\theta = \theta(t)$, $r = r(t)$, and vice versa.

Referring to Figs. 3-4 and 3-5,

$$c = r \sin \phi, \qquad \theta = \theta, \qquad z = r \cos \phi \qquad (1)$$

$$\phi = \cos^{-1} \frac{z}{\sqrt{c^2 + z^2}}, \qquad \theta = \theta, \qquad r = \sqrt{c^2 + z^2} \qquad (2)$$

3.18 Derive the transformation relations between the cartesian coordinates $x = x(t)$, $y = y(t)$, $z = z(t)$ and the spherical coordinates $\phi = \phi(t)$, $\theta = \theta(t)$, $r = r(t)$, and vice versa.

Referring to Figs. 3-3 and 3-5,

$$x = r \sin \phi \cos \theta, \qquad y = r \sin \phi \sin \theta, \qquad z = r \cos \phi \qquad (1)$$

$$\phi = \cos^{-1} \frac{z}{\sqrt{x^2 + y^2 + z^2}}, \qquad \theta = \tan^{-1} \frac{y}{x}, \qquad r = \sqrt{x^2 + y^2 + z^2} \qquad (2)$$

3.19 Derive the transformation relation between the cylindrical unit vectors $\mathbf{e}_c$, $\mathbf{e}_\theta$, $\mathbf{e}_z$ and the spherical unit vectors $\mathbf{e}_\phi$, $\mathbf{e}_\theta$, $\mathbf{e}_r$, and vice versa.

Referring to Fig. P-3.19,

$$\left.\begin{array}{l} \mathbf{e}_c = \mathbf{e}_\phi \cos \phi + \mathbf{e}_r \sin \phi \\ \mathbf{e}_\theta = \mathbf{e}_\theta \\ \mathbf{e}_z = -\mathbf{e}_\phi \sin \phi + \mathbf{e}_r \cos \phi \end{array}\right\} \qquad (1)$$

$$\left.\begin{array}{l} \mathbf{e}_\phi = \mathbf{e}_c \cos \phi - \mathbf{e}_z \sin \phi \\ \mathbf{e}_\theta = \mathbf{e}_\theta \\ \mathbf{e}_r = \mathbf{e}_c \sin \phi + \mathbf{e}_z \cos \phi \end{array}\right\} \qquad (2)$$

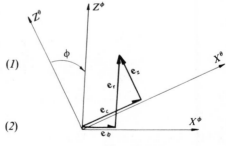

Fig. P-3.19

3.20 Using the results of Problems 3.12 and 3.19, derive the transformation relations between the cartesian unit vectors $\mathbf{i}$, $\mathbf{j}$, $\mathbf{k}$ and the spherical unit vectors $\mathbf{e}_\phi$, $\mathbf{e}_\theta$, $\mathbf{e}_v$, and vice versa.

From (1) and (2) of Problem 3.12,

$$\underbrace{\begin{bmatrix} \mathbf{i} \\ \mathbf{j} \\ \mathbf{k} \end{bmatrix}}_{[\mathbf{e}^0]} = \underbrace{\begin{bmatrix} \cos \theta & -\sin \theta & 0 \\ \sin \theta & \cos \theta & 0 \\ 0 & 0 & 1 \end{bmatrix}}_{[\pi^{0\theta}]} \underbrace{\begin{bmatrix} \mathbf{e}_c \\ \mathbf{e}_\theta \\ \mathbf{e}_z \end{bmatrix}}_{[\mathbf{e}^\theta]}, \qquad \underbrace{\begin{bmatrix} \mathbf{e}_c \\ \mathbf{e}_\theta \\ \mathbf{e}_z \end{bmatrix}}_{[\mathbf{e}^\theta]} = \underbrace{\begin{bmatrix} \cos \theta & \sin \theta & 0 \\ -\sin \theta & \cos \theta & 0 \\ 0 & 0 & 1 \end{bmatrix}}_{[\pi^{\theta 0}]} \underbrace{\begin{bmatrix} \mathbf{i} \\ \mathbf{j} \\ \mathbf{k} \end{bmatrix}}_{[\mathbf{e}^0]} \qquad (1), (2)$$

which are similar to the transformation matrix equations *(3-29)* and *(3-30)*.

From *(1)* and *(2)* of Problem 3.19,

$$
\underbrace{\begin{bmatrix} \mathbf{e}_c \\ \mathbf{e}_\theta \\ \mathbf{e}_z \end{bmatrix}}_{[\mathbf{e}^\theta]} = \underbrace{\begin{bmatrix} \cos\phi & 0 & \sin\phi \\ 0 & 1 & 0 \\ -\sin\phi & 0 & \cos\phi \end{bmatrix}}_{[\pi^{\theta\phi}]} \underbrace{\begin{bmatrix} \mathbf{e}_\phi \\ \mathbf{e}_\theta \\ \mathbf{e}_r \end{bmatrix}}_{[\mathbf{e}^\phi]}, \qquad \underbrace{\begin{bmatrix} \mathbf{e}_\phi \\ \mathbf{e}_\theta \\ \mathbf{e}_r \end{bmatrix}}_{[\mathbf{e}^\phi]} = \underbrace{\begin{bmatrix} \cos\phi & 0 & -\sin\phi \\ 0 & 1 & 0 \\ \sin\phi & 0 & \cos\phi \end{bmatrix}}_{[\pi^{\phi\theta}]} \underbrace{\begin{bmatrix} \mathbf{e}_c \\ \mathbf{e}_\theta \\ \mathbf{e}_z \end{bmatrix}}_{[\mathbf{e}^\theta]} \qquad (3),(4)
$$

which are similar to the transformation matrix equations *(3-38)* and *(3-39)*.

On substituting *(3)* into *(1)*,

$$
\underbrace{\begin{bmatrix} \mathbf{i} \\ \mathbf{j} \\ \mathbf{k} \end{bmatrix}}_{[\mathbf{e}^0]} = \underbrace{\underbrace{\begin{bmatrix} \cos\theta\cos\phi & -\sin\theta & \cos\theta\sin\phi \\ \sin\theta\cos\phi & \cos\theta & \sin\theta\sin\phi \\ -\sin\phi & 0 & \cos\phi \end{bmatrix}}_{[\pi^{0\theta}]\,[\pi^{\theta\phi}]}}_{[\pi^{0\phi}]} \underbrace{\begin{bmatrix} \mathbf{e}_\phi \\ \mathbf{e}_\theta \\ \mathbf{e}_r \end{bmatrix}}_{[\mathbf{e}^\phi]} \qquad (5)
$$

and *(2)* into *(4)*,

$$
\underbrace{\begin{bmatrix} \mathbf{e}_\phi \\ \mathbf{e}_\theta \\ \mathbf{e}_r \end{bmatrix}}_{[\mathbf{e}^\phi]} = \underbrace{\underbrace{\begin{bmatrix} \cos\theta\cos\phi & \sin\theta\cos\phi & \sin\phi \\ -\sin\theta & \cos\theta & 0 \\ \cos\theta\sin\phi & \sin\theta\sin\phi & \cos\phi \end{bmatrix}}_{[\pi^{\phi\theta}]\,[\pi^{\theta 0}]}}_{[\pi^{\phi 0}]} \underbrace{\begin{bmatrix} \mathbf{i} \\ \mathbf{j} \\ \mathbf{k} \end{bmatrix}}_{[\mathbf{e}^0]} \qquad (6)
$$

which are similar to the transformation matrix equations *(3-32)* and *(3-33)*.

3.21 Using the relations *(5)* and *(6)* of Problem 3.20, derive the time derivatives of $\mathbf{e}_\phi$, $\mathbf{e}_\theta$, $\mathbf{e}_r$ given by *(3-25)*.

By *(5)* of Problem 3.20,

$$[\dot{\mathbf{e}}^0] = [\pi^{0\phi}][\dot{\mathbf{e}}^\phi] + [\dot{\pi}^{0\phi}][\mathbf{e}^\phi] = [0] \qquad (1)$$

from which

$$[\dot{\mathbf{e}}^\phi] = -[\pi^{0\phi}]^{-1}[\dot{\pi}^{0\phi}][\mathbf{e}^\phi] \qquad (2)$$

where by orthogonality, $[\pi^{0\phi}]^{-1} = [\pi^{0\phi}]^T = [\pi^{\phi 0}]$. The evaluation of *(2)* then yields

$$
\begin{bmatrix} \dot{\mathbf{e}}_\phi \\ \dot{\mathbf{e}}_\theta \\ \dot{\mathbf{e}}_r \end{bmatrix} = \begin{bmatrix} 0 & \lambda_1 & -\dot{\phi} \\ -\lambda_1 & 0 & -\lambda_2 \\ \dot{\phi} & \lambda_2 & 0 \end{bmatrix} \begin{bmatrix} \mathbf{e}_\phi \\ \mathbf{e}_\theta \\ \mathbf{e}_r \end{bmatrix} \qquad (3)
$$

where $\lambda_1 = \dot{\theta}\cos\phi$ and $\lambda_2 = \dot{\theta}\sin\phi$.

3.22 Derive the equations of space motion in spherical coordinates, *(3-24)*. Given: spherical coordinates $\phi = \phi(t)$, $\theta = \theta(t)$, $r = r(t)$.

Referring to Fig. 3-5, page 56,

$$\mathbf{r} = r\mathbf{e}_r \tag{1}$$

where r is the radius, $\mathbf{e}_r$ is the unit radial vector and the remaining unit vectors in Fig. 3-5 are $\mathbf{e}_\phi$, $\mathbf{e}_\theta$. In terms of the time derivatives *(3)* of Problem 3.21,

$$\mathbf{v} = \dot{\mathbf{r}} = \dot{r}\mathbf{e}_r + r\dot{\mathbf{e}}_r = r\dot{\phi}\mathbf{e}_\phi + (r\dot{\theta}\sin\phi)\mathbf{e}_\theta + \dot{r}\mathbf{e}_r = v_\phi\mathbf{e}_\phi + v_\theta\mathbf{e}_\theta + v_r\mathbf{e}_r \tag{2}$$

$$
\begin{aligned}
\mathbf{a} = \dot{\mathbf{v}} = \ddot{\mathbf{r}} &= \dot{r}\dot{\phi}\mathbf{e}_\phi + r\ddot{\phi}\mathbf{e}_\phi + r\dot{\phi}\dot{\mathbf{e}}_\phi + (\dot{r}\dot{\theta}\sin\phi)\mathbf{e}_\theta + (r\ddot{\theta}\sin\phi)\mathbf{e}_\theta + (r\dot{\theta}^2\cos\phi)\mathbf{e}_\theta \\
&\quad + (r\dot{\theta}\sin\phi)\dot{\mathbf{e}}_\theta + \ddot{r}\mathbf{e}_r + \dot{r}\dot{\mathbf{e}}_r \\
&= (2\dot{r}\dot{\phi} + r\ddot{\phi} - r\dot{\theta}^2\sin\phi\cos\phi)\mathbf{e}_\phi \\
&\quad + (2\dot{r}\dot{\theta}\sin\phi + r\ddot{\theta}\sin\phi + 2r\dot{\phi}\dot{\theta}\cos\phi)\mathbf{e}_\theta + (\ddot{r} - r\dot{\phi}^2 - r\dot{\theta}^2\sin^2\phi)\mathbf{e}_r \\
&= a_\phi\mathbf{e}_\phi + a_\theta\mathbf{e}_\theta + a_r\mathbf{e}_r
\end{aligned}
\tag{3}
$$

3.23 The path of a moving particle is given parametrically by $\phi = \omega t$, $\theta = \omega t$, $r = R$. Find the equations of motion. Given: R, $\omega = $ constants.

Referring to Fig. 3-5,

$$\mathbf{r} = r\mathbf{e}_r = R\mathbf{e}_r$$

By *(3-24)*,

$$\mathbf{v} = \dot{\mathbf{r}} = (R)(\omega)\mathbf{e}_\phi + (R)(\omega)(\sin\omega t)\mathbf{e}_\theta + (0)\mathbf{e}_r = R\omega[\mathbf{e}_\phi + (\sin\omega t)\mathbf{e}_\theta]$$

where $v_\phi = R\omega$, $v_\theta = R\omega\sin\omega t$, $v_r = 0$.

$$
\begin{aligned}
\mathbf{a} = \ddot{\mathbf{r}} &= [2(0)(\omega) + (R)(0) - (R)(\omega^2)(\sin\omega t)(\cos\omega t)]\mathbf{e}_\phi \\
&\quad + [2(0)(\omega)(\sin\omega t) + (R)(0)(\sin\omega t) + 2(R)(\omega)(\omega)(\cos\omega t)]\mathbf{e}_\theta \\
&\quad + [(0) - (R)(\omega^2) - (R)(\omega^2)\sin^2\omega t]\mathbf{e}_r \\
&= -(R\omega^2\sin\omega t\cos\omega t)\mathbf{e}_\phi + (2R\omega^2\cos\omega t)\mathbf{e}_\theta - R\omega^2(1 + \sin^2\omega t)\mathbf{e}_r
\end{aligned}
$$

where $a_\phi = R\omega(1 + \omega\sin\omega t\cos\omega t)$, $a_\theta = 2R\omega^2\cos\omega t$, $a_r = R\omega^2(1 + \sin^2\omega t)$.

3.24 Express the equations of motion of the particle of Problem 3.23 in the cartesian system.

By *(1)* of Problem 3.18,

$$x = (R\sin 2\omega t)/2, \qquad y = R\sin^2\omega t, \qquad z = R\cos\omega t$$

By *(3-21)*,

$$
\begin{aligned}
\mathbf{r} &= (R/2)[(\sin 2\omega t)\mathbf{i} + (2\sin^2\omega t)\mathbf{j} + (2\cos\omega t)\mathbf{k}] \\
\mathbf{v} = \dot{\mathbf{r}} &= R\omega[(2\cos 2\omega t)\mathbf{i} + (\sin 2\omega t)\mathbf{j} - (2\sin\omega t)\mathbf{k}] \\
\mathbf{a} = \ddot{\mathbf{r}} &= -R\omega^2[(4\sin 2\omega t)\mathbf{i} - (2\cos 2\omega t)\mathbf{j} + (2\cos\omega t)\mathbf{k}]
\end{aligned}
$$

EQUATIONS OF MOTION, CURVILINEAR COORDINATES

3.25 The path of a moving particle is given by $\mathbf{r} = (R \cos \omega t)\mathbf{i} + (R \sin \omega t)\mathbf{j} + h\omega t\mathbf{k}$.   Find its equation of motion in curvilinear coordinates.   Given: $R, \omega, h, c = \sqrt{R^2 + h^2}$.

By (3-26),

$$\mathbf{e}_t = \frac{\dot{\mathbf{r}}}{\dot{r}} = \frac{R\omega[(-\sin \omega t)\mathbf{i} + (\cos \omega t)\mathbf{j}] + h\omega\mathbf{k}}{\sqrt{(-R\omega \sin \omega t)^2 + (R\omega \cos \omega t)^2 + (h\omega)^2}} = \frac{R}{c}[(-\sin \omega t)\mathbf{i} + (\cos \omega t)\mathbf{j}] + \frac{h}{c}\mathbf{k}$$

$$\kappa_1 \mathbf{e}_n = \frac{d\mathbf{e}_t}{ds} = \frac{d\mathbf{e}_t/dt}{ds/dt} = \frac{\dot{\mathbf{e}}_t}{\dot{r}} = -\frac{R}{c^2}[(\cos \omega t)\mathbf{i} + (\sin \omega t)\mathbf{j}]$$

where

$$\kappa_1 = \left| \frac{\dot{\mathbf{e}}_t}{\dot{r}} \right| = \sqrt{\left(\frac{-R \cos \omega t}{c^2} \right)^2 + \left(\frac{-R \sin \omega t}{c^2} \right)^2} = \frac{R}{c^2} = \frac{1}{\rho_1}$$

and

$$\mathbf{e}_n = -[(\cos \omega t)\mathbf{i} + (\sin \omega t)\mathbf{j}]$$

The third unit vector given by (3-12) is

$$\mathbf{e}_b = \mathbf{e}_t \times \mathbf{e}_n = \frac{h}{c}[(\sin \omega t)\mathbf{i} - (\cos \omega t)\mathbf{j}] + \frac{R}{c}\mathbf{k}$$

With the unit vectors known, the position vector of the particle in this new system is

$$\mathbf{r} = (\mathbf{r} \cdot \mathbf{e}_t)\mathbf{e}_t + (\mathbf{r} \cdot \mathbf{e}_n)\mathbf{e}_n + (\mathbf{r} \cdot \mathbf{e}_b)\mathbf{e}_b = (h^2\omega t/c)\mathbf{e}_t - R\mathbf{e}_n + (Rh\omega t/c)\mathbf{e}_b$$

By (1-21) the velocity and acceleration vectors in the same system are

$$\mathbf{v} = \dot{r}\mathbf{e}_t = c\omega\mathbf{e}_t$$
$$\mathbf{a} = \ddot{r}\mathbf{e}_t + (\dot{r}^2/\rho_1)\mathbf{e}_n = (0)\mathbf{e}_t + [(\omega c)^2/(c^2/R)]\mathbf{e}_n = R\omega^2\mathbf{e}_n$$

which shows the simplicity of this form of equations of motion.

3.26 Using the results of Problem 3.25, show that the magnitudes of $\mathbf{r}, \mathbf{v}, \mathbf{a}$ are invariants.

The magnitude of $\mathbf{r} = (R \cos \omega t)\mathbf{i} + (R \sin \omega t)\mathbf{j} + h\omega t\mathbf{k}$ is

$$r = \sqrt{r_x^2 + r_y^2 + r_z^2} = \sqrt{(R \cos \omega t)^2 + (R \sin \omega t)^2 + (h\omega t)^2} = \sqrt{R^2 + h^2\omega^2 t^2}$$

and of $\mathbf{r} = (h^2\omega t/c)\mathbf{e}_t + (-R)\mathbf{e}_n + (Rh\omega t/c)\mathbf{e}_b$ is

$$r = \sqrt{r_t^2 + r_n^2 + r_b^2} = \sqrt{(h^2\omega t/c)^2 + (-R)^2 + (Rh\omega t/c)^2} = \sqrt{R^2 + h^2\omega^2 t^2}$$

The magnitude of $\mathbf{v} = -R\omega[(\sin \omega t)\mathbf{i} - (\cos \omega t)\mathbf{j}] + h\omega\mathbf{k}$ is

$$v = \sqrt{v_x^2 + v_y^2 + v_z^2} = \sqrt{(-R\omega \sin \omega t)^2 + (R \cos \omega t)^2 + (h\omega)^2} = c\omega$$

and of $\mathbf{v} = c\omega\mathbf{e}_t$ is by inspection $v = c\omega$.

The magnitude of $\mathbf{a} = -R\omega^2[(\cos \omega t)\mathbf{i} + (\sin \omega t)\mathbf{j}]$ is

$$a = \sqrt{a_x^2 + a_y^2 + a_z^2} = \sqrt{(-R\omega^2 \cos \omega t)^2 + (-R\omega^2 \sin \omega t)^2 + (0)^2} = R\omega^2$$

and of $\mathbf{a} = R\omega^2 \mathbf{e}_n$ is by inspection $a = R\omega^2$.

These relations show the invariant character of the respective magnitudes, which remain unchanged regardless of the system of the vector components.

TRANSFORMATION MATRICES

3.27 A path vector is given in the cartesian system as $\mathbf{r} = 2t\mathbf{i} + t^2\mathbf{j} + 2t\mathbf{k}$. Construct the respective angular transformation matrix $[\pi^{\theta 0}]$ and express this vector in the cylindrical system.

The construction of the angular transformation matrix is based on the geometry of Fig. P-3.12, page 66. Hence in matrix form,

$$\underbrace{\begin{bmatrix} r_c \\ r_\theta \\ r_z \end{bmatrix}}_{[r^\theta]} = \underbrace{\begin{bmatrix} \cos \theta & \sin \theta & 0 \\ -\sin \theta & \cos \theta & 0 \\ 0 & 0 & 1 \end{bmatrix}}_{[\pi^{\theta 0}]} \underbrace{\begin{bmatrix} 2t \\ t^2 \\ 2t \end{bmatrix}}_{[r^0]} = \underbrace{\begin{bmatrix} 2t \cos \theta + t^2 \sin \theta \\ -2t \sin \theta + t^2 \cos \theta \\ 2t \end{bmatrix}}_{[r^\theta]}$$

In vector form,

$$\mathbf{r} = (2t \cos \theta + t^2 \sin \theta)\mathbf{e}_c + (-2t \sin \theta + t^2 \cos \theta)\mathbf{e}_\theta + 2t\mathbf{e}_z$$

which must check,

$$r \stackrel{?}{=} \sqrt{r_x^2 + r_y^2 + r_z^2} = \sqrt{r_c^2 + r_\theta^2 + r_z^2} = t\sqrt{8 + t^2}$$

Note that $\tan \theta = t/2$, $\sin \theta = t/\sqrt{4 + t^2}$, $\cos \theta = 2/\sqrt{4 + t^2}$.

3.28 The path vector of Problem 3.23 is given in the spherical system as $\mathbf{r} = R\mathbf{e}_r$. Using the results of Problem 3.20, express this vector in the cartesian system.

By (3-32), in matrix form,

$$\underbrace{\begin{bmatrix} r_x \\ r_y \\ r_z \end{bmatrix}}_{[r^0]} = \underbrace{\begin{bmatrix} \cos \theta \cos \phi & -\sin \theta & \cos \theta \sin \phi \\ \sin \theta \cos \phi & \cos \theta & \sin \theta \sin \phi \\ -\sin \phi & 0 & \cos \phi \end{bmatrix}}_{[\pi^{0\phi}]} \underbrace{\begin{bmatrix} 0 \\ 0 \\ R \end{bmatrix}}_{[r^\phi]} = \underbrace{\begin{bmatrix} R \cos \theta \sin \phi \\ R \sin \theta \sin \phi \\ R \cos \phi \end{bmatrix}}_{[r^0]}$$

In vector form,

$$\mathbf{r} = (R \sin \theta \cos \phi)\mathbf{i} + (R \sin \theta \sin \phi)\mathbf{j} + (R \cos \phi)\mathbf{k}$$

which again must check,

$$r = \sqrt{r_x^2 + r_y^2 + r_z^2} = \sqrt{R^2 \cos^2 \theta \sin^2 \phi + R^2 \sin^2 \theta \sin^2 \phi + R^2 \cos^2 \phi} = R$$

or

$$r = \sqrt{r_\phi^2 + r_\theta^2 + r_r^2} = \sqrt{(0)^2 + (0)^2 + (R)^2} = R$$

3.29 The velocity vector of Problem 3.26 is given as

$$\mathbf{v} = c\omega\mathbf{e}_t = -R\omega[(\sin \omega t)\mathbf{i} - (\cos \omega t)\mathbf{j}] + h\omega\mathbf{k}$$

in the respective system. Using the results of Problem 3.25, construct the transformation matrix $[\pi^{s0}]$ and show the matrix relation.

The coefficients of $[\pi^{s0}]$ are the direction cosines of the unit vectors $\mathbf{e}_t$, $\mathbf{e}_n$, $\mathbf{e}_b$ in Problem 3.25, i.e.

$$
\underbrace{\begin{bmatrix} v_t \\ v_n \\ v_b \end{bmatrix}}_{[v^s]} = \underbrace{\begin{bmatrix} -\dfrac{R}{c}\sin \omega t & \dfrac{R}{c}\cos \omega t & \dfrac{h}{c} \\ -\cos \omega t & -\sin \omega t & 0 \\ \dfrac{h}{c}\sin \omega t & -\dfrac{h}{c}\cos \omega t & \dfrac{R}{c} \end{bmatrix}}_{[\pi^{s0}]} \underbrace{\begin{bmatrix} -R\omega \sin \omega t \\ R\omega \cos \omega t \\ h\omega \end{bmatrix}}_{[v^0]} = \underbrace{\begin{bmatrix} c\omega \\ 0 \\ 0 \end{bmatrix}}_{[v^s]}
$$

The same transformation applies for $\mathbf{r}$ and $\mathbf{a}$.

3.30 Express in the spherical system the acceleration vector of Problem 3.26 given in the curvilinear system as $\mathbf{a} = R\omega^2\mathbf{e}_n$.

The angular transformation matrix in this case is

$$[\pi^{\phi s}] = [\pi^{\phi 0}][\pi^{0s}]$$

where $[\pi^{\phi 0}]$ is given in (3-33) and $[\pi^{0s}] = [\pi^{s0}]^T$ in Problem 3.29. Hence

$$
\underbrace{\begin{bmatrix} a_\phi \\ a_\theta \\ a_r \end{bmatrix}}_{[a^\phi]} = \underbrace{\begin{bmatrix} \cos \theta \cos \phi & \sin \theta \cos \phi & -\sin \phi \\ -\sin \theta & \cos \theta & 0 \\ \cos \theta \sin \phi & \sin \theta \sin \phi & \cos \phi \end{bmatrix}}_{[\pi^{\phi 0}]} \underbrace{\begin{bmatrix} -\dfrac{R}{c}\sin \omega t & -\cos \omega t & \dfrac{h}{c}\sin \omega t \\ \dfrac{R}{c}\cos \omega t & -\sin \omega t & -\dfrac{h}{c}\cos \omega t \\ \dfrac{h}{c} & 0 & \dfrac{R}{c} \end{bmatrix}}_{[\pi^{0s}]} \begin{bmatrix} 0 \\ R\omega^2 \\ 0 \end{bmatrix}
$$

which yields

$$
\begin{aligned}
\mathbf{a} &= (-\cos \theta \cos \phi \cos \omega t - \sin \theta \cos \phi \sin \omega t)R\omega^2\mathbf{e}_\phi \\
&\quad + (\sin \theta \cos \omega t - \cos \theta \sin \omega t)R\omega^2\mathbf{e}_\theta \\
&\quad\quad + (-\cos \theta \sin \phi \cos \omega t - \sin \theta \sin \phi \sin \omega t)R\omega^2\mathbf{e}_r \\
&= (-\cos \phi)R\omega^2\mathbf{e}_\phi + (-\sin \phi)R\omega^2\mathbf{e}_r
\end{aligned}
$$

By Problem 3.18,

$$\phi = \cos^{-1}\frac{z}{\sqrt{x^2 + y^2 + z^2}} = \cos^{-1}\frac{h\omega t}{R}$$

from which $\cos \phi = h\omega t/R$, $\sin \phi = R/c$, and

$$\theta = \tan^{-1}\frac{y}{x} = \tan^{-1}\frac{R \sin \omega t}{R \cos \omega t}$$

from which $\tan \theta = \tan \omega t$, $\cos \theta = \cos \omega t$, $\sin \theta = \sin \omega t$.

This problem shows clearly how a very involved transformation can be performed with relative ease by means of π-matrices.

Problems

GEOMETRY OF SPACE PATH

3.31 A space path is given parametrically by $x = t \cos (\ln t)$, $y = t \sin (\ln t)$, $z = 7t$. Find the first and second path derivatives of $\mathbf{r} = x(t)\mathbf{i} + y(t)\mathbf{j} + z(t)\mathbf{k}$.

3.32 Compute the unit vectors $\mathbf{e}_t$, $\mathbf{e}_n$, $\mathbf{e}_b$ of the space path of Problem 3.31.

3.33 Using the results of Problems 3.31 and 3.32, construct $[\pi^{0s}]$ and $[\pi^{s0}]$ matrices at $t = 2.718$.

3.34 For the space path of Problem 3.31, find the radius of curvature ρ_1 and the radius of torsion ρ_2.

3.35 Derive the general expressions for the center of curvature and torsion of the space path of Problem 3.31.

EQUATIONS OF MOTION, CARTESIAN SYSTEM

3.36 The path of a moving particle is given by $\mathbf{r} = t\mathbf{i} + (t^2/2)\mathbf{j} + (t^3/6)\mathbf{k}$ where t is time. Find the equations of motion.

3.37 The velocity of a particle is given as $\mathbf{v} = (-200 \sin 4t)\mathbf{i} + (200 \cos t)\mathbf{j} + 20\mathbf{k}$, and its initial position vector at $t = 0$ is $\mathbf{r}_0 = 50\mathbf{i}$. Find the equations of motion.

3.38 The acceleration vector of a particle is given as $\mathbf{a} = 10t\mathbf{k}$ and its initial position vector and velocity vector at $t = 0$ are respectively $\mathbf{r}_0 = 100\mathbf{i} + 200\mathbf{j} + 300\mathbf{k}$, $\mathbf{v}_0 = 20\mathbf{i} + 40\mathbf{j} + 60\mathbf{k}$. Find the equations of motion.

EQUATIONS OF MOTION, CYLINDRICAL COORDINATES

3.39 The path of a moving particle is given parametrically by $c = 10t$, $\theta = 20t$, $z = 30t^2$. Find the equations of motion in the cylindrical system.

3.40 The velocity vector of a particle is $\mathbf{v} = 10\mathbf{e}_c + 200t\mathbf{e}_\theta + 60t\mathbf{e}_z$, and the initial position vector at $t = 0$ is $\mathbf{r}_0 = 100\mathbf{e}_c + 100\mathbf{e}_z$. Find the equations of motion in the cylindrical system.

EQUATIONS OF MOTION, SPHERICAL COORDINATES

3.41 The position vector of a moving particle is

$$\mathbf{r} = (10t/\pi)\mathbf{i} + (20t/\pi)\mathbf{j} + 100\mathbf{k}$$

Find the equations of motion in the spherical system.

3.42 Derive the equations of motion of a particle in the spherical system whose angle ϕ is measured from the XY plane as shown in Fig. P-3.42.

EQUATIONS OF MOTION, CURVILINEAR COORDINATES

3.43 The path of motion of a particle is given by

$$\mathbf{r} = [t \sin (10 \ln t)]\mathbf{i} + [t \cos (10 \ln t)]\mathbf{j} + 10t\mathbf{k}$$

Find the equations of motion of this particle in curvilinear coordinates.

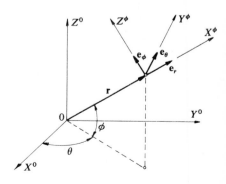

Fig. P-3.42

3.44   Find the equations of curvature and torsion for the path of Problem 3.43.

TRANSFORMATION MATRICES

3.45   The path vector of a particle is $\mathbf{r} = t^2\mathbf{i} + 2t^2\mathbf{j} + 3t^2\mathbf{k}$.   Express this vector in the cylindrical system.

3.46   Express the path vector of Problem 3.45 in the spherical system.

3.47   Express the path vector of Problem 3.45 in the curvilinear system.

Chapter 4

Kinetics of Particles, Space Motion

4.1 EQUATIONS OF MOTION

Classification of Problems

As in plane motion (Section 2.2), the kinetic analysis of particles in space motion recognizes *three distinct types of problems*. The kinetic problems of the first and second kinds are the prime concern of this chapter.

Problem of the First Kind

If $\mathbf{r}(t)$, $\mathbf{v}(t)$, $\mathbf{a}(t)$ and the mass m of the particle are known, the associated force (cause) is again given by (2-2) as

$$\mathbf{F}(t) = m\ddot{\mathbf{r}}(t) \tag{4-1}$$

which is usually expressed in *component form*.

In the *cartesian system*,

$$F_x(t) = ma_x(t), \qquad F_y(t) = ma_y(t), \qquad F_z(t) = ma_z(t) \tag{4-2}$$

In the *cylindrical system*,

$$F_c(t) = ma_c(t), \qquad F_\theta(t) = ma_\theta(t), \qquad F_z(t) = ma_z(t) \tag{4-3}$$

In the *spherical system*,

$$F_\phi(t) = ma_\phi(t), \qquad F_\theta(t) = ma_\theta(t), \qquad F_r(t) = ma_r(t) \tag{4-4}$$

In the *curvilinear system*,

$$F_t(t) = ma_t(t), \qquad F_n(t) = ma_n(t), \qquad F_b(t) = m\overset{0}{\cancel{a_b(t)}} \tag{4-5}$$

where $F_x(t)$, $F_y(t)$, ..., $F_n(t)$, $F_b(t)$ are the components of the *force function* in the respective system and $a_x(t)$, $a_y(t)$, ..., $a_n(t)$, $a_b(t)$ are the components of the corresponding *acceleration* in the same system.

Problem of the Second Kind

If **F** and m are known, the acceleration of the particle is again given by (2-2) as

$$\ddot{\mathbf{r}}(t) = \frac{\mathbf{F}}{m} \qquad (4\text{-}6)$$

where

$$\mathbf{F} = \mathbf{F}(t, s, \dot{s}, \ddot{s}) \qquad (4\text{-}7)$$

may be one or several functions given in the component form corresponding to the system of $\ddot{\mathbf{r}}(t)$.

Four *distinct cases* of **F** listed in Table 2-2, page 23, may occur in space motion and are handled analogically to those of plane motion.

4.2   MOMENTUM AND IMPULSE

Vector Equations

The definitions of *momentum, impulse,* their time derivatives and their vector equations, given in Section 2.3 by equations (2-8) to (2-15), pages 24 and 25, are applicable in space kinetics of particles without modification.

Matrix Equations

Since three-dimensional vectors are involved, the matrix form of these equations is more convenient and is used in this chapter.

The *linear momentum* of a particle and its time derivative [equations (2-8) and (2-9)] are respectively

$$\underbrace{\begin{bmatrix} G_x^0 \\ G_y^0 \\ G_z^0 \end{bmatrix}}_{[G^0]} = m \underbrace{\begin{bmatrix} \dot{x}^0 \\ \dot{y}^0 \\ \dot{z}^0 \end{bmatrix}}_{[\dot{s}^0]}, \qquad \underbrace{\begin{bmatrix} \dot{G}_x^0 \\ \dot{G}_y^0 \\ \dot{G}_z^0 \end{bmatrix}}_{[\dot{G}^0]} = m \underbrace{\begin{bmatrix} \ddot{x}^0 \\ \ddot{y}^0 \\ \ddot{z}^0 \end{bmatrix}}_{[\ddot{s}^0]} = \underbrace{\begin{bmatrix} F_x^0 \\ F_y^0 \\ F_z^0 \end{bmatrix}}_{[F^0]} \qquad (4\text{-}8), (4\text{-}9)$$

where the superscript 0 identifies the reference system.

The *angular momentum* of the same particle and its time derivative [equations (2-10) and (2-11)] are respectively

$$\underbrace{\begin{bmatrix} H_x^0 \\ H_y^0 \\ H_z^0 \end{bmatrix}}_{[H^0]} = m \underbrace{\begin{bmatrix} 0 & -z^0 & y^0 \\ z^0 & 0 & -x^0 \\ -y^0 & x^0 & 0 \end{bmatrix}}_{[r^0]} \underbrace{\begin{bmatrix} \dot{x}^0 \\ \dot{y}^0 \\ \dot{z}^0 \end{bmatrix}}_{[\dot{s}^0]} \qquad (4\text{-}10)$$

$$\underbrace{\begin{bmatrix} \dot{H}_x^0 \\ \dot{H}_y^0 \\ \dot{H}_z^0 \end{bmatrix}}_{[\dot{H}^0]} = m \underbrace{\begin{bmatrix} 0 & -z^0 & y^0 \\ z^0 & 0 & -x^0 \\ -y^0 & x^0 & 0 \end{bmatrix}}_{[r^0]} \underbrace{\begin{bmatrix} \ddot{x}^0 \\ \ddot{y}^0 \\ \ddot{z}^0 \end{bmatrix}}_{[\ddot{s}^0]} = \underbrace{\begin{bmatrix} M_x^0 \\ M_y^0 \\ M_z^0 \end{bmatrix}}_{[M^0]} \qquad (4\text{-}11)$$

where $[r^0]$ is the *moment arm matrix* in the reference system.*

---

*J. J. Tuma, "Statics", Quantum Publishers, New York, 1974, Chapter 7, p. 153.

If the resultants of forces and moments acting on the particle in motion are zero, then

$$[\dot{G}^0] = m[\ddot{s}^0] = [F^0] = [0] \qquad (4\text{-}12)$$

$$[\dot{H}^0] = m[r^0][\ddot{s}^0] = [M^0] = [0] \qquad (4\text{-}13)$$

which are the matrix formulations of the *principles of conservation of linear* and *angular momentum* respectively.

The assembly of (*4-12*) and (*4-13*) into one matrix equation is

$$
\begin{bmatrix}
\dot{G}^0_x \\
\dot{G}^0_y \\
\dot{G}^0_z \\
\hline
\dot{H}^0_x \\
\dot{H}^0_y \\
\dot{H}^0_z
\end{bmatrix}
= m
\begin{bmatrix}
1 & 0 & 0 \\
0 & 1 & 0 \\
0 & 0 & 1 \\
\hline
0 & -z^0 & y^0 \\
z^0 & 0 & -x^0 \\
-y^0 & x^0 & 0
\end{bmatrix}
\begin{bmatrix}
\ddot{x}^0 \\
\ddot{y}^0 \\
\ddot{z}^0
\end{bmatrix}
=
\begin{bmatrix}
0 \\
0 \\
0 \\
\hline
0 \\
0 \\
0
\end{bmatrix}
$$

which is the generalization of the *equations of equilibrium*, of which the equations of static equilibrium are a special case.*

The *linear and angular impulses* of a particle in motion corresponding to the time interval $t_2 - t_1$ [equations (*2-14*) and (*2-15*)] are respectively

$$
\underbrace{\int_{t_1}^{t_2}
\begin{bmatrix}
F^0_x \\
F^0_y \\
F^0_z
\end{bmatrix} dt}_{[F^0]}
=
\underbrace{\int_{t_1}^{t_2}
\begin{bmatrix}
\dot{G}^0_x \\
\dot{G}^0_y \\
\dot{G}^0_z
\end{bmatrix} dt}_{[\dot{G}^0]}
=
\underbrace{
\begin{bmatrix}
G^0_{2x} - G^0_{1x} \\
G^0_{2y} - G^0_{1y} \\
G^0_{2z} - G^0_{1z}
\end{bmatrix}}_{[G^0_2 - G^0_1]}
\qquad (4\text{-}14)
$$

$$
\underbrace{\int_{t_1}^{t_2}
\begin{bmatrix}
M^0_x \\
M^0_y \\
M^0_z
\end{bmatrix} dt}_{[M^0]}
=
\underbrace{\int_{t_1}^{t_2}
\begin{bmatrix}
\dot{H}^0_x \\
\dot{H}^0_y \\
\dot{H}^0_z
\end{bmatrix} dt}_{[\dot{H}^0]}
=
\underbrace{
\begin{bmatrix}
H^0_{2x} - H^0_{1x} \\
H^0_{2y} - H^0_{1y} \\
H^0_{2z} - H^0_{1z}
\end{bmatrix}}_{[H^0_2 - H^0_1]}
$$

$$
=
\underbrace{
\begin{bmatrix}
0 & -z^0_2 & y^0_2 \\
z_2 & 0 & -x^0_2 \\
-y^0_2 & x^0_2 & 0
\end{bmatrix}}_{[r^0_2]}
\underbrace{
\begin{bmatrix}
G^0_{2x} \\
G^0_{2y} \\
G^0_{2z}
\end{bmatrix}}_{[G^0_2]}
-
\underbrace{
\begin{bmatrix}
0 & -z^0_1 & y^0_1 \\
z^0_1 & 0 & -x^0_1 \\
-y^0_1 & x^0_1 & 0
\end{bmatrix}}_{[r^0_1]}
\underbrace{
\begin{bmatrix}
G^0_{1x} \\
G^0_{1y} \\
G^0_{1z}
\end{bmatrix}}_{[G^0_1]}
\qquad (4\text{-}15)
$$

where $[r^0_1]$ and $[r^0_2]$ are the moment arm matrices in the reference system at t_1 and t_2 respectively, and $[G^0_1]$, $[G^0_2]$ and $[H^0_1]$, $[H^0_2]$ are the linear and angular momenta at t_1 and t_2 respectively.

The obvious advantage of the matrix forms (*4-8*)–(*4-15*) is their transformation capability, since once they are given or computed in one system, they can be easily transformed to any other system by direct application of π-matrices developed in Section 3.3, page 56.

---

*J. J. Tuma, "Statics", Quantum Publishers, New York, 1974, Chapter 7, p. 153.

4.3   POWER, WORK, ENERGY

Scalar Equations

The definitions of *power, mechanical work, kinetic energy* and *potential energy*, and their scalar expressions, given in Section 2.4 by (2-16)–(2-22), pages 25–27, are again applicable in space kinetics of particles without modification.

Matrix Equations

As in Section 4.2, the matrix form of these equations is more convenient and as such is developed in this section.

The *power (2-16)* is

$$P = \begin{bmatrix} \dot{x}^0 \\ \dot{y}^0 \\ \dot{z}^0 \end{bmatrix}^T \begin{bmatrix} F_x^0 \\ F_y^0 \\ F_z^0 \end{bmatrix} = m \begin{bmatrix} \dot{x}^0 \\ \dot{y}^0 \\ \dot{z}^0 \end{bmatrix}^T \begin{bmatrix} \ddot{x}^0 \\ \ddot{y}^0 \\ \ddot{z}^0 \end{bmatrix} = \tfrac{1}{2}m \frac{d\left[[\dot{s}^0]^T[\dot{s}^0]\right]}{dt} = \tfrac{1}{2}m \underbrace{d[(\dot{x}^0)^2 + (\dot{y}^0)^2 + (\dot{z}^0)^2]/dt}_{d(v^0)^2/dt} = \dot{T}$$

$$\underbrace{[\dot{s}^0]^T}_{} \quad \underbrace{[F^0]}_{} \qquad \underbrace{[\dot{s}^0]^T}_{} \quad \underbrace{[\ddot{s}^0]}_{}$$

(4-16)

where v^0 is the speed.

The *kinetic energy (2-17)* is

$$T = \tfrac{1}{2}m \begin{bmatrix} \dot{x}^0 \\ \dot{y}^0 \\ \dot{z}^0 \end{bmatrix}^T \begin{bmatrix} \dot{x}^0 \\ \dot{y}^0 \\ \dot{z}^0 \end{bmatrix} = \tfrac{1}{2}m\underbrace{[(\dot{x}^0)^2 + (\dot{y}^0)^2 + (\dot{z}^0)^2]}_{(v^0)^2}$$

$$\underbrace{[\dot{s}^0]^T}_{} \quad \underbrace{[\dot{s}^0]}_{}$$

(4-17)

where $[\dot{s}^0]^T[\dot{s}^0] = (v^0)^2$ is an *invariant*.

The *mechanical work* given by (2-18a, b, c) is respectively

$$U = \int_{s_1^0}^{s_2^0} [F_x^0 \quad F_y^0 \quad F_z^0] \begin{bmatrix} dx^0 \\ dy^0 \\ dz^0 \end{bmatrix} = T_2 - T_1 \qquad (4\text{-}18a)$$

$$U = \int_{s_1^0}^{s_2^0} [G_x^0 \quad G_y^0 \quad G_z^0] \begin{bmatrix} d\dot{x}^0 \\ d\dot{y}^0 \\ d\dot{z}^0 \end{bmatrix} = T_2 - T_1 \qquad (4\text{-}18b)$$

$$U = \int_{t_1}^{t_2} [\dot{x}^0 \quad \dot{y}^0 \quad \dot{z}^0] \begin{bmatrix} F_x^0 \\ F_y^0 \\ F_z^0 \end{bmatrix} dt = T_2 - T_1 \qquad (4\text{-}18c)$$

and can be expressed as

$$U = \tfrac{1}{2}m\left[[\dot{s}_2^0]^T[\dot{s}_2^0] - [\dot{s}_1^0]^T[\dot{s}_1^0] \right] = T_2 - T_1 \qquad (4\text{-}18)$$

which is the matrix form of the *classical work-energy equation (2-18)*.

If the *force field* in *(2-19)* is a space field, then

$$\mathbf{F} = -\nabla V(x,y,z) = -\frac{\partial V(x,y,z)}{\partial x}\mathbf{i} - \frac{\partial V(x,y,z)}{\partial y}\mathbf{j} - \frac{\partial V(x,y,z)}{\partial z}\mathbf{k} = -\frac{\partial V_x}{\partial x}\mathbf{i} - \frac{\partial V_y}{\partial y}\mathbf{j} - \frac{\partial V_z}{\partial z}\mathbf{k} \quad (4\text{-}19)$$

where $V(x,y,z)$ is the potential energy (energy of position).

The *work integral (2-18a)* can then be expressed as

$$U = -\int_{s_1^0}^{s_2^0}\underbrace{\begin{bmatrix}\partial V_{x/\partial x}^0 \\ \partial V_{y/\partial y}^0 \\ \partial V_{z/\partial z}^0\end{bmatrix}^T \begin{bmatrix}dx^0 \\ dy^0 \\ dz^0\end{bmatrix}}_{[\partial V^0/\partial s]^T \, [ds^0]} = V_1 - V_2 \qquad (4\text{-}20)$$

where $[\partial V^0/\partial s^0]^T[ds^0] = dV^0$ is again an invariant.

The generalization of Definitions 2.14–2.16, pages 26 and 27, and their analytical expressions follow the pattern of *(4-18)–(4-20)*, and no additional explanation is necessary.

Illustrative Problems

EQUATIONS OF MOTION, CONSTANT FORCE

4.1 Consider a particle of mass m acted on by a force $\mathbf{F} = 2m\mathbf{j}$ in the cartesian system. Find the matrix equations of motion of this particle. Given: $x(0) = 0$, $y(0) = 0$, $z(0) = 0$, $\dot{x}(0) = 2$, $\dot{y}(0) = 0$, $\dot{z}(0) = 1$. See Fig. P-4.1.

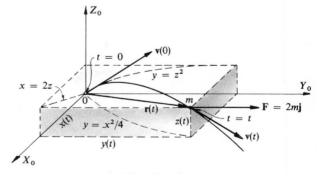

Fig. P-4.1

By *(4-6)*,

$$\begin{bmatrix}\ddot{x} \\ \ddot{y} \\ \ddot{z}\end{bmatrix} = \frac{1}{m}\begin{bmatrix}F_x \\ F_y \\ F_z\end{bmatrix} \qquad (1)$$

By direct integration,

$$\begin{bmatrix}\dot{x} \\ \dot{y} \\ \dot{z}\end{bmatrix} = \begin{bmatrix}C_{1x} \\ C_{1y} \\ C_{1z}\end{bmatrix} + \frac{t}{m}\begin{bmatrix}F_x \\ F_y \\ F_z\end{bmatrix}, \qquad \begin{bmatrix}x \\ y \\ z\end{bmatrix} = \begin{bmatrix}C_{2x} \\ C_{2y} \\ C_{2z}\end{bmatrix} + t\begin{bmatrix}C_{1x} \\ C_{1y} \\ C_{1z}\end{bmatrix} + \frac{t^2}{2m}\begin{bmatrix}F_x \\ F_y \\ F_z\end{bmatrix} \qquad (2),(3)$$

where $C_{1x}, C_{1y}, C_{1z}, C_{2x}, C_{2y}, C_{2z}$ are constants of integration and the superscript 0 is omitted.

At $t = 0$, (2) and (3) yield respectively

$$\dot{x}(0) = C_{1x}, \qquad \dot{y}(0) = C_{1y}, \qquad \dot{z}(0) = C_{1z}$$
$$x(0) = C_{2x}, \qquad y(0) = C_{2y}, \qquad z(0) = C_{2z}$$

In terms of these values, the equations of motion (1), (2) and (3) are

$$\begin{bmatrix} \ddot{x} \\ \ddot{y} \\ \ddot{z} \end{bmatrix} = \begin{bmatrix} 0 \\ 2 \\ 0 \end{bmatrix}, \qquad \begin{bmatrix} \dot{x} \\ \dot{y} \\ \dot{z} \end{bmatrix} = \begin{bmatrix} 2 \\ 2t \\ 1 \end{bmatrix}, \qquad \begin{bmatrix} x \\ y \\ z \end{bmatrix} = \begin{bmatrix} 2t \\ t^2 \\ t \end{bmatrix} \qquad (4), (5), (6)$$

which are identical to those of Problem 3.9, page 65.

4.2   Find the causes necessary to produce and sustain the motion of the particle in Problem 3.15, page 67.   See Fig. P-4.2.

The matrix forms of the kinematic equations of Problem 3.15 are

$$\begin{bmatrix} r_c \\ r_\theta \\ r_z \end{bmatrix} = \begin{bmatrix} R \\ 0 \\ ht \end{bmatrix}, \qquad \begin{bmatrix} v_c \\ v_\theta \\ v_z \end{bmatrix} = \begin{bmatrix} 0 \\ R \\ h \end{bmatrix}, \qquad \begin{bmatrix} a_c \\ a_\theta \\ a_z \end{bmatrix} = \begin{bmatrix} -R \\ 0 \\ 0 \end{bmatrix}$$
$$[r^\theta] \qquad\qquad [v^\theta] \qquad\qquad [a^\theta]$$

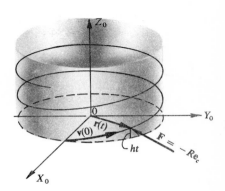

Fig. P-4.2

The causes required to produce and sustain this motion are

$$\begin{bmatrix} G_c \\ G_\theta \\ G_z \end{bmatrix} = m \begin{bmatrix} 0 \\ R \\ h \end{bmatrix}, \qquad \begin{bmatrix} F_c \\ F_\theta \\ F_z \end{bmatrix} = m \begin{bmatrix} -R \\ 0 \\ 0 \end{bmatrix}$$
$$[G^\theta] \quad [v^\theta] \qquad\qquad [F^\theta] \quad [a^\theta]$$

where $[\dot{G}^\theta] \neq [F^\theta]$, since not only the magnitudes of $G_c, G_\theta, ..., F_\theta, F_z$ change with time, but also their directions change with time (Problem 4.3).

4.3   Solve Problem 4.2 in the cartesian system.

The kinematic equations of Problem 3.15 are

$$\begin{bmatrix} r_x \\ r_y \\ r_z \end{bmatrix} = \begin{bmatrix} R \cos t \\ R \sin t \\ ht \end{bmatrix}, \qquad \begin{bmatrix} v_x \\ v_y \\ v_z \end{bmatrix} = \begin{bmatrix} -R \sin t \\ R \cos t \\ h \end{bmatrix}, \qquad \begin{bmatrix} a_x \\ a_y \\ a_z \end{bmatrix} = \begin{bmatrix} -R \cos t \\ -R \sin t \\ 0 \end{bmatrix}$$
$$[r^0] \qquad\qquad\qquad [v^0] \qquad\qquad\qquad [a^0]$$

The causes required to produce and sustain this motion are

$$\begin{bmatrix} G_x \\ G_y \\ G_z \end{bmatrix} = m \begin{bmatrix} -R \sin t \\ R \cos t \\ h \end{bmatrix}, \qquad \begin{bmatrix} F_x \\ F_y \\ F_z \end{bmatrix} = m \begin{bmatrix} -R \cos t \\ -R \sin t \\ 0 \end{bmatrix}$$
$$[G^0] \qquad\qquad\qquad [F^0]$$

where $[\dot{G}^0] = [F^0]$, since the directions of G_x, G_y, ..., F_y, F_z remain constant and only their magnitudes change with time.

The relationships of $[G^\theta]$ to $[G^0]$ and of $[F^\theta]$ to $[F^0]$ are respectively

$$[G^\theta] = [\pi^{\theta 0}][G^0], \qquad [F^\theta] = [\pi^{\theta 0}][F^0]$$

where $[\pi^{\theta 0}]$ is given by (3-30). Then

$$[\dot{G}^\theta] = [\pi^{\theta 0}][\dot{G}^0] = m\begin{bmatrix} \cos t & \sin t & 0 \\ -\sin t & \cos t & 0 \\ 0 & 0 & 1 \end{bmatrix}\begin{bmatrix} -R\cos t \\ -R\sin t \\ 0 \end{bmatrix} = m\begin{bmatrix} -R \\ 0 \\ 0 \end{bmatrix} = [F^\theta]$$

which shows the use of π-matrices in the differentiation of dynamics vectors.

EQUATIONS OF MOTION, F(t)

4.4   Discuss the solution of the kinetic problem of the second kind, if $\mathbf{F}(t)$ and $\mathbf{r}(0)$, $\dot{\mathbf{r}}(0)$, m are given values.   See Fig. P-4.4.

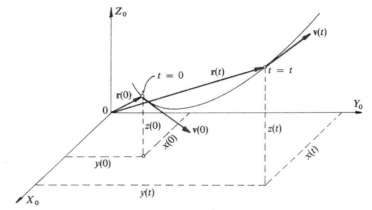

Fig. P-4.4

By (4-6), in the cartesian system,

$$\begin{bmatrix} \ddot{x} \\ \ddot{y} \\ \ddot{z} \end{bmatrix} = \frac{1}{m}\begin{bmatrix} F_x(t) \\ F_y(t) \\ F_z(t) \end{bmatrix} \tag{1}$$

By direct integration,

$$\begin{bmatrix} \dot{x} \\ \dot{y} \\ \dot{z} \end{bmatrix} = \begin{bmatrix} C_{1x} \\ C_{1y} \\ C_{1z} \end{bmatrix} + \frac{1}{m}\int_0^t \begin{bmatrix} F_x(t) \\ F_y(t) \\ F_z(t) \end{bmatrix} dt \tag{2}$$

$$\begin{bmatrix} x \\ y \\ z \end{bmatrix} = \begin{bmatrix} C_{2x} \\ C_{2y} \\ C_{2z} \end{bmatrix} + t\begin{bmatrix} C_{1x} \\ C_{1y} \\ C_{1z} \end{bmatrix} + \frac{1}{m}\int_0^t\int_0^t \begin{bmatrix} F_x(t) \\ F_y(t) \\ F_z(t) \end{bmatrix} dt\,dt \tag{3}$$

where C_{1x}, C_{1y}, ..., C_{2y}, C_{2z} are constants of integration and the superscript 0 is omitted.

At $t = 0$, (2) and (3) yield respectively,

$$\dot{x}(0) = C_{1x}, \qquad \dot{y}(0) = C_{1y}, \qquad \dot{z}(0) = C_{1z}$$

$$x(0) = C_{2x}, \qquad y(0) = C_{2y}, \qquad z(0) = C_{2z} \tag{4}$$

In terms of these values, the time-transport matrix equation constructed as an assembly of (2) and (3) is

$$
\begin{bmatrix} 1 \\ \hline x(t) \\ y(t) \\ z(t) \\ \hline \dot{x}(t) \\ \dot{y}(t) \\ \dot{z}(t) \end{bmatrix}
=
\left[
\begin{array}{c|ccc|ccc}
1 & 0 & 0 & 0 & 0 & 0 & 0 \\
\hline
\int_0^t \int_0^t F_x(t)\,dt\,dt/m & 1 & 0 & 0 & t & 0 & 0 \\
\int_0^t \int_0^t F_y(t)\,dt\,dt/m & 0 & 1 & 0 & 0 & t & 0 \\
\int_0^t \int_0^t F_z(t)\,dt\,dt/m & 0 & 0 & 1 & 0 & 0 & t \\
\hline
\int_0^t F_x(t)\,dt/m & 0 & 0 & 0 & 1 & 0 & 0 \\
\int_0^t F_y(t)\,dt/m & 0 & 0 & 0 & 0 & 1 & 0 \\
\int_0^t F_z(t)\,dt/m & 0 & 0 & 0 & 0 & 0 & 1
\end{array}
\right]
\begin{bmatrix} 1 \\ \hline x(0) \\ y(0) \\ z(0) \\ \hline \dot{x}(0) \\ \dot{y}(0) \\ \dot{z}(0) \end{bmatrix}
\tag{5}
$$

$$\underbrace{}_{[\hat{A}_t]} \qquad \underbrace{}_{[\hat{T}_{t0}]} \qquad \underbrace{}_{[\hat{A}_0]}$$

where $[\hat{A}_0], [\hat{A}_t]$ are the kinematic vectors at $t = 0$, $t = t$ respectively, and $[\hat{T}_{t0}]$ is the kinematic-transport matrix between the respective time stations $t = 0$, $t = t$.

The matrix equation (5) is the three-dimensional generalization of (5) in Problem 1.10, page 11.

4.5   Find the inverse relationship $[\hat{A}_0] = [\hat{T}_{0t}] [\hat{A}_t]$.

The submatrix form of (5) of Problem 4.4 is

$$\begin{bmatrix} [I] \\ [A_t] \end{bmatrix} = \begin{bmatrix} [I] & [0] \\ [\psi_{t0}] & [T_{t0}] \end{bmatrix} \begin{bmatrix} [I] \\ [A_0] \end{bmatrix} \tag{1}$$

where the lower submatrix equation is

$$[A_t] = [\psi_{t0}] + [T_{t0}] [A_0] \tag{2}$$

From (2),

$$[A_0] = -[T_{t0}]^{-1}[\psi_{t0}] + [T_{t0}]^{-1}[A_t] \tag{3}$$

where by inspection,

$$[T_{t0}]^{-1} = \left[\begin{array}{ccc|ccc} 1 & 0 & 0 & -t & 0 & 0 \\ 0 & 1 & 0 & 0 & -t & 0 \\ 0 & 0 & 1 & 0 & 0 & -t \\ \hline 0 & 0 & 0 & 1 & 0 & 0 \\ 0 & 0 & 0 & 0 & 1 & 0 \\ 0 & 0 & 0 & 0 & 0 & 1 \end{array}\right] = [T_{0t}] \qquad (4)$$

and

$$-[T_{t0}]^{-1}[\psi_{t0}] = \left[\begin{array}{ccc|ccc} -1 & 0 & 0 & t & 0 & 0 \\ 0 & -1 & 0 & 0 & t & 0 \\ 0 & 0 & -1 & 0 & 0 & t \\ \hline 0 & 0 & 0 & -1 & 0 & 0 \\ 0 & 0 & 0 & 0 & -1 & 0 \\ 0 & 0 & 0 & 0 & 0 & -1 \end{array}\right] \left[\begin{array}{c} \int_0^t \int_0^t F_x(t)\,dt\,dt \\ \int_0^t \int_0^t F_y(t)\,dt\,dt \\ \int_0^t \int_0^t F_z(t)\,dt\,dt \\ \int_0^t F_x(t)\,dt \\ \int_0^t F_y(t)\,dt \\ \int_0^t F_z(t)\,dt \end{array}\right] \frac{1}{m}$$

$$= \frac{1}{m} \left[\begin{array}{c} t\int_0^t F_x(t)\,dt - \int_0^t \int_0^t F_x(t)\,dt\,dt \\ t\int_0^t F_y(t)\,dt - \int_0^t \int_0^t F_y(t)\,dt\,dt \\ t\int_0^t F_z(t)\,dt - \int_0^t \int_0^t F_z(t)\,dt\,dt \\ \hline -\int_0^t F_x(t)\,dt \\ -\int_0^t F_y(t)\,dt \\ -\int_0^t F_z(t)\,dt \end{array}\right] = [\psi_{0t}] \qquad (5)$$

Then (3) in terms of (4) and (5) becomes

$$[A_0] = [\psi_{0t}] + [T_{0t}][A_t] \qquad (6)$$

By enlarging the size of $[T_{0t}]$ and including the force function $[\psi_{0t}]$ in the transport matrix, the closed form becomes

$$\underbrace{\begin{bmatrix} [I] \\ [A_0] \end{bmatrix}}_{[\hat{A}_0]} = \underbrace{\begin{bmatrix} [I] & [0] \\ [\psi_{0t}] & [T_{0t}] \end{bmatrix}}_{[\hat{T}_{0t}]} \underbrace{\begin{bmatrix} [I] \\ [A_t] \end{bmatrix}}_{[\hat{A}_t]} \qquad (7)$$

which is the desired inverse relationship, since

$$[\hat{T}_{t0}][\hat{T}_{0t}] = [I] \qquad (8)$$

4.6   Show the application of the transport matrix equations of Problems 4.4 and 4.5 to the kinetics of particles.

Once the transport matrix equation (5) of Problem 4.4 and its inverse (7) of Problem 4.5 are available for a given time interval $t_i - t_0$, their extension to the analysis of the multistation problem is accomplished by matrix multiplication.

At $t = t_i$,

$$[\hat{A}_i] = [\hat{T}_{i0}][\hat{A}_0] \qquad (1)$$

At $t = t_j$,

$$[\hat{A}_j] = [\hat{T}_{ji}][\hat{A}_i] \qquad (2)$$

At $t = t_k$,

$$[\hat{A}_k] = [\hat{T}_{kj}][\hat{A}_j] \qquad (3)$$

where $[\hat{A}_0]$, $[\hat{A}_i]$, $[\hat{A}_j]$, $[\hat{A}_k]$ are the state kinematic vectors at the time stations 0, i, j, k respectively and $[\hat{T}_{i0}]$, $[\hat{T}_{ji}]$, $[\hat{T}_{kj}]$ are the transport matrices of the time intervals $(t_i - t_0)$, $(t_j - t_i)$, $(t_k - t_j)$ respectively.
By successive substitutions of (1) into (2) and (2) into (3),

$$[\hat{A}_k] = \underbrace{[\hat{T}_{kj}][\hat{T}_{ji}][\hat{T}_{i0}]}_{[\hat{T}_{k0}]} [\hat{A}_0] \qquad (4)$$

where

$$[\hat{T}_{k0}] = \begin{bmatrix} [I] & [0] \\ [\psi_{k0}] & [T_{k0}] \end{bmatrix} \qquad (5)$$

is the new transport matrix relating the initial state vector $[\hat{A}_0]$ to the new state vector $[\hat{A}_k]$.
This matrix is characteristic for a given motion, is independent of the kinematic conditions at either end of the total time interval $t_k - t_0$, and may include any number of subintervals.

By inspection, the inverse of (4) is

$$[\hat{A}_0] = \underbrace{[\hat{T}_{0i}][\hat{T}_{ij}][\hat{T}_{jk}]}_{[\hat{T}_{0k}]}[\hat{A}_k] \tag{6}$$

where $[\hat{T}_{0k}] = [\hat{T}_{k0}]^{-1}$.

Equation (4) gives the kinematic transport in the direction of motion and (6) gives the kinematic transport in the opposite direction.

There are always twelve kinematic end conditions involved, of which six are always known, and six are unknown. The transport equation (4) or (6) provides the necessary six equations for the solution of these unknowns.

EQUATIONS OF MOTION, F(s)

4.7   A particle of mass m is constrained by three orthogonal linear springs of stiffness k_x, k_y, k_z acting along the respective cartesian axes as shown in Fig. P-4.7. Derive equations of motion of m in terms of the initial conditions $\mathbf{r}(0)$ and $\dot{\mathbf{r}}(0)$.

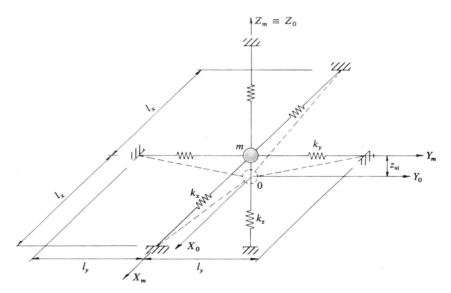

Fig. P-4.7

First allow the particle to move downward along the Z_m axis by

$$z_{st} = W/k_z \tag{1}$$

under the action of its weight.

Then select this position of static equilibrium (designated by 0) as the origin of a new system of coordinate axes X_0, Y_0, Z_0, from which the initial kinematic vectors $\mathbf{r}(0)$ and $\dot{\mathbf{r}}(0)$ can be measured.

Since z_{st} is assumed to be small, the angular rotations of the horizontal springs,

$$z_{st}/l_x \approx 0, \qquad z_{st}/l_y \approx 0 \tag{2}$$

may be disregarded.

At this new position, the forces acting against the motion of the particle are proportional to the respective displacement, i.e.

$$F_x(x) = -2k_x x, \qquad F_y(y) = -2k_y y, \qquad F_z(z) = -2k_z z$$

and by (4-6),

$$
\begin{bmatrix} \ddot{x} \\ \ddot{y} \\ \ddot{z} \end{bmatrix} = -\frac{2}{m} \begin{bmatrix} k_x x \\ k_y y \\ k_z z \end{bmatrix} = - \begin{bmatrix} \lambda_x^2 x \\ \lambda_y^2 y \\ \lambda_z^2 z \end{bmatrix}
\tag{3}
$$

where $\lambda_x^2 = 2k_x/m$, $\lambda_y^2 = 2k_y/m$, $\lambda_z^2 = 2k_z/m$.

The matrix differential equation (3) consists of three independent linear differential equations (of second order with constant coefficients) of known integrals, i.e.

$$
\begin{bmatrix} x \\ y \\ z \end{bmatrix} = \begin{bmatrix} C_{1x} \cos \lambda_x t \\ C_{1y} \cos \lambda_y t \\ C_{1z} \cos \lambda_z t \end{bmatrix} + \begin{bmatrix} C_{2x} \sin \lambda_x t \\ C_{2y} \sin \lambda_y t \\ C_{2z} \sin \lambda_z t \end{bmatrix}
\tag{4}
$$

where $C_{1x}, C_{1y}, C_{1z}, C_{2x}, C_{2y}, C_{2z}$ are constants of integration to be determined from the initial conditions. At $t = 0$, equation (4) becomes

$$
\begin{bmatrix} x(0) \\ y(0) \\ z(0) \end{bmatrix} = \begin{bmatrix} C_{1x} \cos \lambda_x(0) \\ C_{1y} \cos \lambda_y(0) \\ C_{1z} \cos \lambda_z(0) \end{bmatrix} + \begin{bmatrix} C_{2x} \sin \lambda_x(0) \\ C_{2y} \sin \lambda_y(0) \\ C_{2z} \sin \lambda_z(0) \end{bmatrix} = \begin{bmatrix} C_{1x} \\ C_{1y} \\ C_{1z} \end{bmatrix}
\tag{5}
$$

and at the same time, the time derivative of (4) is

$$
\begin{bmatrix} \dot{x}(0) \\ \dot{y}(0) \\ \dot{z}(0) \end{bmatrix} = - \begin{bmatrix} C_{1x}\lambda_x \sin \lambda_x(0) \\ C_{1y}\lambda_y \sin \lambda_y(0) \\ C_{1z}\lambda_z \sin \lambda_z(0) \end{bmatrix} + \begin{bmatrix} C_{2x}\lambda_x \cos \lambda_x(0) \\ C_{2y}\lambda_y \cos \lambda_y(0) \\ C_{2z}\lambda_z \cos \lambda_z(0) \end{bmatrix} = \begin{bmatrix} C_{2x}\lambda_x \\ C_{2y}\lambda_y \\ C_{2z}\lambda_z \end{bmatrix}
\tag{6}
$$

In terms of (5) and (6), equation (4) becomes

$$
\begin{bmatrix} x \\ y \\ z \end{bmatrix} = \begin{bmatrix} x(0) \cos \lambda_x t \\ y(0) \cos \lambda_y t \\ z(0) \cos \lambda_z t \end{bmatrix} + \begin{bmatrix} (\dot{x}(0)/\lambda_x) \sin \lambda_x t \\ (\dot{y}(0)/\lambda_y) \sin \lambda_y t \\ (\dot{z}(0)/\lambda_z) \sin \lambda_z t \end{bmatrix}
$$

which defines the position of m at t in terms of the initial displacements $x(0)$, $y(0)$, $z(0)$ and the initial speeds $\dot{x}(0)$, $\dot{y}(0)$, $\dot{z}(0)$.

Consequently, the motion occurs if and only if $\mathbf{r}(0) \neq 0$ and/or $\dot{\mathbf{r}}(0) \neq 0$. If $\mathbf{r}(0) = 0$ and $\dot{\mathbf{r}}(0) = 0$, the particle is at rest (static equilibrium) and no motion is impending.

The motion discussed above is called small linear vibration (oscillation) of m and is further studied in Chapter 11.

EQUATIONS OF MOTION, $F(\dot{s})$

4.8 A particle of mass m is ejected from the origin of the cartesian system (Fig. P-4.8) with velocity

$$\mathbf{v}(0) = (\alpha_v \mathbf{i} + \beta_v \mathbf{j} + \gamma_v \mathbf{k})v(0)$$

and subjected to a velocity drag (air resistance)

$$F(t) = -(\dot{x}(t)\mathbf{i} + \dot{y}(t)\mathbf{j} + \dot{z}(t)\mathbf{k})c$$

where α_v, β_v, γ_v are the direction cosines of $\mathbf{v}(0)$, and c is the coefficient of resistance. Find the matrix equations of motion of this projectile. Given: $x(0) = 0$, $y(0) = 0$, $z(0) = 0$, $v(0) = v_0$, α_v, β_v, γ_v, m and c.

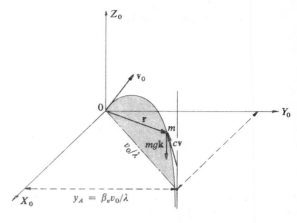

Fig. P-4.8

By (4-6), in the cartesian system,

$$\begin{bmatrix} \ddot{x} \\ \ddot{y} \\ \ddot{z} \end{bmatrix} = \frac{1}{m} \begin{bmatrix} -c\dot{x} \\ -c\dot{y} \\ -c\dot{z} - mg \end{bmatrix} \qquad (1)$$

where $-mg$ is the gravity force.

The integrals of (1) with respect to t are

$$\begin{bmatrix} \dot{x} \\ \dot{y} \\ \dot{z} \end{bmatrix} = -\lambda \begin{bmatrix} C_{1x}e^{-\lambda t} \\ C_{1y}e^{-\lambda t} \\ C_{1z}e^{-\lambda t} + g/\lambda^2 \end{bmatrix}, \qquad \begin{bmatrix} x \\ y \\ z \end{bmatrix} = \begin{bmatrix} C_{2x} + C_{1x}e^{-\lambda t} \\ C_{2y} + C_{1y}e^{-\lambda t} \\ C_{2z} + C_{1z}e^{-\lambda t} - gt/\lambda \end{bmatrix} \qquad (2), (3)$$

where C_{1x}, C_{1y}, C_{1z}, C_{2x}, C_{2y}, C_{2z} are constants of integration and $\lambda = c/m$ is sometimes called the ballistic coefficient.

At $t = 0$, equations (2) and (3) yield

$$C_{1x} = -\alpha_v v_0/\lambda, \qquad C_{1y} = -\beta_v v_0/\lambda, \qquad C_{1z} = -(\gamma_v v_0 + g/\lambda)/\lambda$$
$$C_{2x} = \alpha_v v_0/\lambda, \qquad C_{2y} = \beta_v v_0/\lambda, \qquad C_{2z} = (\gamma_v v_0 + g/\lambda)/\lambda$$

In terms of these constants the equations of motion (2) and (3) are respectively

$$\begin{bmatrix} \dot{x} \\ \dot{y} \\ \dot{z} \end{bmatrix} = v_0 \begin{bmatrix} \alpha_v e^{-\lambda t} \\ \beta_v e^{-\lambda t} \\ \gamma_v e^{-\lambda t} - g(1 - e^{-\lambda t})/\lambda v_0 \end{bmatrix}, \qquad \begin{bmatrix} x \\ y \\ z \end{bmatrix} = \frac{1}{\lambda} \begin{bmatrix} \alpha_v v_0(1 - e^{-\lambda t}) \\ \beta_v v_0(1 - e^{-\lambda t}) \\ (\gamma_v v_0 + g/\lambda)(1 - e^{-\lambda t}) - gt \end{bmatrix} \qquad (4), (5)$$

4.9 Analyze the equations of motion of Problem 4.8 and show the shape of the trajectory.

If $\lambda = 0$ (no air resistance), the trajectory defined by (5) of Problem 4.8 is a plane parabola. If $\lambda > 0$, the trajectory is a plane curve (below this parabola) approaching asymptotically the vertical which intersects the XY plane at x_A, y_A (Fig. P-4.8).

The coordinates of the asymptote are computed from the first and second row in (5) and are

$$x_A = \lim_{t \to \infty} x(t) = \alpha_v v_0/\lambda, \qquad y_A = \lim_{t \to \infty} y(t) = \beta_v v_0/\lambda \qquad (1)$$

The terminal velocity $(t \to \infty)$ of the particle computed from (4) of Problem 4.8 is

$$\dot{x}_A = \lim_{t \to \infty} \dot{x}(t) = 0, \qquad \dot{y}_A = \lim_{t \to \infty} \dot{y}(t) = 0, \qquad \dot{z}_A = \lim_{t \to \infty} \dot{z}(t) = -g/\lambda \qquad (2)$$

For small values of λ,

$$e^{-\lambda t} \approx 1 - \lambda t + (\lambda t)^2/2 \qquad (3)$$

and the matrix equation of the trajectory (5) becomes

$$\begin{bmatrix} x \\ y \\ z \end{bmatrix} = v_0 t \begin{bmatrix} \alpha_v(1 - \lambda t/2) \\ \beta_v(1 - \lambda t/2) \\ \gamma_v(1 - \lambda t/2) - gt/(2v_0) \end{bmatrix} \qquad (4)$$

which for $\lambda = 0$ reduces to the equations of the plane parabola.

For $\lambda t \lesssim 0.17$, the error of this approximation is $\varepsilon_T \lesssim 0.1$ percent; and for $\lambda t \lesssim 0.35$, $\varepsilon_T \lesssim 1$ percent.

The equation of the plane of this motion obtained by dividing the first equation of (4) by the second equation of (4) is

$$x/y = \alpha_v/\beta_v \qquad (5)$$

and is valid for both cases ($\lambda = 0$ and $\lambda > 0$).

MOTION WITH CONSTRAINTS

4.10 A spherical pendulum of length l and mass m undergoes conical motion of constant radius $c = l \sin \phi_0$ (Fig. P-4.10a). Find the equations of motion of m and the tension S in the string. Given: m, l, ϕ_0.

By (4-4),

$$\begin{bmatrix} F_\phi(t) \\ F_\theta(t) \\ F_r(t) \end{bmatrix} = \begin{bmatrix} -mg \sin \phi_0 \\ 0 \\ mg \cos \phi_0 - S \end{bmatrix} = \begin{bmatrix} ma_\phi \\ ma_\theta \\ ma_r \end{bmatrix} \qquad (1)$$

where S is the unknown tension in the spring, ϕ_0 is a given angle and a_ϕ, a_θ, a_r are given by (3-24).

Since $r = l = $ constant and $\phi_0 = $ constant,

$$a_\phi = -l\dot{\theta}^2 \sin \phi_0 \cos \phi_0$$

$$a_\theta = l\ddot{\theta} \sin \phi_0 \qquad (2)$$

$$a_r = -l\dot{\theta}^2 \sin^2 \phi_0$$

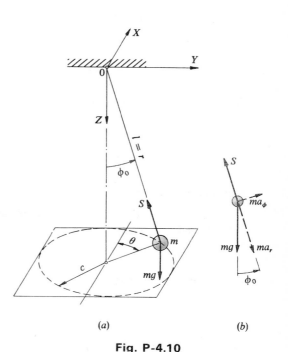

(a)   (b)

Fig. P-4.10

Then (*1*) in terms of (*2*) is

$$
\begin{bmatrix} -mg \sin \phi_0 \\ 0 \\ mg \cos \phi_0 - S \end{bmatrix} = m \begin{bmatrix} -l\dot{\theta}^2 \sin \phi_0 \cos \phi_0 \\ l\ddot{\theta} \sin \phi_0 \\ -l\dot{\theta}^2 \sin^2 \phi_0 \end{bmatrix} \tag{3}
$$

From the first equation of (*3*), the angular velocity of *m* is

$$
\dot{\theta} = \sqrt{g/(l \cos \phi_0)}
$$

From the second equation of (*3*), the angular acceleration is

$$
\ddot{\theta} = 0
$$

From the third equation of (*3*), the tension in the string is

$$
S = mg \cos \phi_0 + mgl \sin^2 \phi_0 / l \cos \phi_0 = mg/\cos \phi_0
$$

which must satisfy the condition of equilibrium along the line of action of the constraint (string) as shown in Fig. P-4.10*b*.

4.11   A particle of mass *m* rests at 1 on the top of a smooth fixed sphere of radius *R* (Fig. P-4.11).   If the particle is displaced from 1 with $\dot{\phi}(0) = \omega_1$, at which position and with what speed will it leave the surface of the sphere?   Given: *R*, *m*, ω_1.

By (*4-4*),

$$
\begin{bmatrix} F_\phi(t) \\ F_\theta(t) \\ F_r(t) \end{bmatrix} = \begin{bmatrix} mg \sin \phi \\ 0 \\ -mg \cos \phi + N \end{bmatrix} = \begin{bmatrix} ma_\phi \\ ma_\theta \\ ma_r \end{bmatrix} \tag{1}
$$

where *N* is the unknown normal force of the particle on the surface of the sphere and ϕ is the time-dependent position angle.

The three acceleration components in (*1*) are again given by (*3-24*).

Since the motion is in the vertical plane *XZ* ($\theta = 0$) and

$$
R = r = \text{constant} \tag{2}
$$

the acceleration components (*3-24*) reduce to

$$
a_\phi = R\ddot{\phi}
$$

$$
a_\theta = 0
$$

$$
a_r = -R\dot{\phi}^2 \tag{3}
$$

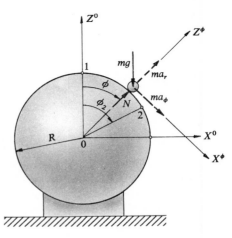

Fig. P-4.11

Then (*1*) in terms of (*3*) is

$$\begin{bmatrix} mg \sin \phi \\ 0 \\ -mg \cos \phi + N \end{bmatrix} = m \begin{bmatrix} R\ddot{\phi} \\ 0 \\ -R\dot{\phi}^2 \end{bmatrix}$$

(4)

From the first equation in (*4*),

$$\ddot{\phi} = \frac{g}{R} \sin \phi$$

(5)

and from the third equation in (*4*),

$$\dot{\phi}^2 = \frac{g}{R} \cos \phi - \frac{N}{Rm}$$

(6)

where

$$\dot{\phi} = \frac{d\phi}{dt} = \omega, \qquad \ddot{\phi} = \frac{d\omega}{d\phi} \frac{d\phi}{dt} = \frac{d\omega}{d\phi} \omega$$

(7), (8)

Then (*5*) in terms of (*8*) becomes

$$\frac{d\omega}{d\phi} \omega = \frac{g}{R} \sin \phi$$

and on integrating,

$$\int_0^\omega \omega \, d\omega = \frac{g}{R} \int_0^\phi \sin \phi \, d\phi \ + \ C$$

$$\omega^2/2 = (g/R)(1 - \cos \phi) \ + \ C$$

$$\omega = \sqrt{(2g/R)(1 - \cos \phi) + 2C}$$

where at $\phi = 0$, $\omega = \omega_1$ and $2C = \omega_1^2$.

At the point of departure 2, $\phi = \phi_2$, $N = 0$, and

$$\omega_2 = \dot{\phi}_2 = \sqrt{(2g/R)(1 - \cos \phi_2) + \omega_1^2}$$

(9)

In terms of (*9*), equation (*6*) can be written as

$$(2g/R)(1 - \cos \phi_2) + \omega_1^2 = (g/R) \cos \phi_2 - \cancel{N/Rm}^{\,0}$$

(10)

from which

$$\phi_2 = \cos^{-1}(2/3 + R\omega_1^2/3g)$$

(11)

When $\omega_1 = 0$, equation (*11*) reduces to $\phi_2 = \cos^{-1} 2/3 = 48.2°$.

The speed of departure at 2 is

$$v_2 = R\omega_2 = R\sqrt{(2g/R)[1 - (2/3 + R\omega_1^2/3g)] + \omega_1^2}$$

which for $\omega_1 = 0$ becomes $v_2 = \sqrt{2gR/3}$.

...mine the superelevation of the highway curve of radius R (Fig. P-4.12) which will produce equal reaction on the outer and inner wheels of a car of mass m moving with uniform speed v along the curve.   Given: m, R, v.

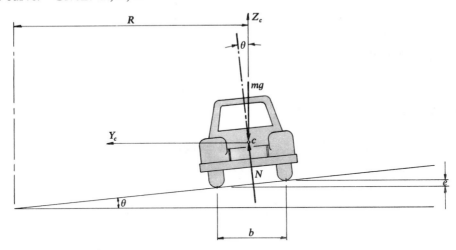

Fig. P-4.12

By (4-5),

$$\begin{bmatrix} F_t(t) \\ F_n(t) \\ F_b(t) \end{bmatrix} = \begin{bmatrix} 0 \\ N \sin \theta \\ -mg + N \cos \theta \end{bmatrix} = \begin{bmatrix} ma_t \\ ma_n \\ ma_b \end{bmatrix} \tag{1}$$

where N is the resultant of force on the wheels and must pass through the center of gravity of the car. The three acceleration components in (1) are given by (1-21), page 6, as

$$a_t = \dot{v}, \qquad a_n = v^2/\rho, \qquad a_b = 0 \tag{2}$$

where $\rho = R$; and since $v = $ constant, $\dot{v} = 0$.

Then (1) in terms of (2) is

$$\begin{bmatrix} 0 \\ N \sin \theta \\ -mg + N \cos \theta \end{bmatrix} = m \begin{bmatrix} 0 \\ v^2/R \\ 0 \end{bmatrix} \tag{3}$$

From the third equation in (3),

$$N = mg/\cos \theta \tag{4}$$

and from the second equation in (3) with N given by (4),

$$\tan \theta = v^2/gR \tag{5}$$

The superelevation, defined as the difference between the elevations of the outer and inner wheel levels, is

$$e = b \tan \theta = bv^2/gR \tag{6}$$

Note that this solution is valid only for the condition of equal reactions (see Problem 4.13).

FRICTION RESISTANCE

4.13 A concrete highway of radius of curvature $R = 400$ ft, width 40 ft and superelevation 2 ft has a kinetic coefficient of friction $\mu_k = 0.2$ (Fig. P-4.13).   What is the maximum speed of the car traveling on this road before skidding radially?

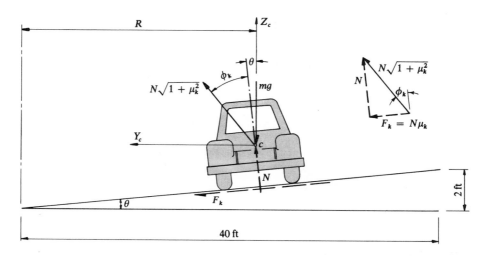

Fig. P-4.13

In terms of the angle of kinetic friction,* $\phi_k = \tan^{-1}\mu_k$, (3) of Problem 4.12 becomes

$$\begin{bmatrix} 0 \\ N\sqrt{1 + \mu_k^2}\,\sin\left(\theta + \phi_k\right) \\ N\sqrt{1 + \mu_k^2}\,\cos\left(\theta + \phi_k\right) - mg \end{bmatrix} = m \begin{bmatrix} 0 \\ v^2/R \\ 0 \end{bmatrix} \qquad (1)$$

From the third equation in (1),

$$N = \frac{mg}{\sqrt{1 + \mu_k^2}\,\cos\left(\theta + \phi_k\right)} \qquad (2)$$

and from the second equation in (1) with N now given by (2),

$$v = \sqrt{gR\tan\left(\theta + \phi_k\right)} = 57 \text{ ft/sec} = 38.9 \text{ mph}$$

where $g = 32.2$ ft/sec^2, $R = 400$ ft, $\theta = \tan^{-1} 2/40 = 2.86°$, $\phi_k = \tan^{-1} 0.2 = 11.31°$, $\tan\left(\theta + \phi_k\right) = 0.25267$.

MOMENTUM AND IMPULSE

4.14 Using the linear impulse equation (4-14), find the velocity of the particle in Problem 4.1.

Let $[G_1^0] = [G^0(0)] = m[\dot{s}(0)]$, $[G_2^0] = [G^0(t)] = m[\dot{s}(t)]$, $[F^0] = [F^0(t)]$.   Then by (4-14) in terms of the values given in Problem 4.1,

*J. J. Tuma, "Statics", Quantum Publishers, New York, 1974, Chapter 10, p. 225.

$$m \begin{bmatrix} \dot{x}^0(t) \\ \dot{y}^0(t) \\ \dot{z}^0(t) \end{bmatrix} = m \begin{bmatrix} 2 \\ 0 \\ 1 \end{bmatrix} + \int_0^t \begin{bmatrix} 0 \\ 2m \\ 0 \end{bmatrix} dt = m \begin{bmatrix} 2 \\ 2t \\ 1 \end{bmatrix}$$

$$\underbrace{\phantom{m \begin{bmatrix} \dot{x}^0(t) \\ \dot{y}^0(t) \\ \dot{z}^0(t) \end{bmatrix}}}_{[\dot{s}^0(t)]} \quad \underbrace{\phantom{m \begin{bmatrix} 2 \\ 0 \\ 1 \end{bmatrix}}}_{[\dot{s}^0(0)]} \quad \underbrace{\phantom{\int_0^t \begin{bmatrix} 0 \\ 2m \\ 0 \end{bmatrix} dt}}_{[F^0(t)]}$$

which is equivalent to (2) in Problem 4.1.

4.15 The linear momentum of a particle of mass m at t is $\mathbf{G} = (2\mathbf{i} + 2t\mathbf{j} + \mathbf{k})m$. Find the force causing the motion.

By (4-9),

$$\begin{bmatrix} F_x^0 \\ F_y^0 \\ F_z^0 \end{bmatrix} = \begin{bmatrix} \dot{G}_x^0 \\ \dot{G}_y^0 \\ \dot{G}_z^0 \end{bmatrix} = m \begin{bmatrix} 0 \\ 2 \\ 0 \end{bmatrix}$$

which is the inverse of Problem 4.14.

4.16 See Fig. P-4.16.   A projectile of mass m_1 is fired with velocity $\mathbf{v}_1 = (3\mathbf{i} + 4\mathbf{j})$ ft/sec into a block of mass m_2 resting on the $X_0 Y_0$ plane.   Find the displacement of the block if the coefficient of kinetic friction is μ_k.   Given: $m_1 = m_2 = m$, $\mathbf{v}_1$, $\mu_k = 0.20$, $g = 32.2$ ft/sec^2.

By the principle of conservation of momentum,

$$m_1 v_1 = (m_1 + m_2) v_2$$

from which

$$v_2 = \frac{m_1}{m_1 + m_2} v_1 = \tfrac{1}{2}\sqrt{3^2 + 4^2} = 2.5 \text{ ft/sec}$$

The magnitude of kinetic friction is $F_k = -\mu_k m_2 g = -m_2 a_k = -6.44m$ where $-a_k =$ deceleration.

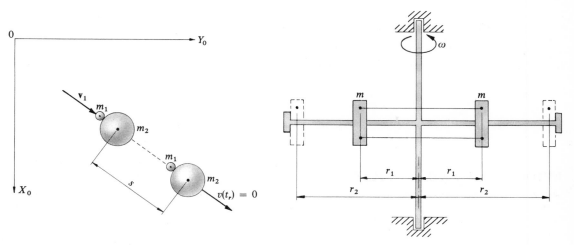

Fig. P-4.16   Fig. P-4.17

The speed of $(m_1 + m_2)$ is then

$$v = v_2 + v_k = 2.5 - 6.44t$$

where $v_k = -a_k t = $ speed of friction resistance.
   At rest, $v(t_r) = 0$ from which $t_r = 2.5/6.44 = 0.38$ sec.
   The displacement is then $s = a_k t_r^2/2 = (6.44)(0.38)^2/2 = 6.43$ ft.

4.17 Refer to Fig. P-4.17.   A smooth horizontal bar of negligible weight rotates with a constant angular speed ω_1 about a vertical shaft with two blocks of equal mass m held at a distance r_1 from the shaft by strings.   If the strings are cut, the sliders move to their new positions at the distance r_2. Compute the new angular velocity of the shaft.   Given: m, r_1, r_2, ω_1.

   The conservation of angular momentum requires that $2mr_1v_1 = 2mr_2v_2$ where in circular motion $v_1 = r_1\omega_1$, $v_2 = r_2\omega_2$.
   Thus the new angular speed is $\omega_2 = r_1^2\omega_1/r_2^2$.   For $r_1 = l$ and $r_2 = 2l$, $\omega_2 = \omega_1/4$.

4.18 Find the angular impulse required to maintain a constant angular speed ω_1 in Problem 4.17.
   By (4-15),

$$\int_0^t \dot{H}\, dt = H_2 - H_1 = 2mr_2^2\omega_1 - 2mr_1^2\omega_1 = 2m\omega_1(r_2^2 - r_1^2)$$

For $r_1 = l$ and $r_2 = 2l$, $\displaystyle\int_0^t \dot{H}\, dt = 6l^2 m\omega_1$.

WORK AND ENERGY

4.19 A particle of weight W slides inside a smooth spiral tube of constant helix angle γ.   If the release speed at 1 is zero, what is the terminal speed at 2 (Fig. P-4.19)?

   Since the gravity force is derivable from a potential, by (2-20)

$$\frac{Wv_2^2}{2g} - \frac{Wv_1^2}{2g} = \underbrace{\int_h^0 -W\, dz}_{U}$$

where $v_1 = 0$ and U is independent of the helical path.   Then $v_2 = \sqrt{2hg}$, the speed of free fall.

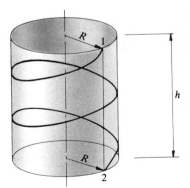

Fig. P-4.19

4.20 A pipe-sleeve slider (Fig. P-4.20) of mass m slides along the straight rod $\overline{12}$ from 1 to 2 under the action of gravity and the force in the spring attached to it.   The unstretched length of the spring is a and its spring stiffness is k.   If the initial velocity of the slider is zero, what is its terminal velocity at 2?   Given: W, a, b, h, k.

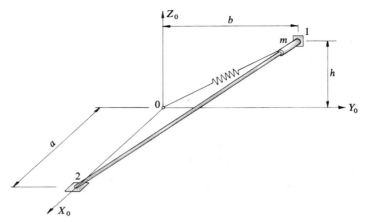

Fig. P-4.20

By (2-22),

$$T_2 - T_1 = V_1 - V_2$$

where $T_1 = Wv_1^2/2g = 0$, $T_2 = Wv_2^2/2g$, $V_1 = Wh + (k/2)(\sqrt{b^2 + h^2} - a)^2$, $V_2 = 0$. Thus

$$\frac{Wv_2^2}{2g} = Wh + (k/2)(\sqrt{b^2 + h^2} - a)^2 \qquad \text{or} \qquad v_2 = \sqrt{2hg + (kg/W)(\sqrt{b^2 + h^2} - a)^2}$$

which for $k = 0$ reduces to $v_2 = \sqrt{2hg}$.

4.21 Using the principle of conservation of energy, solve Problem 4.11.

Selecting 0 as the datum, the potential and kinetic energies at 1 and 2 are respectively

$$V_1 = mgR \qquad\qquad T_1 = m(R\omega_1)^2/2 \tag{1}$$
$$V_2 = mgR \cos \phi_2 \qquad T_2 = m(R\omega_2)^2/2 \tag{2}$$

In terms of (1) and (2), equation (2-22) yields

$$(R\omega_2)^2 = 2gR(1 - \cos \phi_2) - (R\omega_1)^2 \tag{3}$$

Since at 2, $N = 0$, from the second equation in (4-5),

$$-mg \cos \phi_2 = m(R\omega_2)^2/R \tag{4}$$

On eliminating ω_2 from (3) and (4), $\phi_2 = \cos^{-1}(2/3 + R\omega_1^2/3g)$ which is identical to (11) of Problem 4.11.

Problems

EQUATIONS OF MOTION

4.22 Consider a particle of mass m acted upon by a force $\mathbf{F} = 10m\mathbf{i} + 20m\mathbf{j} + 30m\mathbf{k}$ in the cartesian system. Find the matrix equations of motion. Given: $x(0) = 4$, $y(0) = 5$, $z(0) = 0$, $\dot{x}(0) = 0$, $\dot{y}(0) = 6$, $\dot{z}(0) = 0$.

4.23 A particle of mass m is acted upon by a force $\mathbf{F} = (a \cos \omega t)\mathbf{i} + (b \sin \omega t)\mathbf{j} + ht\mathbf{k}$ in the cartesian system. Find the matrix equations of motion. Given: m, a, b, h, ω, $\mathbf{r}(0) = 0$, $\dot{\mathbf{r}}(0) = 0$.

4.24 Construct the transport matrix equation for the particle of Problem 4.22 in the time interval $t_1 - t_0$. Use the results of Problem 4.4. Given: $t_0 = 0$, $t_1 = 10$.

4.25 Construct the transport matrix equation for the particle of Problem 4.23 in the time interval $t_2 - t_1$. Use the results of Problem 4.4. Given: $t_1 = \pi/\omega$, $t_2 = 2\pi/\omega$.

4.26 Using the transport matrix equation of Problem 4.24, compute the kinematic vectors at $t_1 = 10$, $t_2 = 20$, $t_3 = 30$.

4.27 For the moving projectile of Problem 4.8, find the maximum height and the time required to reach this height.

MOTION WITH CONSTRAINTS

4.28 For a particle of weight W which slides inside the smooth helical tube of Problem 4.19, find the contact force N at 2. Given: R, h, γ, W.

4.29 A ball of weight W is rigidly attached to a straight inclined bar $\overline{0m}$ of length l which rotates about the Z_0 axis (Fig. P-4.29) with a constant angular speed ω. Neglecting the mass of the bar, find its equations of motion and the axial force in it. Given: l, W, ϕ, ω.

4.30 The particle of Problem 4.11 is given a horizontal velocity $v_1 = \sqrt{gR}$ at 1. Find the angle ϕ_2 at which it leaves the fixed sphere and the speed of departure v_2.

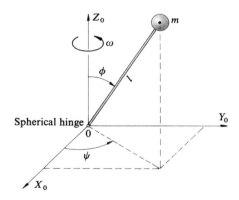

Fig. P-4.29

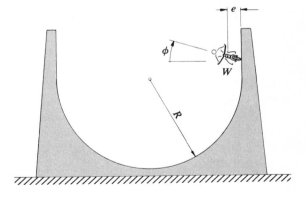

Fig. P-4.32

FRICTION RESISTANCE

4.31 Work Problem 4.11 if the coefficient of kinetic friction $\mu_k = 0.2$.

4.32 Find the minimum uniform speed v which the motorcyclist riding around in a circular drum of radius R (Fig. P-4.32) must maintain to prevent slipping, and the angle ϕ which he must make with the normal to the drum's wall to prevent tipping. Given: W = weight of driver and motorcycle, R, e, and μ_k = coefficient of friction between the tires and the drum's wall.

MOMENTUM AND IMPULSE

4.33   A small ball of weight W moves with constant velocity along a horizontal circle at the end of a cord of length l_1 which makes an angle θ_1 with the vertical.   By pulling the string through the opening at 0, its effective length reduces to l_2 and the angle changes to θ_2 (Fig. P-4.33).   Find θ_2 for given l_1, l_2 and θ_1.

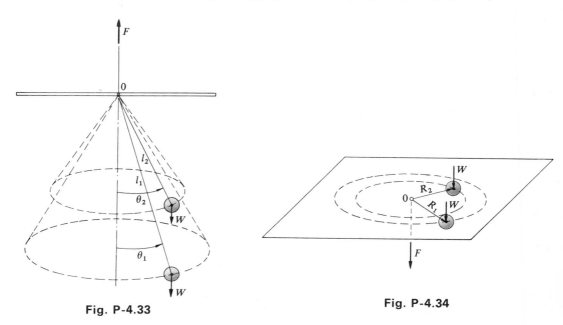

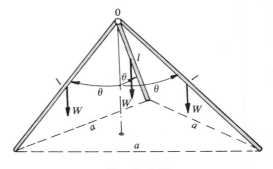

Fig. P-4.33

Fig. P-4.34

4.34   A small ball of weight W attached at the end of a string moves in a circular path of radius R_1 with constant speed v_1 on a horizontal plane as shown in Fig. P-4.34.   Find the velocity v_2 of the ball if the effective length of the string is reduced to R_2 by drawing it slowly through the hole at 0.

4.35   Find the angular impulse required to maintain a constant angular speed in Problem 4.34.

WORK AND ENERGY

4.36   Using the work-energy equation (*4-18*), derive the equations of motion of the particle of Problem 4.7.

4.37   Using the work-energy equation (*4-18*), solve Problem 4.30.

4.38   Three identical bars of weight W and length l are hinged together at 0 (Fig. P-4.38) and supported by a smooth horizontal plane.   Derive the equation of motion of this assembly in terms of the angle θ that each bar makes with the vertical.

Fig. P-4.38

Chapter 5

Dynamics of Systems of Particles

5.1 CHARACTERISTICS OF A SYSTEM

Mathematical Models

Although the *single particle model* introduced in the preceding chapters offers an adequate representation of some mechanical systems, in general most mechanical systems must be treated as collections of particles and represented by *multiparticle models*.

Two types of multiparticle models used in dynamic analysis are:

(a) *Discrete parameter model*, a collection of a finite number of particles, each of which is defined by a set of discrete characteristics (discrete parameters) specific for that particle.

(b) *Distributed parameter model*, a collection of an infinite number of particles, each of which is defined by a set of distributed characteristics which are continuous, single-valued and differentiable, but may have a finite number of discontinuities in the region of the system.

The parameters of these models are the mass, force, moment, position, velocity and acceleration, and their combinations such as the mass center, momentum, impulse, power, work and energy. Only discrete parameter models are considered in this chapter.

Mass Center

If the positions of N particles of mass $m_1, m_2, \ldots, m_N$ are given by their respective position vectors $\mathbf{r}_{01}, \mathbf{r}_{02}, \ldots, \mathbf{r}_{0N}$, then their *mass center c* is defined as the point located by the vector (Fig. 5-1)

$$\mathbf{r}_{0c} = \frac{\mathbf{r}_{01}m_1 + \mathbf{r}_{02}m_2 + \ldots + \mathbf{r}_{0N}m_N}{m_1 + m_2 + \ldots + m_N} = \frac{\displaystyle\sum_N \mathbf{r}_{0s}m_s}{\displaystyle\sum_N m_s} \tag{5-1}$$

where $\sum_N m_s = m$ is the total mass of the system and $\sum_N \mathbf{r}_{0s}m_s = \sum_N \mathbf{Q}_{0s} = \mathbf{Q}_0$ is the moment of the total mass about 0.

In the *cartesian system*,

$$\mathbf{r}_{0c} = \frac{\displaystyle\sum_N x_{0s}m_s}{\displaystyle\sum_N m_s}\,\mathbf{i} + \frac{\displaystyle\sum_N y_{0s}m_s}{\displaystyle\sum_N m_s}\,\mathbf{j} + \frac{\displaystyle\sum_N z_{0s}m_s}{\displaystyle\sum_N m_s}\,\mathbf{k} = x_{0c}\mathbf{i} + y_{0c}\mathbf{j} + z_{0c}\mathbf{k} \tag{5-2}$$

where x_{0c}, y_{0c}, z_{0c} are the *coordinates of the mass center*, measured from the fixed point 0.

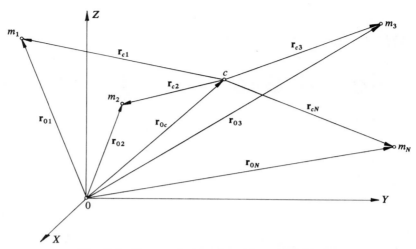

Fig. 5.1 Center of mass of a system of particles.

Since the mechanical systems in this book are assumed to be in a uniform gravitational field, their respective *mass centers* are also their *gravity centers*.

5.2 MOTION RELATIVE TO A FIXED POINT

Equations of Motion

For a discrete parameter model, each particle of which obeys Newton's laws, the differential equation of motion is obtained by the linear superposition of the differential equations of motion of the respective particles, i.e.

$$\sum_{N} \ddot{\mathbf{r}}_{0s} m_s = \sum_{N} \mathbf{F}_s, \qquad s = 1, 2, \ldots, N \tag{5-3}$$

where the left side is the *inertial function* of the system and the right side the *resultant force function* (Fig. 5-2).

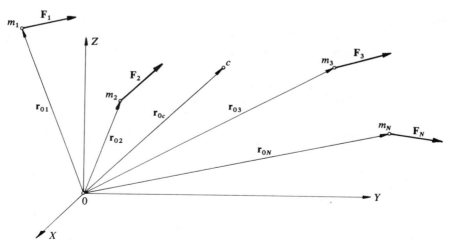

Fig. 5-2 Unbalanced forces in a system of particles.

Since by (5-1),

$$\sum_N \mathbf{r}_{0s} m_s = \mathbf{r}_{0c} m$$

the inertial function can be expressed in terms of $\mathbf{r}_{0c}$ as

$$\sum_N \ddot{\mathbf{r}}_{0s} m_s = \ddot{\mathbf{r}}_{0c} m \qquad (5\text{-}4)$$

and the *equation of motion* (5-3) can be written as

$$\mathbf{F} = \ddot{\mathbf{r}}_{0c} m \qquad \text{or} \qquad \ddot{\mathbf{r}}_{0c} = \mathbf{F}/m \qquad (5\text{-}5), (5\text{-}6)$$

where $\ddot{\mathbf{r}}_{0c}$ is the acceleration vector of the mass center and

$$\mathbf{F} = \mathbf{F}(t, s, \dot{s}, \ddot{s}) \qquad (5\text{-}7)$$

is the force resultant.

      Equations (5-5) and (5-6) are the multiparticle equivalents of the single particle equations (2-5) and (2-6), respectively.   This formal similarity is of a great practical importance, making possible the application of the methods of single particle analysis to the analysis of multiparticle systems (problems of the first kind, and problems of the second kind, Sections 2.2 and 4.1).

Linear and Angular Momentum

      The relations (5-1), (5-5) and (5-6) also allow the extension of the concept of momentum and impulse to the system of particles.

      The *total linear momentum* $\mathbf{G}$ of this system of particles in motion is

$$\mathbf{G} = \sum_N \mathbf{G}_s = \sum_N \dot{\mathbf{r}}_{0s} m_s = \dot{\mathbf{r}}_{0c} m \qquad (5\text{-}8)$$

where $\dot{\mathbf{r}}_{0c}$ is the velocity vector of the mass center.

      The *time derivative of the total linear momentum* $\dot{\mathbf{G}}$ of the same system is

$$\dot{\mathbf{G}} = \sum_N \dot{\mathbf{G}}_s = \ddot{\mathbf{r}}_{0c} m = \mathbf{F} \qquad (5\text{-}9)$$

where $\mathbf{F}$ is the force resultant introduced in (5-5) and (5-6).

      The *total angular momentum* $\mathbf{H}$ of the same system is

$$\mathbf{H} = \sum_N (\mathbf{r}_{0s} \times \mathbf{G}_s) = \sum_N (\mathbf{r}_{0s} \times \dot{\mathbf{r}}_{0s} m_s) = \sum_N (\mathbf{Q}_{0s} \times \dot{\mathbf{r}}_{0s}) \qquad (5\text{-}10)$$

where $\mathbf{Q}_{0s}$ is the moment of mass m_s about 0 introduced in (5-1).

      The *time derivative of the total angular momentum* $\dot{\mathbf{H}}$ of the same system is

$$\dot{\mathbf{H}} = \sum_N (\mathbf{r}_{0s} \times \dot{\mathbf{G}}_s) + \sum_N (\dot{\mathbf{r}}_{0s} \times \mathbf{G}_s) = \sum_N (\mathbf{r}_{0s} \times \mathbf{F}_s) = \mathbf{M} \qquad (5\text{-}11)$$

where $\mathbf{M}$ is the moment resultant about 0.

Conservation of Momentum

If the *resultant of forces* acting on the system of particles in motion is *zero* ($\mathbf{F} = 0$), then

$$\dot{\mathbf{G}} = \ddot{\mathbf{r}}_{0c}m = \mathbf{F} = 0 \qquad \text{and} \qquad \mathbf{G} = \text{constant} \qquad (5\text{-}12)$$

which is the system generalization of the *principle of conservation of linear momentum* (Definition 2.8).

If the *resultant of moments* acting on the system of particles in motion is *zero* ($\mathbf{M} = 0$), then

$$\dot{\mathbf{H}} = \sum_{N} (\mathbf{r}_{0s} \times \mathbf{F}_s) = \mathbf{M} = 0 \qquad \text{and} \qquad \mathbf{H} = \text{constant} \qquad (5\text{-}13)$$

which is the system generalization of the *principle of conservation of angular momentum* (Definition 2.9).

Linear and Angular Impulse

The *linear impulse of forces* acting on the system of particles during the time interval $t_2 - t_1$ equals the linear impulse of their resultant during the same time interval, i.e.

$$\sum_{N} \int_{t_1}^{t_2} \mathbf{F}_s \, dt = \sum_{N} \int_{t_1}^{t_2} \dot{\mathbf{G}}_s \, dt = \sum_{N} [\mathbf{G}_{s,2} - \mathbf{G}_{s,1}] = \mathbf{G}_2 - \mathbf{G}_1 = \int_{t_1}^{t_2} \mathbf{F} \, dt \qquad (5\text{-}14)$$

where $\mathbf{G}_2, \mathbf{G}_1$ is the total linear momentum at t_2, t_1 respectively, and the total linear impulse equals the change in total linear momentum (Definition 2.10).

The *angular impulse of forces* acting on the system of N particles during the time interval $t_2 - t_1$ equals the angular impulse of their resultant during the same time interval, i.e.

$$\sum_{N} \int_{t_1}^{t_2} \mathbf{M}_s \, dt = \sum_{N} \int_{t_1}^{t_2} \dot{\mathbf{H}}_s \, dt = \sum_{N} [\mathbf{H}_{s,2} - \mathbf{H}_{s,1}] = \mathbf{H}_2 - \mathbf{H}_1 = \int_{t_1}^{t_2} \mathbf{M} \, dt \qquad (5\text{-}15)$$

where $\mathbf{H}_2, \mathbf{H}_1$ is the total angular momentum at t_2, t_1 respectively, and the total angular impulse equals the change in total angular momentum (Definition 2.11).

5.3   MOTION RELATIVE TO THE MASS CENTER

Position Vector and Moment of Mass

The *position vector of the particle s* in the system of N particles in motion with respect to a fixed point 0 and its time derivatives can also be written as

$$\mathbf{r}_{0s} = \mathbf{r}_{0c} + \mathbf{r}_{cs}, \qquad \dot{\mathbf{r}}_{0s} = \dot{\mathbf{r}}_{0c} + \dot{\mathbf{r}}_{cs}, \qquad \ddot{\mathbf{r}}_{0s} = \ddot{\mathbf{r}}_{0c} + \ddot{\mathbf{r}}_{cs} \qquad (5\text{-}16)$$

where $\mathbf{r}_{0c}$ is the position vector of the mass center with respect to 0 and $\mathbf{r}_{cs}$ is the position vector of the particle with respect to this mass center.

The *total moment of mass of all particles* with respect to a fixed point 0 and its time derivatives can be written in terms of (5-16) as

$$\left.\begin{aligned}
\mathbf{Q}_0 &= \sum_{N} \mathbf{r}_{0s}m_s = \sum_{N} (\mathbf{r}_{0c}m_s + \mathbf{r}_{cs}m_s) = \mathbf{r}_{0c}m \\[2mm]
\dot{\mathbf{Q}}_0 &= \sum_{N} \dot{\mathbf{r}}_{0s}m_s = \sum_{N} (\dot{\mathbf{r}}_{0c}m_s + \dot{\mathbf{r}}_{cs}m_s) = \dot{\mathbf{r}}_{0c}m = \mathbf{G} \\[2mm]
\ddot{\mathbf{Q}}_0 &= \sum_{N} \ddot{\mathbf{r}}_{0s}m_s = \sum_{N} (\ddot{\mathbf{r}}_{0c}m_s + \ddot{\mathbf{r}}_{cs}m_s) = \ddot{\mathbf{r}}_{0c}m = \dot{\mathbf{G}} = \mathbf{F}
\end{aligned}\right\} \qquad (5\text{-}17)$$

where $\mathbf{G}$ and $\mathbf{F}$ are defined by (5-8) and (5-9) respectively.

Linear Momentum

Since in (5-17)

$$\mathbf{Q}_c = \sum_N \mathbf{r}_{cs} m_s = 0, \qquad \dot{\mathbf{Q}}_c = \sum_N \dot{\mathbf{r}}_{cs} m_s = 0, \qquad \ddot{\mathbf{Q}}_c = \sum_N \ddot{\mathbf{r}}_{cs} m_s = 0 \qquad (5\text{-}18)$$

it may be concluded that:

(1) The *moment of mass* of all particles with respect to the mass center is zero.

$$\int_0^t \mathbf{G}_c \, dt = \mathbf{Q}_c = 0 \qquad (5\text{-}19)$$

(2) The *linear momentum* of a system of particles with respect to the mass center is zero.

$$\mathbf{G}_c = \dot{\mathbf{Q}}_c = 0 \qquad (5\text{-}20)$$

(3) The *resultant of forces* acting on a system of particles with respect to the mass center is zero.

$$\dot{\mathbf{G}}_c = \mathbf{F}_c = 0 \qquad (5\text{-}21)$$

Angular Momentum

By (5-10), in terms of (5-16), the total angular momentum of the system with respect to 0 is

$$\mathbf{H} = \sum_N (\mathbf{r}_{0s} \times \mathbf{G}_s) = \sum_N \left[(\mathbf{r}_{0c} + \mathbf{r}_{cs}) \times (\dot{\mathbf{r}}_{0c} + \dot{\mathbf{r}}_{cs}) m_s \right]$$

$$= \mathbf{r}_{0c} \times \underbrace{\dot{\mathbf{r}}_{0c} m}_{\mathbf{G}_{0c}} + \sum_N (\mathbf{r}_{cs} \times \underbrace{\dot{\mathbf{r}}_{cs} m_s}_{\mathbf{G}_{cs}}) = \mathbf{H}_{0c} + \mathbf{H}_c \qquad (5\text{-}22)$$

where $\mathbf{H}_{0c}$ is the angular momentum of the mass located at c about 0 and $\mathbf{H}_c$ is the sum of angular momenta of $m_1, m_2, \ldots, m_N$ located at 1, 2, $\ldots$, N respectively about c.

By (5-11), in terms of (5-16), the *time derivative of the total angular momentum* of the system of particles with respect to 0 is

$$\dot{\mathbf{H}} = \sum_N (\mathbf{r}_{0s} \times \mathbf{F}_s) = \sum_N \left[(\mathbf{r}_{0c} + \mathbf{r}_{cs}) \times \mathbf{F}_s \right] = \mathbf{M}_{0c} + \mathbf{M}_c \qquad (5\text{-}23)$$

where $\mathbf{M}_{0c}$ is the moment of the force resultant located at c about 0, and $\mathbf{M}_c$ is the sum of moments of all forces located at their respective points of action with respect to c.

5.4 WORK AND ENERGY

Kinetic Energy

The *total kinetic energy* T of the system of N particles with respect to the fixed point 0 is

$$T = \tfrac{1}{2} \sum_N (\dot{\mathbf{r}}_{0s} \cdot \dot{\mathbf{r}}_{0s} m_s) = \tfrac{1}{2} \sum_N \dot{r}_{0s}^2 m_s \qquad (5\text{-}24)$$

In terms of (5-16),

$$T = \frac{1}{2} \sum_N \left[(\dot{\mathbf{r}}_{0c} + \dot{\mathbf{r}}_{cs}) \cdot (\dot{\mathbf{r}}_{0c} + \dot{\mathbf{r}}_{cs}) m_s \right] = \frac{1}{2} \dot{\mathbf{r}}_{0c} \cdot \dot{\mathbf{r}}_{0c} m + \frac{1}{2} \sum_N (\dot{\mathbf{r}}_{cs} \cdot \dot{\mathbf{r}}_{cs} m_s)$$

$$= \frac{1}{2} \dot{r}_{0c}^2 m + \frac{1}{2} \sum_N (\dot{r}_{cs}^2 m_s) = T_{0c} + T_c \tag{5-25}$$

where T_{0c} is the translatory energy of the total mass located at c with respect to 0, and T_c is the sum of the kinetic energies of masses with respect to c.

Mechanical Work—Kinetic Energy

The *total mechanical work* U done by the forces in moving the respective N particles along prescribed paths from configuration 1 to configuration 2 (Fig. 5-3) is

$$U = \sum_N \int_1^2 \mathbf{F}_s \cdot d\mathbf{r}_s = \sum_N \frac{1}{2} m_s (\dot{r}_{s,2}^2 - \dot{r}_{s,1}^2) = \sum_N (T_{s,2} - T_{s,1}) = T_2 - T_1 \tag{5-26}$$

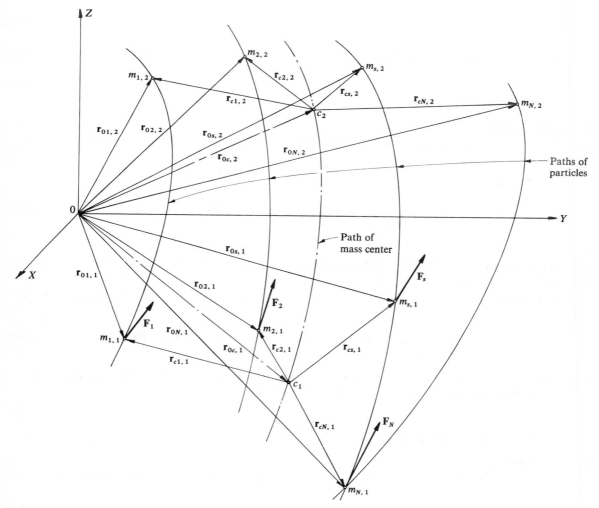

Fig. 5.3 Paths of a system of particles acted upon by a system of forces.

where T_2, T_1 are the total kinetic energies of configurations 2, 1 respectively.

In terms of (5-16),

$$U = \sum_N \int_1^2 \mathbf{F}_s \cdot d(\mathbf{r}_{0c} + \mathbf{r}_{cs}) = \tfrac{1}{2}m(\dot{r}^2_{0c,\,2} - \dot{r}^2_{0c,\,1}) + \sum_N \tfrac{1}{2}m_s(\dot{r}^2_{cs,\,2} - \dot{r}^2_{cs,\,1})$$

$$= T_{0c,\,2} - T_{0c,\,1} + T_{c,\,2} - T_{c,\,1} = \Delta T_{0c} + \Delta T_c = U_{0c} + U_c \tag{5-27}$$

where $T_{0c,\,2} - T_{0c,\,1}$ and $T_{c,\,2} - T_{c,\,1}$ are the changes in the respective kinetic energies of (5-25) corresponding to the change in configuration from 1 to 2.

Mechanical Work—Potential Energy

If the *force field* is *conservative* so that the force of each particle is given as

$$\mathbf{F}_s = -\nabla V_s \tag{5-28}$$

where V_s is the *potential energy* of the particle s, then the *total mechanical work* U of the system of N particles is

$$U = \sum_N \int_1^2 \mathbf{F}_s \cdot d\mathbf{r}_s = -\sum_N \int_1^2 dV_s = \sum_N (V_{s,\,1} - V_{s,\,2}) = V_1 - V_2 \tag{5-29}$$

where $(V_1 - V_2)$ is the change in the potential energy of the system due to the respective change in position.

In terms of (5-16),

$$U = \sum_N \int_1^2 \mathbf{F}_s \cdot d\mathbf{r}_s = -\sum_N \int_1^2 \nabla V_s \cdot d(\mathbf{r}_{0c} + \mathbf{r}_{cs}) = -\sum_N \int_1^2 \nabla V_s \cdot d\mathbf{r}_{0c} - \sum_N \int_1^2 \nabla V_s \cdot d\mathbf{r}_{cs}$$

$$= V_{0c,\,1} - V_{0c,\,2} + V_{c,\,1} - V_{c,\,2} = -\Delta V_{0c} - \Delta V_c = U_{0c} + U_c \tag{5-30}$$

where $V_{0c,\,1} - V_{0c,\,2}$ and $V_{c,\,1} - V_{c,\,2}$ are the changes in potential energy analogous to those of (5-27).

Conservation of Energy

When the system of N particles having potential energy is acted upon by forces, then the work-energy equations (5-26) and (5-29) may be combined into

$$T_1 + V_1 = T_2 + V_2 \tag{5-31}$$

where $T_1 + V_1 = T_2 + V_2 = E$ is called the *total energy* which, as (5-31) indicates, *remains constant* (principle of conservation of energy).

Illustrative Problems

MASS CENTER

5.1 Locate the mass center of the following system of three particles: $m_1 = 100 \text{ kg}_m$, $m_2 = 200 \text{ kg}_m$, $m_3 = 300 \text{ kg}_m$, $\mathbf{r}_{01} = (10t\mathbf{i} + 10t^2\mathbf{j} + 10\mathbf{k}) \text{ m}$, $\mathbf{r}_{02} = (20t\mathbf{i} + 10\mathbf{j}) \text{ m}$, $\mathbf{r}_{03} = (10\mathbf{i} + 20t\mathbf{k}) \text{ m}$.

In (5-1),

$$m = \sum_N m_s = 100 + 200 + 300 = 600 \text{ kg}_m$$

$$\mathbf{Q}_0 = \sum_N \mathbf{r}_{0s}m_s = (10t\mathbf{i} + 10t^2\mathbf{j} + 10\mathbf{k})100 + (20t\mathbf{i} + 10\mathbf{j})200 + (10\mathbf{i} + 20t\mathbf{k})300$$

$$= [(5000t + 3000)\mathbf{i} + (1000t^2 + 2000)\mathbf{j} + (6000t + 1000)\mathbf{k}] \text{ kg}_m\text{-m}$$

The position vector of the mass center is

$$\mathbf{r}_{0c} = \frac{\mathbf{Q}_0}{m} = \frac{(5000t + 3000)\mathbf{i} + (1000t^2 + 2000)\mathbf{j} + (6000t + 1000)\mathbf{k}}{600}$$

$$= [(8.33t + 5)\mathbf{i} + (1.66t^2 + 3.33)\mathbf{j} + (10t + 1.66)\mathbf{k}] \text{ m}$$

MOTION RELATIVE TO A FIXED POINT

5.2 For the system of 3 particles of Problem 5.1, find the forces required to sustain their motion.

By (2-2) and in terms of $\mathbf{r}_{01}, \mathbf{r}_{02}, \mathbf{r}_{03}$ of Problem 5.1, the differential equations of motion of the respective particles are

$$\begin{array}{lll} \ddot{\mathbf{r}}_{01}m_1 = \mathbf{F}_1 & (20\mathbf{j})100 = \mathbf{F}_1 & \mathbf{F}_1 = (2000\mathbf{j}) \text{ kg} \\ \ddot{\mathbf{r}}_{02}m_2 = \mathbf{F}_2 & (0)200 = \mathbf{F}_2 & \mathbf{F}_2 = 0 \\ \ddot{\mathbf{r}}_{03}m_3 = \mathbf{F}_3 & (0)300 = \mathbf{F}_3 & \mathbf{F}_3 = 0 \end{array}$$

This shows that particle 1 is in a state of uniformly accelerated motion under the action of an unbalanced force $\mathbf{F}_1$, whereas particles 2 and 3 are in a state of uniform motion with no force required to sustain it. These results must satisfy (5-5): $\ddot{\mathbf{r}}_{0c}m = (3.33\mathbf{j})(600) = \mathbf{F}$ from which $\mathbf{F} = (2000\mathbf{j}) \text{ kg}$.

5.3 For the system of three particles of mass $m_1 = 100 \text{ kg}_m$, $m_2 = 200 \text{ kg}_m$, $m_3 = 300 \text{ kg}_m$ acted upon by forces $\mathbf{F}_1 = (3000\mathbf{i} + 3000\mathbf{j}) \text{ kg}$, $\mathbf{F}_2 = (6000\mathbf{j} + 12,000\mathbf{k}) \text{ kg}$, $\mathbf{F}_3 = (3000\mathbf{i} + 6000\mathbf{k})$ kg respectively, find the equations of motion of their mass center with respect to a fixed point 0. Given: $\mathbf{r}_{0c}(0) = 0$, $\dot{\mathbf{r}}_{0c}(0) = 0$.

This is a kinetic problem of the second kind, Case 1, Table 2-1, page 22, which can be formulated in terms of (5-6) as

$$\ddot{\mathbf{r}}_{0c} = \frac{\mathbf{F}}{m} = \frac{[(3000\mathbf{i} + 3000\mathbf{j}) + (6000\mathbf{j} + 12,000\mathbf{k}) + (3000\mathbf{i} + 6000\mathbf{k})]}{100 + 200 + 300} = (10\mathbf{i} + 15\mathbf{j} + 30\mathbf{k}) \text{ m/sec}^2$$

$$\dot{\mathbf{r}}_{0c} = t(10\mathbf{i} + 15\mathbf{j} + 30\mathbf{k}) \text{ m/sec}$$

$$\mathbf{r}_{0c} = t^2(5\mathbf{i} + 7.5\mathbf{j} + 15\mathbf{k}) \text{ m}$$

By the same approach,

$$\mathbf{r}_{01} = t^2(15\mathbf{i} + 15\mathbf{j})\,\text{m}, \qquad \mathbf{r}_{02} = t^2(15\mathbf{i} + 30\mathbf{k})\,\text{m}, \qquad \mathbf{r}_{03} = t^2(5\mathbf{i} + 10\mathbf{k})\,\text{m}$$

which must satisfy (5-2).

$$\mathbf{r}_{0c} = \frac{t^2(15\mathbf{i} + 15\mathbf{j})100 + t^2(15\mathbf{j} + 30\mathbf{k})200 + t^2(5\mathbf{i} + 10\mathbf{k})300}{100 + 200 + 300} = t^2(5\mathbf{i} + 7.5\mathbf{j} + 15\mathbf{k})\,\text{m}$$

MOMENTUM RELATIVE TO A FIXED POINT

5.4 Find the linear momentum of the system of particles in Problem 5.1 with respect to 0.

The linear momentum (5-8) is

$$\mathbf{G} = \dot{\mathbf{r}}_{0c}m = (8.33\mathbf{i} + 3.33t\mathbf{j} + 10\mathbf{k})\,(600)\,\text{kg}_m\text{-m/sec}$$

Note: $1\,\text{kg}_m = 1\,\text{kg-sec}^2/\text{m}$ and so

$$\mathbf{G} = (5000\mathbf{i} + 2000t\mathbf{j} + 6000\mathbf{k})\,\text{kg-sec}$$

By (5-9), $\dot{\mathbf{G}} = (2000\mathbf{j})\,\text{kg} = \mathbf{F}$, which is the force resultant of Problem 5.2.

5.5 Find the angular momentum of the system of particles in Problem 5.1 with respect to 0.
From Problem 5.1,

$$\mathbf{Q}_{01} = (10t\mathbf{i} + 10t^2\mathbf{j} + 10\mathbf{k})100 \qquad \dot{\mathbf{r}}_{01} = 10\mathbf{i} + 20t\mathbf{j}$$
$$\mathbf{Q}_{02} = (20t\mathbf{i} + 10\mathbf{j})200 \qquad\qquad\quad \dot{\mathbf{r}}_{02} = 20\mathbf{i}$$
$$\mathbf{Q}_{03} = (10\mathbf{i} + 20t\mathbf{k})300 \qquad\qquad \dot{\mathbf{r}}_{03} = 20\mathbf{k}$$

and by (5-10), the angular momentum is

$$\mathbf{H} = \mathbf{Q}_{01} \times \dot{\mathbf{r}}_{01} + \mathbf{Q}_{02} \times \dot{\mathbf{r}}_{02} + \mathbf{Q}_{03} \times \dot{\mathbf{r}}_{03}$$

$$= 100\begin{vmatrix} \mathbf{i} & \mathbf{j} & \mathbf{k} \\ 10t & 10t^2 & 10 \\ 10 & 20t & 0 \end{vmatrix} + 200\begin{vmatrix} \mathbf{i} & \mathbf{j} & \mathbf{k} \\ 20t & 10 & 0 \\ 20 & 0 & 0 \end{vmatrix} + 300\begin{vmatrix} \mathbf{i} & \mathbf{j} & \mathbf{k} \\ 10 & 0 & 20t \\ 0 & 0 & 20 \end{vmatrix}$$

$$= [-20{,}000t\mathbf{i} - 50{,}000\mathbf{j} + (10{,}000t^2 - 40{,}000)\mathbf{k}]\,\text{kg-m-sec}$$

The time derivative of $\mathbf{H}$ is

$$\dot{\mathbf{H}} = -20{,}000(\mathbf{i} - t\mathbf{k})\,\text{kg-m} = \mathbf{M}$$

which is the moment of $\mathbf{F}$ [equation (5-11)] about 0.
A useful numerical check of these which sometimes involves cross product calculations is

$$\mathbf{M} = \sum_N \mathbf{r}_{0s} \times \mathbf{F}_s = \mathbf{r}_{01} \times \mathbf{F}_1 + \mathbf{r}_{02} \times \mathbf{F}_2{}^0 + \mathbf{r}_{03} \times \mathbf{F}_3{}^0$$

$$= \begin{vmatrix} \mathbf{i} & \mathbf{j} & \mathbf{k} \\ 10t & 10t^2 & 10 \\ 0 & 2000 & 0 \end{vmatrix} = -20{,}000(\mathbf{i} - t\mathbf{k}) \text{ kg-m} = \dot{\mathbf{H}}$$

where $\mathbf{F}_1, \mathbf{F}_2, \mathbf{F}_3$ are the computed forces in Problem 5.2.

IMPULSE RELATIVE TO A FIXED POINT

5.6   Find the linear impulse of the system of particles of Problem 5.1 during the time interval $t_2 - t_1$.
Given: $t_1 = 10$ sec, $t_2 = 30$ sec.

The forces of this system (Problem 5.2) are $\mathbf{F}_1 = (2000\mathbf{j})$ kg, $\mathbf{F}_2 = 0$, $\mathbf{F}_3 = 0$.
The linear impulse (5-14) is then

$$\text{L.I.} = \sum_N \int_{t_1}^{t_2} \mathbf{F}_s \, dt = \mathbf{j} \int_{10}^{30} 2000 \, dt = \mathbf{j} \left[2000t \right]_{10}^{30} = (40{,}000\mathbf{j}) \text{ kg-sec}$$

which can be checked (Problem 5.4) by

$$\mathbf{G}_2 - \mathbf{G}_1 = [5000\mathbf{i} + (2000)(30)\mathbf{j} + 6000\mathbf{k}] - [5000\mathbf{i} + (2000)(10)\mathbf{j} + 6000\mathbf{k}] = (40{,}000\mathbf{j}) \text{ kg-sec}$$

5.7   Find the angular impulse of the system of particles of Problem 5.1 during the time interval $t_2 - t_1$.
Given: $t_1 = 10$ sec, $t_2 = 30$ sec.

The forces are (Problem 5.2): $\mathbf{F}_1 = (2000\mathbf{j})$ kg, $\mathbf{F}_2 = 0$, $\mathbf{F}_3 = 0$. The angular impulse (5-15) is
then

$$\text{A.I.} = \sum_N \int_{t_1}^{t_2} \mathbf{M}_s \, dt = -\mathbf{i} \int_{10}^{30} 20{,}000 \, dt + \mathbf{k} \int_{10}^{30} 20{,}000t \, dt = (-400{,}000\mathbf{i} + 8{,}000{,}000\mathbf{k}) \text{ kg-m-sec}$$

where $\mathbf{M}_s$ is the computed moment in Problem 5.5.
Similarly as in Problem 5.6, this can be checked by

$$\mathbf{H}_2 - \mathbf{H}_1 = (-600{,}000\mathbf{i} - 500\mathbf{j} + 9{,}020{,}000\mathbf{k}) - (-200{,}000\mathbf{i} - 500\mathbf{j} + 1{,}020{,}000\mathbf{k})$$
$$= (-400{,}000\mathbf{i} + 8{,}000{,}000\mathbf{k}) \text{ kg-m-sec}$$

MOTION RELATIVE TO THE MASS CENTER

5.8   Derive equations (5-17)–(5-21).

From Fig. 5-1,

$$\mathbf{Q}_0 = \sum_N \mathbf{r}_{0s} m_s = \sum_N (\mathbf{r}_{0c} + \mathbf{r}_{cs}) m_s = \mathbf{r}_{0c} \sum_N m_s + \sum_N \mathbf{r}_{cs} m_s = \mathbf{Q}_{0c} + \mathbf{Q}_c$$

where $\sum_N m_s = m$ and by the definition of mass center, $\mathbf{Q}_c = \sum_N \mathbf{r}_{cs} m_s = 0$. Hence $\mathbf{Q}_0 = \mathbf{Q}_{0c} + \overset{0}{\cancel{\mathbf{Q}_c}} = \mathbf{r}_{0c} m$
and

$$\dot{\mathbf{Q}}_0 = \sum_N \dot{\mathbf{r}}_{0s} m_s = \dot{\mathbf{Q}}_{0c} + \overset{0}{\cancel{\dot{\mathbf{Q}}_c}} = \mathbf{G}_{0c} + \overset{0}{\cancel{\mathbf{G}_c}} = \dot{\mathbf{r}}_{0c} m = \mathbf{G}$$

$$\ddot{\mathbf{Q}}_0 = \sum_N \ddot{\mathbf{r}}_{0s} m_s = \ddot{\mathbf{Q}}_{0c} + \cancel{\ddot{\mathbf{Q}}_c}^{0} = \mathbf{F}_{0c} + \cancel{\mathbf{F}_c}^{0} = \ddot{\mathbf{r}}_{0c} m = \dot{\mathbf{G}} = \mathbf{F}$$

From above it may be concluded that the moment of mass, the linear momentum and the force resultant with respect to a fixed point 0 equal the products of their respective mass center vectors ($\mathbf{r}_{0c}, \dot{\mathbf{r}}_{0c}, \ddot{\mathbf{r}}_{0c}$) and the total mass m applied at these centers.

5.9 Derive equation (5-22): $\mathbf{H} = \mathbf{H}_{0c} + \mathbf{H}_c$.

Following the reasoning of Problem 5.8, and by the definition of $\mathbf{H}$ given in (5-10),

$$\mathbf{H} = \sum_N (\mathbf{r}_{0s} \times \mathbf{G}_s) = \sum_N (\mathbf{r}_{0s} \times \dot{\mathbf{r}}_{0s} m_s) = \sum_N [(\mathbf{r}_{0c} + \mathbf{r}_{cs}) \times (\dot{\mathbf{r}}_{0c} + \dot{\mathbf{r}}_{cs}) m_s]$$

where by Problem 5.8,

$$\sum_N (\mathbf{r}_{cs} \times \dot{\mathbf{r}}_{0c} m_s) = \left(\sum_N \mathbf{r}_{cs} m_s\right) \times \dot{\mathbf{r}}_{0c} = \cancel{\mathbf{Q}_c}^{0} \times \mathbf{r}_{0c} = 0$$

$$\sum_N (\mathbf{r}_{0c} \times \dot{\mathbf{r}}_{cs} m_s) = \mathbf{r}_{0c} \times \left(\sum_N \dot{\mathbf{r}}_{cs} m_s\right) = \dot{\mathbf{r}}_{0c} \times \cancel{\dot{\mathbf{Q}}_c}^{0} = 0$$

Therefore

$$\mathbf{H} = \sum_N (\mathbf{r}_{0c} \times \dot{\mathbf{r}}_{0c} m_s) + \sum_N (\mathbf{r}_{cs} \times \dot{\mathbf{r}}_{cs} m_s) = \mathbf{r}_{0c} \times \mathbf{G}_{0c} + \sum_N (\mathbf{r}_{cs} \times \mathbf{G}_{cs}) = \mathbf{H}_{0c} + \mathbf{H}_c$$

Thus the total angular momentum of the system with respect to 0 consists of two parts:

(a) The cross product of the position vector $\mathbf{r}_{0c}$ of the mass center c with respect to 0 and the total linear momentum of the system with respect to 0, $\mathbf{H}_{0c}$.

(b) The sum of cross products of the position vectors $\mathbf{r}_{cs}$ of the particle with respect to c and the respective linear momentum of the particle with respect to c, $\mathbf{H}_c$.

5.10 Derive equation (5-23): $\dot{\mathbf{H}} = \mathbf{M}_{0c} + \mathbf{M}_c$.

The time derivative of $\mathbf{H} = \sum_N (\mathbf{r}_{0s} \times \mathbf{G}_s)$ is

$$\dot{\mathbf{H}} = \sum_N (\mathbf{r}_{0s} \times \dot{\mathbf{G}}_s + \dot{\mathbf{r}}_{0s} \times \mathbf{G}_s) = \sum_N (\mathbf{r}_{0s} \times \mathbf{F}) = \sum_N [(\mathbf{r}_{0c} + \mathbf{r}_{cs}) \times \mathbf{F}_s] = \mathbf{r}_{0c} \times \mathbf{F} + \sum_N (\mathbf{r}_{cs} \times \mathbf{F}_s)$$

$$= \mathbf{M}_{0c} + \mathbf{M}_c$$

where $\sum_N (\dot{\mathbf{r}}_{0s} \times \mathbf{G}_s) = \sum_N (\dot{\mathbf{r}}_{0s} \times \dot{\mathbf{r}}_{0s} m_s) = 0$ and $\sum_N \mathbf{F}_s = \mathbf{F}$.

This result is formally similar to the result of Problem 5.9; the total moment with respect to 0 of the forces acting on the system consists of two parts:

(a) The cross product of the position vector $\mathbf{r}_{0c}$ of the mass center c with respect to 0 and the resultant $\mathbf{F}$ of all forces applied at c, $\mathbf{M}_{0c}$.

(b) The sum of cross products of the position vectors $\mathbf{r}_{cs}$ of the particle with respect to c and the respective force $\mathbf{F}_s$ acting on the particle s, $\mathbf{M}_c$.

WORK AND ENERGY

5.11 Derive equation (5-25): $T = T_{0c} + T_c$.

The total kinetic energy of the system of N particles moving along the respective paths under the action of the respective forces $\mathbf{F}_1, \mathbf{F}_2, \ldots, \mathbf{F}_N$ is by definition, for any position,

$$T = \tfrac{1}{2} \sum_N [\dot{\mathbf{r}}_{0s} \cdot \dot{\mathbf{r}}_{0s} m_s] = \tfrac{1}{2} \sum_N \dot{r}_{0s}^2 m_s$$

In terms of (5-16),

$$T = \tfrac{1}{2} \sum_N [(\dot{\mathbf{r}}_{0c} + \dot{\mathbf{r}}_{cs}) \cdot (\dot{\mathbf{r}}_{0c} + \dot{\mathbf{r}}_{cs}) m_s]$$

$$= \tfrac{1}{2} \sum_N (\dot{\mathbf{r}}_{0c} \cdot \dot{\mathbf{r}}_{0c} m_s) + \sum_N (\dot{\mathbf{r}}_{0c} \cdot \dot{\mathbf{r}}_{cs} m_s) + \tfrac{1}{2} \sum_N (\dot{\mathbf{r}}_{cs} \cdot \dot{\mathbf{r}}_{cs} m_s)$$

$$= \tfrac{1}{2} \dot{\mathbf{r}}_{0c} \cdot \dot{\mathbf{r}}_{0c} m + \tfrac{1}{2} \sum_N (\dot{\mathbf{r}}_{cs} \cdot \dot{\mathbf{r}}_{cs} m_s) = \tfrac{1}{2} \dot{r}_{0c}^2 m + \tfrac{1}{2} \sum_N \dot{r}_{cs}^2 m_s = T_{0c} + T_c$$

where by the definition of mass center,

$$\sum_N (\dot{\mathbf{r}}_{0c} \cdot \dot{\mathbf{r}}_{cs} m_s) = \dot{\mathbf{r}}_{0c} \cdot \left(\sum_N \dot{\mathbf{r}}_{cs} m_s \right) = 0$$

As in Problems 5.9 and 5.10, the total kinetic energy of a system of particles with respect to a fixed point 0 consists of two parts:

(a) The kinetic energy T_{0c} produced by the total mass m moving with velocity $\dot{\mathbf{r}}_{0c}$ along the path of c relative to 0.

(b) The kinetic energy T_c produced by the respective masses $m_1, m_2, \ldots, m_N$ moving with their relative velocities $\dot{\mathbf{r}}_{c1}, \dot{\mathbf{r}}_{c2}, \ldots, \dot{\mathbf{r}}_{cN}$ along their respective paths relative to the path of c.

5.12 Derive equation (5-27): $U = \Delta T_{0c} + \Delta T_c = U_{0c} + U_c$.

The total mechanical work of the forces $\mathbf{F}_1, \mathbf{F}_2, \ldots, \mathbf{F}_N$ moving the particles of mass $m_1, m_2, \ldots, m_N$ along their respective paths $\mathbf{r}_{01}, \mathbf{r}_{02}, \ldots, \mathbf{r}_{0N}$ from configuration 1 to configuration 2 (Fig. 5-3, page 104) is

$$U = \sum_N \int_1^2 \mathbf{F}_s \cdot d\mathbf{r}_s = \sum_N \int_1^2 \ddot{\mathbf{r}}_s m_s \cdot d\mathbf{r}_s = \sum_N m_s \int_1^2 \frac{d\dot{\mathbf{r}}_s}{dt} \frac{d\mathbf{r}_s}{dt} dt$$

$$= \sum_N \tfrac{1}{2} m_s \left[\dot{\mathbf{r}}_s \cdot \dot{\mathbf{r}}_s \right]_{t_1}^{t_2} = \sum_N \tfrac{1}{2} m_s \left[\dot{r}_s^2 \right]_{t_1}^{t_2} = \sum_N \tfrac{1}{2} m_s (\dot{r}_{s,2}^2 - \dot{r}_{s,1}^2) = \sum_N (T_{s,2} - T_{s,1}) = T_2 - T_1$$

where for simplicity the subscript 0 is omitted.

In terms of (5-16),

$$U = \sum_N \int_1^2 \mathbf{F}_s \cdot d(\mathbf{r}_{0c} + \mathbf{r}_{cs}) = \sum_N m_s \int_{t_1}^{t_2} \frac{d(\dot{\mathbf{r}}_{0c} + \dot{\mathbf{r}}_{cs})}{dt} \cdot \frac{d(\mathbf{r}_{0c} + \mathbf{r}_{cs})}{dt} dt$$

$$= \sum_N m_s \int_{t_1}^{t_2} \frac{d\dot{\mathbf{r}}_{0c}}{dt} \cdot \dot{\mathbf{r}}_{0c} \, dt + \sum_N m_s \int_{t_1}^{t_2} \frac{d\dot{\mathbf{r}}_{0c}}{dt} \cdot \dot{\mathbf{r}}_{cs} \, dt + \sum_N m_s \int_{t_1}^{t_2} \frac{d\dot{\mathbf{r}}_{cs}}{dt} \cdot \dot{\mathbf{r}}_{0c} \, dt + \sum_N m_s \int_{t_1}^{t_2} \frac{d\dot{\mathbf{r}}_{cs}}{dt} \cdot \dot{\mathbf{r}}_{cs} \, dt$$

$$= \sum_N \tfrac{1}{2} m_s \left[\dot{\mathbf{r}}_{0c} \cdot \dot{\mathbf{r}}_{0c} \right]_{t_1}^{t_2} + \sum_N \tfrac{1}{2} m_s \left[\dot{\mathbf{r}}_{cs} \cdot \dot{\mathbf{r}}_{cs} \right]_{t_1}^{t_2} = \sum_N \tfrac{1}{2} m (\dot{r}_{0c,\,2}^2 - \dot{r}_{0c,\,1}^2) + \sum_N \tfrac{1}{2} m_s (\dot{r}_{cs,\,2}^2 - \dot{r}_{cs,\,1}^2)$$

$$= T_{0c,\,2} - T_{0c,\,1} + T_{c,\,2} - T_{c,\,1} = U_{0c} + U_c$$

where

$$\sum_N m_s \int_{t_1}^{t_2} \frac{d\dot{\mathbf{r}}_{0c}}{dt} \cdot \dot{\mathbf{r}}_{cs}\, dt + \sum_N m_s \int_{t_1}^{t_2} \frac{d\dot{\mathbf{r}}_{cs}}{dt} \cdot \dot{\mathbf{r}}_{0c}\, dt = \sum_N m_s \int_{t_1}^{t_2} \frac{d(\dot{\mathbf{r}}_{0c} \cdot \dot{\mathbf{r}}_{cs})}{dt}\, dt$$

$$= \sum_N \left[m_s \dot{\mathbf{r}}_{0c} \cdot \dot{\mathbf{r}}_{cs} \right]_{t_1}^{t_2} = \left[\dot{\mathbf{r}}_{0c} \cdot \left(\sum_N \dot{\mathbf{r}}_{cs} m_s \right) \right]_{t_1}^{t_2} = 0$$

The interpretation and comparison of the above results with those of Problems 5.8–5.12 is given in Problem 5.13.

5.13 Compare the analytical forms of the mass moment **Q**, linear momentum **G**, resultant of forces **F**, angular momentum **H**, moment of forces **M**, kinetic energy T, and mechanical work U expressed in terms of $\mathbf{r}_{0s} = \mathbf{r}_{0c} + \mathbf{r}_{cs}$ in Problems 5.8–5.12.

All seven derived functions **Q**, **G**, **F**, **H**, **M**, T, U, if expressed in terms of $\mathbf{r}_{0s} = \mathbf{r}_{0c} + \mathbf{r}_{cs}$, split into two parts stated symbolically as

$$\underbrace{\Psi(\mathbf{r}_{0s})}_{\Psi} = \underbrace{\Psi(\mathbf{r}_{0c})}_{\Psi_{0c}} + \underbrace{\Psi(\mathbf{r}_{cs})}_{\Psi_c}$$

In particular,

$$\mathbf{Q} = \mathbf{Q}_{0c} + \cancel{\mathbf{Q}_c}^{\,0}$$

$$\mathbf{G} = \mathbf{G}_{0c} + \cancel{\mathbf{G}_c}^{\,0} \qquad\qquad \mathbf{H} = \mathbf{H}_{0c} + \mathbf{H}_c \qquad\qquad T = T_{0c} + T_c$$

$$\mathbf{F} = \mathbf{F}_{0c} + \cancel{\mathbf{F}_c}^{\,0} \qquad\qquad \mathbf{M} = \mathbf{M}_{0c} + \mathbf{M}_c \qquad\qquad U = U_{0c} + U_c$$

The summary shown above is not only of theoretical value by showing the formal affinity of these functions but is also of mnemonic value, allowing a rapid construction of these functions.

As shown later in Chapters 7–10, these analogies are perfectly general and are true for the discrete parameter models as well as for the distributed parameter models, and this is their most important characteristic.

APPLICATIONS OF WORK-ENERGY EQUATIONS

5.14 Using the work-energy equation (5-26), determine the work performed by the system of Problem 5.1 during the time interval $t_2 - t_1$.   Given: $t_1 = 10$ sec, $t_2 = 30$ sec.

By (5-26), the mechanical work of the system is

$$U = \sum_3 \int_{t_1}^{t_2} \mathbf{F}_s \cdot d\mathbf{r}_s = \int_{t_1}^{t_2} \mathbf{F}_1 \cdot d\mathbf{r}_{01} + \int_{t_1}^{t_2} \mathbf{F}_2 \cdot d\mathbf{r}_{02} + \int_{t_1}^{t_2} \mathbf{F}_3 \cdot d\mathbf{r}_{03}$$

Since $\mathbf{F}_1 = (2000\mathbf{j})$ kg, $\mathbf{F}_2 = 0$, $\mathbf{F}_3 = 0$,

$$U = \int_{10}^{30} (2000\mathbf{j}) \cdot \underbrace{(10\mathbf{i} + 20t\mathbf{j})\, dt}_{d\mathbf{r}_{01}} = \int_{10}^{30} 40{,}000t\, dt = \left[20{,}000t^2 \right]_{10}^{30} = 16 \times 10^6 \text{ m-kg}$$

This result must also satisfy the right side of (5-26).

$$T_2 - T_1 = \sum_3 \tfrac{1}{2} m_s(\dot{r}_{s,2}^2 - \dot{r}_{s,1}^2) = \tfrac{1}{2}m_1(\dot{r}_{1,2}^2 - \dot{r}_{1,1}^2) + \tfrac{1}{2}m_2(\dot{r}_{2,2}^2 - \dot{r}_{2,1}^2) + \tfrac{1}{2}m_3(\dot{r}_{3,2}^2 - \dot{r}_{3,1}^2)$$

where $m_1 = 100$, $m_2 = 200$, $m_3 = 300 \text{ kg}_m$. We have $\dot{r}_{01} = \sqrt{100 + 400t^2}$, $\dot{r}_{02} = 20$, $\dot{r}_{03} = 20$ m/sec. Since $\dot{r}_{02}$, $\dot{r}_{03}$ are constant they do not contribute to the change in kinetic energy and so

$$T_2 - T_1 = \tfrac{1}{2}m_1(\dot{r}_{1,2}^2 - \dot{r}_{1,1}^2) = (50)\left[100 + 400t^2 \right]_{10}^{30} = 16 \times 10^6 \text{ m-kg}$$

5.15 Two blocks of weight W_a and W_b are connected by a rope which passes over a pulley as shown in Fig. P-5.15. Neglecting the mass and friction of pulley and rope, find the acceleration of these blocks. Assume at $t_1 = 0$, $y_a(0) = 0$, $y_b(b) = 0$, $\dot{y}_a(0) = 0$, $\dot{y}_b(0) = 0$, $W_a < W_b$.

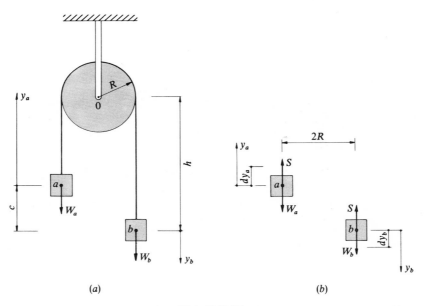

(a) (b)

Fig. P-5.15

By (5-26),

$$\underbrace{\int_0^{y_a} -W_a\, dy_a + \int_0^{y_b} W_b\, dy_b}_{U} = \underbrace{\frac{W_a}{2g}\dot{y}_a^2 + \frac{W_b}{2g}\dot{y}_b^2}_{T_2 - T_1} \qquad (1)$$

where $T_1 = 0$, $y_a = y_b = y$, $\dot{y}_a = \dot{y}_b = \dot{y}$. Then

$$-W_a y + W_b y = \frac{W_a}{2g}\dot{y}^2 + \frac{W_b}{2g}\dot{y}^2 \tag{2}$$

and on differentiating and dividing by $\dot{y}$,

$$\ddot{y} = g(W_b - W_a)/(W_a + W_b) = gA, \qquad \dot{y} = gtA, \qquad y = gt^2 A/2$$

where A is the free-fall reduction constant. For example for $W_b = 2W_a$, $A = \frac{1}{3}$; for $W_b = 3W_a$, $A = \frac{1}{2}$; ...; for $W_b = nW_a$, $A = (n-1)/(n+1)$; and of course for $n = 1$, $A = 0$.

The same result follows from the principle of conservation of energy (5-31).

If at $t = 0$, $V_1 = 0$, $T_1 = 0$ and at $t_2 = t$, $V_2 = W_a y_a - W_b y_b$, $T_2 = (W_a/2g)\dot{y}_a^2 + (W_b/2g)\dot{y}_b^2$, then

$$V_1 + T_1 = V_2 + T_2 \qquad \text{or} \qquad 0 = W_a y_a - W_b y_b + \frac{W_a}{2g}\dot{y}_a^2 + \frac{W_b}{2g}\dot{y}_b^2 \tag{3}$$

which is identical to (2).

5.16 Since the tension S in the rope was not included in the work-energy equation (5-26) of Problem 5.15, a question arises as to whether the result is correct. Derive the differential equation of motion with the effect of rope tension S included.

By (5-26),

$$\underbrace{\int_0^{y_a}(-W_a + S)\,dy_a + \int_0^{y_b}(W_b - S)\,dy_b}_{U} = \underbrace{\frac{W_a}{2g}\dot{y}_a^2 + \frac{W_b}{2g}\dot{y}_b^2}_{T_2 - T_1}$$

where the work done by S cancels and the differential equation of motion is the same as in Problem 5.15.

The force S is called the workless constraint, the effect of which is necessary for the writing of the equation of motion of a single particle but may be disregarded in the work-energy equation of the system.

5.17 Two blocks of weight W_a and W_b are connected by a rope which passes over a pulley as shown in Fig. P-5.17. Neglecting the mass and friction of rope and pulley, and the friction of block a on the plane of contact, find the differential equation of motion of this system. Assume at $t_1 = 0$, $x_a(0) = 0$, $y_b(0) = 0$, $\dot{x}_a(0) = \dot{s}_1$, $\dot{y}_b(0) = \dot{s}_1$, $W_a < W_b$.

By (5-26),

$$\underbrace{\int_0^{x_a}(-W_a \sin\alpha)\,dx_a + \int_0^{y_b}W_b\,dy_b}_{U} = \underbrace{\frac{W_a}{2g}\dot{s}_2^2 + \frac{W_b}{2g}\dot{s}_2^2}_{T_2} \underbrace{- \frac{W_a}{2g}\dot{s}_1^2 - \frac{W_b}{2g}\dot{s}_1^2}_{-T_1}$$

where $x_a(t) = y_b(t) = s_2$, $\dot{x}_a(0) = \dot{y}_b(0) = \dot{s}_1$, $\dot{x}_a(t) = \dot{y}_b(t) = \dot{s}_2$. Then

$$(W_b - W_a \sin\alpha)s_2 = \frac{W_a + W_b}{2g}(\dot{s}_2^2 - \dot{s}_1^2)$$

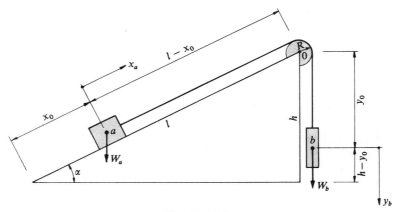

Fig. P-5.17

and on differentiating and dividing by $\dot{s}_2$,

$$\ddot{s} = g(W_b - W_a \sin \alpha)/(W_a + W_b) = gB$$

$$\dot{s} = \dot{s}_1 + gtB, \qquad s = \dot{s}_1 t + gt^2 B/2$$

which is again a reduced free-fall equation.   The reduction constant B for $\alpha = 90°$ becomes the reduction constant A of Problem 5.15.
As in Problem 5.16, the rope tension is a workless constraint.

Problems

MASS CENTER

5.18   Locate the mass center of blocks a and b of Problem 5.15 with respect to the center of the pulley 0.   Given: W_a, W_b, R, h, c.

5.19   Locate the mass center of blocks a and b of Problem 5.17 with respect to the center of the pulley 0.   Given: W_a, W_b, R, l, h, x_0, y_0, α.

MOTION RELATIVE TO A FIXED POINT

5.20   For blocks a and b of Problem 5.15, find the equations of motion of their mass center with respect to the center of the pulley 0.   Given: same as in Problem 5.18.

5.21   For blocks a and b of Problem 5.17, find the equations of motion of their mass center with respect to the center of the pulley 0.   Given: same as in Problem 5.19.

MOMENTUM RELATIVE TO A FIXED POINT

5.22   Find the linear momentum of blocks a and b of Problem 5.15 with respect to the center of the pulley 0. Given: $W_a = 1000 \text{ lb}$, $W_b = 2000 \text{ lb}$, $h = 20 \text{ ft}$, $c = 10 \text{ ft}$, $R = 1 \text{ ft}$, $g = 32.2 \text{ ft/sec}^2$.

5.23   Find the linear momentum of blocks a and b of Problem 5.17 with respect to the center of the pulley 0. Given: $W_a = 1000 \text{ kg}$, $W_b = 2000 \text{ kg}$, $x_0 = 10 \text{ m}$, $y_0 = 10 \text{ m}$, $l = 100 \text{ m}$, $h = 50 \text{ m}$, $\alpha = 30°$, $R = 1 \text{ m}$, $g = 9.8 \text{ m/sec}^2$.

5.24 Find the angular momentum of blocks *a* and *b* of Problem 5.15 with respect to the center of the pulley 0. Given: same as in Problem 5.22.

5.25 Find the angular momentum of blocks *a* and *b* of Problem 5.17 with respect to the center of the pulley 0. Given: same as in Problem 5.23.

IMPULSE RELATIVE TO A FIXED POINT

5.26 Find the linear impulse of blocks *a* and *b* of Problem 5.15 with respect to the center of the pulley 0. Given: same as in Problem 5.22.

5.27 Find the linear impulse of blocks *a* and *b* of Problem 5.17 with respect to the center of the pulley 0. Given: same as in Problem 5.23.

5.28 Find the angular impulse of blocks *a* and *b* of Problem 5.15 with respect to the center of the pulley 0. Given: same as in Problem 5.22.

5.29 Find the angular impulse of blocks *a* and *b* of Problem 5.17 with respect to the center of the pulley 0. Given: same as in Problem 5.23.

WORK AND ENERGY

5.30 Derive the work-energy equation for a system of particles in the cartesian system of coordinates.

5.31 Derive the work-energy equation for a system of particles in the cylindrical system of coordinates.

5.32 Derive the work-energy equation for a system of particles in the spherical system of coordinates.

5.33 Using the work-energy equation (*5-25*), derive the equations of motion for each block of the system shown in Fig. P-5.33. Neglect the weight of pulley and ropes, and their friction. Given: $W_a = 1000$ lb, $W_b = 2000$ lb, $R = 3$ ft, $l = 20$ ft, $g = 32.2$ ft/sec², $y_a(0) = 0$, $y_b(0) = 0$, $\dot{y}_a(0) = 0$, $\dot{y}_b(b) = 0$.

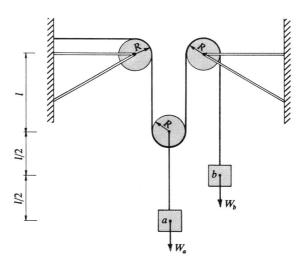

Fig. P-5.33

5.34 Using the principle of conservation of energy, solve Problem 5.17.

5.35 Using the principle of conservation of energy, solve Problem 5.33.

Chapter 6

Moving Reference Systems

6.1 PLANE MOTION—VECTOR EQUATIONS

Moving Axes

In the study of motion of particles introduced in the preceding chapters, the reference systems used were assumed to be stationary (fixed).   Frequently, however, it is convenient and/or necessary to use a reference system which, itself, is moving.   The motion defined in such a system is called the *relative motion* and its coordinate system is called the *moving reference system.*

Translation

The simplest type of motion of the reference system is that of *pure translation* in which the moving axes X_c^0, Y_c^0 translate in the plane of the stationary (fixed) axes X_0^0, Y_0^0.

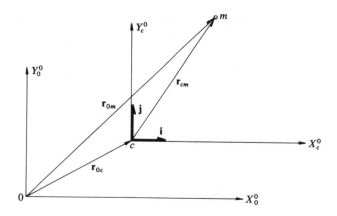

Fig. 6-1 Plane translation.

In such a case the *equations of motion* of the particle m (Fig. 6-1) referred to the origin 0 are

$$\mathbf{r}_{0m} = \mathbf{r}_{0c} + \mathbf{r}_{cm} = (x_{0c} + x_{cm})\mathbf{i} + (y_{0c} + y_{cm})\mathbf{j} \qquad (6\text{-}1)$$

$$\mathbf{v}_{0m} = \dot{\mathbf{r}}_{0m} = \dot{\mathbf{r}}_{0c} + \dot{\mathbf{r}}_{cm} = (\dot{x}_{0c} + \dot{x}_{cm})\mathbf{i} + (\dot{y}_{0c} + \dot{y}_{cm})\mathbf{j} \qquad (6\text{-}2)$$

$$\mathbf{a}_{0m} = \dot{\mathbf{v}}_{0m} = \ddot{\mathbf{r}}_{0m} = \ddot{\mathbf{r}}_{0c} + \ddot{\mathbf{r}}_{cm} = (\ddot{x}_{0c} + \ddot{x}_{cm})\mathbf{i} + (\ddot{y}_{0c} + \ddot{y}_{cm})\mathbf{j} \qquad (6\text{-}3)$$

where $\mathbf{r}_{0c}$, $\dot{\mathbf{r}}_{0c}$, $\ddot{\mathbf{r}}_{0c}$ are kinematic vectors of the origin c of the translating system referred to the stationary axes X_0^0, Y_0^0; $\mathbf{r}_{cm}$, $\dot{\mathbf{r}}_{cm}$, $\ddot{\mathbf{r}}_{cm}$ are kinematic vectors of the particle m referred to the translating axes X_c^0, Y_c^0; and $\mathbf{i}$, $\mathbf{j}$ are unit vectors of constant direction whose time derivatives are zero.

Rotation

If the origin of the reference system is stationary ($0 \equiv c$) but the angular position of the axes X_c^l, Y_c^l changes with time (rotation of axes), the *equations of motion* of the particle m (Fig. 6-2) are

$$\mathbf{r}_{cm} = x_{cm}\mathbf{i} + y_{cm}\mathbf{j} \qquad (6\text{-}4)$$
$$\mathbf{v}_{cm} = \mathbf{r}_{cm}^* = \dot{x}_{cm}\mathbf{i} + \dot{y}_{cm}\mathbf{j} + x_{cm}\dot{\mathbf{i}} + y_{cm}\dot{\mathbf{j}} \qquad (6\text{-}5)$$
$$\mathbf{a}_{cm} = \mathbf{v}_{cm}^* = \mathbf{r}_{cm}^{**} = \ddot{x}_{cm}\mathbf{i} + \ddot{y}_{cm}\mathbf{j} + 2(\dot{x}_{cm}\dot{\mathbf{i}} + \dot{y}_{cm}\dot{\mathbf{j}}) + x_{cm}\ddot{\mathbf{i}} + y_{cm}\ddot{\mathbf{j}} \qquad (6\text{-}6)$$

where $\mathbf{r}_{cm}^*$ and $\mathbf{r}_{cm}^{**}$ are respectively the first and second total time derivatives of the position vector $\mathbf{r}_{cm}$ and include not only the time derivatives of x_{cm} and y_{cm} but also the time derivatives of $\mathbf{i}$ and $\mathbf{j}$.

The *time derivatives* of the rotating unit vectors are

$$\dot{\mathbf{i}} = \dot{\theta}_z\mathbf{j} \qquad \dot{\mathbf{j}} = -\dot{\theta}_z\mathbf{i} \qquad (6\text{-}7)$$
$$\ddot{\mathbf{i}} = -\dot{\theta}_z^2\mathbf{i} + \ddot{\theta}_z\mathbf{j} \qquad \ddot{\mathbf{j}} = -\ddot{\theta}_z\mathbf{i} - \dot{\theta}_z^2\mathbf{j} \qquad (6\text{-}8)$$

where $\dot{\theta}_z$ and $\ddot{\theta}_z$ are respectively the magnitudes of the angular velocity and of the angular acceleration of the rotating axes (Problems 6.1 and 6.2).

In terms of (6-7) and (6-8) and with

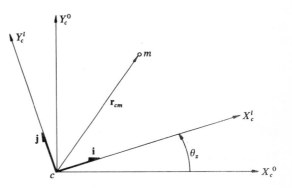

Fig. 6-2 Plane rotation.

$$\left. \begin{array}{l} \dot{\mathbf{r}}_{cm} = \dot{x}_{cm}\mathbf{i} + \dot{y}_{cm}\mathbf{j} \\ \ddot{\mathbf{r}}_{cm} = \ddot{x}_{cm}\mathbf{i} + \ddot{y}_{cm}\mathbf{j} \end{array} \right\} \quad (6\text{-}9), \qquad \left. \begin{array}{l} \boldsymbol{\omega} = \dot{\theta}_z\mathbf{k} \\ \dot{\boldsymbol{\omega}} = \ddot{\theta}_z\mathbf{k} \end{array} \right\} \quad (6\text{-}10)$$

the *velocity and acceleration vectors* (6-5) and (6-6) become respectively

$$\mathbf{v}_{cm} = \mathbf{r}_{cm}^* = \dot{\mathbf{r}}_{cm} + \boldsymbol{\omega} \times \mathbf{r}_{cm} \qquad (6\text{-}11)$$
$$\mathbf{a}_{cm} = \mathbf{v}_{cm}^* = \mathbf{r}_{cm}^{**} = \ddot{\mathbf{r}}_{cm} + \dot{\boldsymbol{\omega}} \times \mathbf{r}_{cm} + 2\boldsymbol{\omega} \times \dot{\mathbf{r}}_{cm} + \boldsymbol{\omega} \times (\boldsymbol{\omega} \times \mathbf{r}_{cm}) \qquad (6\text{-}12)$$

where $\dot{\mathbf{r}}_{cm}$ and $\ddot{\mathbf{r}}_{cm}$ are respectively the *relative (apparent) velocity* and *acceleration* referred to the rotating axes and $\mathbf{r}_{cm}^*$ and $\mathbf{r}_{cm}^{**}$ are the *absolute (true) velocity* and *acceleration* referred to the stationary axes.

General Motion

Finally, a general case of plane motion of the reference system is that of simultaneous translation and rotation of the axes X_c^l, Y_c^l in the plane of the stationary axes X_n^0, Y_n^0 (Fig. 6-3).

In this case the *equations of motion* obtained by the superposition of the equations of translation and rotation are

$$\mathbf{r}_{0m} = \mathbf{r}_{0c} + \mathbf{r}_{cm} \qquad (6\text{-}13)$$
$$\mathbf{v}_{0m} = \dot{\mathbf{r}}_{0c} + \dot{\mathbf{r}}_{cm} + \boldsymbol{\omega} \times \mathbf{r}_{cm} \qquad (6\text{-}14)$$

$$\mathbf{a}_{Om} = \ddot{\mathbf{r}}_{Oc} + \ddot{\mathbf{r}}_{cm} + \dot{\boldsymbol{\omega}} \times \mathbf{r}_{cm} + 2\boldsymbol{\omega} \times \dot{\mathbf{r}}_{cm} + \boldsymbol{\omega} \times (\boldsymbol{\omega} \times \mathbf{r}_{cm}) \qquad (6\text{-}15)$$

where the symbols used are those introduced in (6-1)–(6-3) and (6-11)–(6-12).

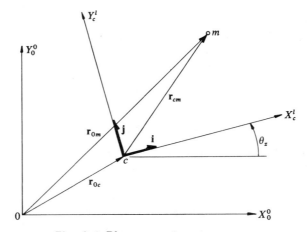

Fig. 6-3 Plane general motion.

6.2   PLANE MOTION—MATRIX EQUATIONS

Translation

The *matrix equivalents* of the vector equations (6-1), (6-2), (6-3) are respectively

$$\underbrace{\begin{bmatrix} x_{Om}^0 \\ y_{Om}^0 \end{bmatrix}}_{[s_{Om}^0]} = \underbrace{\begin{bmatrix} x_{Oc}^0 \\ y_{Oc}^0 \end{bmatrix}}_{[s_{Oc}^0]} + \underbrace{\begin{bmatrix} x_{cm}^0 \\ y_{cm}^0 \end{bmatrix}}_{[s_{cm}^0]} \qquad (6\text{-}16)$$

$$\underbrace{\begin{bmatrix} \dot{x}_{Om}^0 \\ \dot{y}_{Om}^0 \end{bmatrix}}_{[\dot{s}_{Om}^0]} = \underbrace{\begin{bmatrix} \dot{x}_{Oc}^0 \\ \dot{y}_{Oc}^0 \end{bmatrix}}_{[\dot{s}_{Oc}^0]} + \underbrace{\begin{bmatrix} \dot{x}_{cm}^0 \\ \dot{y}_{cm}^0 \end{bmatrix}}_{[\dot{s}_{cm}^0]} \qquad (6\text{-}17)$$

$$\underbrace{\begin{bmatrix} \ddot{x}_{Om}^0 \\ \ddot{y}_{Om}^0 \end{bmatrix}}_{[\ddot{s}_{Om}^0]} = \underbrace{\begin{bmatrix} \ddot{x}_{Oc}^0 \\ \ddot{y}_{Oc}^0 \end{bmatrix}}_{[\ddot{s}_{Oc}^0]} + \underbrace{\begin{bmatrix} \ddot{x}_{cm}^0 \\ \ddot{y}_{cm}^0 \end{bmatrix}}_{[\ddot{s}_{cm}^0]} \qquad (6\text{-}18)$$

where the superscript 0 identifies the angular position of the reference axes.

Rotation

The *matrix equivalents* of the vector equations (6-4)–(6-6) are respectively

$$\underbrace{\begin{bmatrix} x_{cm}^0 \\ y_{cm}^0 \end{bmatrix}}_{[s_{cm}^0]} = \underbrace{\begin{bmatrix} \cos\theta_z & -\sin\theta_z \\ \sin\theta_z & \cos\theta_z \end{bmatrix}}_{[\pi^{0l}]} \underbrace{\begin{bmatrix} x_{cm}^l \\ y_{cm}^l \end{bmatrix}}_{[s_{cm}^l]} \qquad (6\text{-}19)$$

$$\underbrace{\begin{bmatrix} x_{cm}^{0*} \\ y_{cm}^{0*} \end{bmatrix}}_{[s_{cm}^{0*}]} = \underbrace{\begin{bmatrix} \cos\theta_z & -\sin\theta_z \\ \sin\theta_z & \cos\theta_z \end{bmatrix}}_{[\pi^{0l}]} \underbrace{\begin{bmatrix} \dot{x}_{cm}^l \\ \dot{y}_{cm}^l \end{bmatrix}}_{[\dot{s}_{cm}^l]} + \dot{\theta}_z \underbrace{\begin{bmatrix} -\sin\theta_z & -\cos\theta_z \\ \cos\theta_z & -\sin\theta_z \end{bmatrix}}_{[\dot{\pi}^{0l}]} \underbrace{\begin{bmatrix} x_{cm}^l \\ y_{cm}^l \end{bmatrix}}_{[s_{cm}^l]} \tag{6-20}$$

$$\underbrace{\begin{bmatrix} x_{cm}^{0**} \\ y_{cm}^{0**} \end{bmatrix}}_{[s_{cm}^{0**}]} = \underbrace{\begin{bmatrix} \cos\theta_z & -\sin\theta_z \\ \sin\theta_z & \cos\theta_z \end{bmatrix}}_{[\pi^{0l}]} \underbrace{\begin{bmatrix} \ddot{x}_{cm}^l \\ \ddot{y}_{cm}^l \end{bmatrix}}_{[\ddot{s}_{cm}^l]} + 2\dot{\theta}_z \underbrace{\begin{bmatrix} -\sin\theta_z & -\cos\theta_z \\ \cos\theta_z & -\sin\theta_z \end{bmatrix}}_{2[\dot{\pi}^{0l}]} \underbrace{\begin{bmatrix} \dot{x}_{cm}^l \\ \dot{y}_{cm}^l \end{bmatrix}}_{[\dot{s}_{cm}^l]} - \dot{\theta}_z^2 \underbrace{\begin{bmatrix} \cos\theta_z & -\sin\theta_z \\ \sin\theta_z & \cos\theta_z \end{bmatrix}}_{[\ddot{\pi}^{0l}]} \underbrace{\begin{bmatrix} x_{cm}^l \\ y_{cm}^l \end{bmatrix}}_{[s_{cm}^l]}$$

$$(6-21)$$

where the superscripts 0 and *l* identify the stationary and rotating axes respectively and the single and double asterisks identify the first and second total derivatives.

Equations (6-19)–(6-21) can be written *in the rotating system* as

$$[s_{cm}^l] = [s_{cm}^l] \tag{6-22}$$
$$[v_{cm}^l] = [s_{cm}^{l*}] = [\dot{s}_{cm}^l] + [\Gamma][s_{cm}^l] \tag{6-23}$$
$$[a_{cm}^l] = [v_{cm}^{l*}] = [s_{cm}^{l**}] = [\ddot{s}_{cm}^l] + 2[\Gamma][\dot{s}_{cm}^l] + [\Delta][s_{cm}^l] \tag{6-24}$$

where

$$[\Gamma] = \begin{bmatrix} 0 & -\dot{\theta}_z \\ \dot{\theta}_z & 0 \end{bmatrix}, \qquad [\dot{\Gamma}] = \begin{bmatrix} 0 & -\ddot{\theta}_z \\ \ddot{\theta}_z & 0 \end{bmatrix}, \qquad [\Delta] = \begin{bmatrix} -\dot{\theta}_z^2 & -\ddot{\theta}_z \\ \ddot{\theta}_z & -\dot{\theta}_z^2 \end{bmatrix} = [\dot{\Gamma}] + [\Gamma]^2$$

and $[\Gamma][s_{cm}^l]$ is equivalent to $\boldsymbol{\omega} \times \mathbf{r}_{cm}$ in (6-11),

$[\Gamma][\dot{s}_{cm}^l]$ is equivalent to $\boldsymbol{\omega} \times \dot{\mathbf{r}}_{cm}$ in (6-12),

$[\dot{\Gamma}][s_{cm}^l]$ is equivalent to $\dot{\boldsymbol{\omega}} \times \mathbf{r}_{cm}$ in (6-12),

$[\Gamma]^2[s_{cm}^l]$ is equivalent to $\boldsymbol{\omega} \times (\boldsymbol{\omega} \times \mathbf{r}_{cm})$ in (6-12).

General Motion

The *matrix equivalents* of the vector equations (6-13)–(6-15) written in the stationary system in terms of (6-16)–(6-18) and (6-19)–(6-21) are

$$[s_{0m}^0] = [s_{0c}^0] + [\pi^{0l}][s_{cm}^l] \tag{6-25}$$
$$[v_{0m}^0] = [\dot{s}_{0c}^0] + [\pi^{0l}][\dot{s}_{cm}^l] + [\dot{\pi}^{0l}][s_{cm}^l] \tag{6-26}$$
$$[a_{0m}^0] = [\ddot{s}_{0c}^0] + [\pi^{0l}][\ddot{s}_{cm}^0] + 2[\dot{\pi}^{0l}][\dot{s}_{cm}^l] + [\ddot{\pi}^{0l}][s_{cm}^l] \tag{6-27}$$

6.3   SPACE MOTION—VECTOR EQUATIONS

Translation

In the case of space translation of axes X_c^0, Y_c^0, Z_c^0 with respect to the stationary reference axes X_0^0, Y_0^0, Z_0^0 (Fig. 6-4), the *vector equations of motion* are

$$\mathbf{r}_{0m} = \mathbf{r}_{0c} + \mathbf{r}_{cm} = (x_{0c} + x_{cm})\mathbf{i} + (y_{0c} + y_{cm})\mathbf{j} + (z_{0c} + z_{cm})\mathbf{k} \tag{6-28}$$
$$\mathbf{v}_{0m} = \dot{\mathbf{r}}_{0m} = \dot{\mathbf{r}}_{0c} + \dot{\mathbf{r}}_{cm} = (\dot{x}_{0c} + \dot{x}_{cm})\mathbf{i} + (\dot{y}_{0c} + \dot{y}_{cm})\mathbf{j} + (\dot{z}_{0c} + \dot{z}_{cm})\mathbf{k} \tag{6-29}$$
$$\mathbf{a}_{0m} = \dot{\mathbf{v}}_{0m} = \ddot{\mathbf{r}}_{0m} = \ddot{\mathbf{r}}_{0c} + \ddot{\mathbf{r}}_{cm} = (\ddot{x}_{0c} + \ddot{x}_{cm})\mathbf{i} + (\ddot{y}_{0c} + \ddot{y}_{cm})\mathbf{j} + (\ddot{z}_{0c} + \ddot{z}_{cm})\mathbf{k} \tag{6-30}$$

where **i, j, k** are constants and their time derivatives are zero.

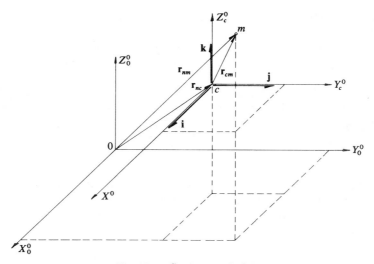

Fig. 6-4 Space translation.

Rotation

In the case of space rotation of axes X_c^l, Y_c^l, Z_c^l with respect to the stationary axes X_c^0, Y_c^0, Z_c^0 (Fig. 6-5), the *vector equations of motion* are

$$\mathbf{r}_{cm} = x_{cm}\mathbf{i} + y_{cm}\mathbf{j} + z_{cm}\mathbf{k} \tag{6-31}$$

$$\mathbf{v}_{cm} = \mathbf{r}_{cm}^* = \dot{x}_{cm}\mathbf{i} + \dot{y}_{cm}\mathbf{j} + \dot{z}_{cm}\mathbf{k} + x_{cm}\dot{\mathbf{i}} + y_{cm}\dot{\mathbf{j}} + z_{cm}\dot{\mathbf{k}} \tag{6-32}$$

$$\mathbf{a}_{cm} = \mathbf{v}_{cm}^* = \mathbf{r}_{cm}^{**} = \ddot{x}_{cm}\mathbf{i} + \ddot{y}_{cm}\mathbf{j} + \ddot{z}_{cm}\mathbf{k} + 2(\dot{x}_{cm}\dot{\mathbf{i}} + \dot{y}_{cm}\dot{\mathbf{j}} + \dot{z}_{cm}\dot{\mathbf{k}}) + x_{cm}\ddot{\mathbf{i}} + y_{cm}\ddot{\mathbf{j}} + z_{cm}\ddot{\mathbf{k}} \tag{6-33}$$

where $\mathbf{i}$, $\mathbf{j}$, $\mathbf{k}$ are functions of time and have time derivatives.

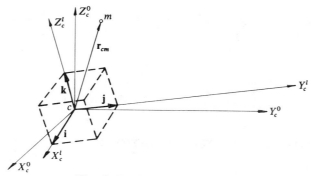

Fig. 6-5 Space rotation.

These *time derivatives* are

$$\left.\begin{aligned} \dot{\mathbf{i}} &= \dot{\theta}_z\mathbf{j} - \dot{\theta}_y\mathbf{k} \\ \dot{\mathbf{j}} &= -\dot{\theta}_z\mathbf{i} + \dot{\theta}_x\mathbf{k} \\ \dot{\mathbf{k}} &= \dot{\theta}_y\mathbf{i} - \dot{\theta}_x\mathbf{j} \end{aligned}\right\} \tag{6-34}$$

$$\left.\begin{aligned} \ddot{\mathbf{i}} &= -(\dot{\theta}_y^2 + \dot{\theta}_z^2)\mathbf{i} + (\dot{\theta}_x\dot{\theta}_y + \ddot{\theta}_z)\mathbf{j} + (\dot{\theta}_x\dot{\theta}_z - \ddot{\theta}_y)\mathbf{k} \\ \ddot{\mathbf{j}} &= (\dot{\theta}_y\dot{\theta}_x - \ddot{\theta}_z)\mathbf{i} - (\dot{\theta}_z^2 + \dot{\theta}_x^2)\mathbf{j} + (\dot{\theta}_y\dot{\theta}_z + \ddot{\theta}_x)\mathbf{k} \\ \ddot{\mathbf{k}} &= (\dot{\theta}_z\dot{\theta}_x + \ddot{\theta}_y)\mathbf{i} + (\dot{\theta}_z\dot{\theta}_y - \ddot{\theta}_x)\mathbf{j} - (\dot{\theta}_x^2 + \dot{\theta}_y^2)\mathbf{k} \end{aligned}\right\} \tag{6-35}$$

where $\dot\theta_x$, $\dot\theta_y$, $\dot\theta_z$ and $\ddot\theta_x$, $\ddot\theta_y$, $\ddot\theta_z$ are the scalar components of the angular velocity and acceleration of the rotating axes (Problems 6.12 and 6.13).

In terms of $(6\text{-}34)$, $(6\text{-}35)$ and with

$$\left.\begin{aligned}\mathbf{\dot r}_{cm} &= \dot x_{cm}\mathbf{i} + \dot y_{cm}\mathbf{j} + \dot z_{cm}\mathbf{k}\\ \mathbf{\ddot r}_{cm} &= \ddot x_{cm}\mathbf{i} + \ddot y_{cm}\mathbf{j} + \ddot z_{cm}\mathbf{k}\end{aligned}\right\} \quad (6\text{-}36) \qquad\qquad \left.\begin{aligned}\boldsymbol{\omega} &= \dot\theta_x\mathbf{i} + \dot\theta_y\mathbf{j} + \dot\theta_z\mathbf{k}\\ \boldsymbol{\dot\omega} &= \ddot\theta_x\mathbf{i} + \ddot\theta_y\mathbf{j} + \ddot\theta_z\mathbf{k}\end{aligned}\right\} \quad (6\text{-}37)$$

the *velocity and acceleration vectors* $(6\text{-}32)$ and $(6\text{-}33)$ become respectively

$$\mathbf{v}_{cm} = \mathbf{r}^*_{cm} = \mathbf{\dot r}_{cm} + \boldsymbol{\omega}\times\mathbf{r}_{cm} \tag{6-38}$$

$$\mathbf{a}_{cm} = \mathbf{v}^*_{cm} = \mathbf{r}^{**}_{cm} = \mathbf{\ddot r}_{cm} + \boldsymbol{\dot\omega}\times\mathbf{r}_{cm} + 2\boldsymbol{\omega}\times\mathbf{\dot r}_{cm} + \boldsymbol{\omega}\times(\boldsymbol{\omega}\times\mathbf{r}_{cm}) \tag{6-39}$$

where $\mathbf{\dot r}_{cm}$ and $\mathbf{\ddot r}_{cm}$ are the *relative (apparent) velocity* and *acceleration* referred to the rotating axes, $\mathbf{r}^*_{cm}$ and $\mathbf{r}^{**}_{cm}$ are the *absolute (true) velocity* and *acceleration* referred to the stationary axes, and $\boldsymbol{\omega}$, $\boldsymbol{\dot\omega}$ are the angular velocity and acceleration of the rotating system with respect to the stationary system.

Formally $(6\text{-}38)$ and $(6\text{-}39)$ are identical to $(6\text{-}11)$ and $(6\text{-}12)$ but involve three-dimensional vectors; and the cross products $2\boldsymbol{\omega}\times\mathbf{\dot r}_{cm}$ and $\boldsymbol{\omega}\times(\boldsymbol{\omega}\times\mathbf{r}_{cm})$, called respectively the *Coriolis* and *centripetal accelerations*, are more complex (Table 6-1).

Table 6-1

Coriolis acceleration	Centripetal acceleration
In equation $(6\text{-}39)$, $$2\boldsymbol{\omega}\times\mathbf{\dot r}_{cm} = 2\begin{vmatrix} \mathbf{i} & \mathbf{j} & \mathbf{k} \\ \dot\theta_x & \dot\theta_y & \dot\theta_z \\ \dot x_{cm} & \dot y_{cm} & \dot z_{cm} \end{vmatrix}$$	In equation $(6\text{-}39)$, $$\boldsymbol{\omega}\times(\boldsymbol{\omega}\times\mathbf{r}_{cm}) = \begin{vmatrix} \boldsymbol{\omega} & \boldsymbol{\omega}\cdot\boldsymbol{\omega} \\ \mathbf{r}_{cm} & \boldsymbol{\omega}\cdot\mathbf{r}_{cm} \end{vmatrix}$$
In equation $(6\text{-}49)$, $$2[\Gamma][\dot s^l_{cm}] = 2\begin{bmatrix} 0 & -\dot\theta_z & \dot\theta_y \\ \dot\theta_z & 0 & -\dot\theta_x \\ -\dot\theta_y & \dot\theta_x & 0 \end{bmatrix}\begin{bmatrix} \dot x^l_{cm} \\ \dot y^l_{cm} \\ \dot z^l_{cm} \end{bmatrix}$$	In equation $(6\text{-}49)$, $$[\Gamma]^2[s^l_{cm}] = \begin{bmatrix} -(\dot\theta_y^2 + \dot\theta_z^2) & \dot\theta_x\dot\theta_y & \dot\theta_x\dot\theta_z \\ \dot\theta_y\dot\theta_x & -(\dot\theta_z^2 + \dot\theta_x^2) & \dot\theta_y\dot\theta_z \\ \dot\theta_z\dot\theta_x & \dot\theta_z\dot\theta_y & -(\dot\theta_x^2 + \dot\theta_y^2) \end{bmatrix}\begin{bmatrix} x^l_{cm} \\ y^l_{cm} \\ z^l_{cm} \end{bmatrix}$$

General Motion

Similarly the vector equations of motion referred to a translating and rotating system of axes are formally identical to $(6\text{-}13)$–$(6\text{-}15)$, but again include three-dimensional vectors.

6.4   SPACE MOTION—MATRIX EQUATIONS
Transformation Matrices

The *transformation relations* between the vector components in the X_c^l, Y_c^l, Z_c^l system and their equivalents in the X_c^0, Y_c^0, Z_c^0 system and vice versa are given by the *angular transformation matrices* $[\pi^{0l}]$ and $[\pi^{l0}]$ as

$$\underbrace{\begin{bmatrix} V^0_{cm} \\ V^0_{cm} \\ V^0_{cm} \end{bmatrix}}_{[V^0_{cm}]} = \underbrace{\begin{bmatrix} \alpha_x & \alpha_y & \alpha_z \\ \beta_x & \beta_y & \beta_z \\ \gamma_x & \gamma_y & \gamma_z \end{bmatrix}}_{[\pi^{0l}]}\underbrace{\begin{bmatrix} V^l_{cm} \\ V^l_{cm} \\ V^l_{cm} \end{bmatrix}}_{[V^l_{cm}]}, \qquad \underbrace{\begin{bmatrix} V^l_{cm} \\ V^l_{cm} \\ V^l_{cm} \end{bmatrix}}_{[V^l_{cm}]} = \underbrace{\begin{bmatrix} \alpha_x & \beta_x & \gamma_x \\ \alpha_y & \beta_y & \gamma_y \\ \alpha_z & \beta_z & \gamma_z \end{bmatrix}}_{[\pi^{l0}]}\underbrace{\begin{bmatrix} V^0_{cm} \\ V^0_{cm} \\ V^0_{cm} \end{bmatrix}}_{[V^0_{cm}]} \qquad (6\text{-}40),(6\text{-}41)$$

where V_{cm}, V_{cm}, V_{cm} are components of a particular kinematic vector.

Since the instantaneous position of X_c^l, Y_c^l, Z_c^l can be always constructed by rotating X_c^0, Y_c^0, Z_c^0 successively through θ_z, θ_y, θ_x as shown in Fig. 6-6, the *coefficients of the angular transformation matrices must be a result of a triple matrix product*, each matrix of which corresponds to one rotation about one axis, i.e.

$$[\pi^{0l}] = \underbrace{\begin{bmatrix} \cos\theta_z & -\sin\theta_z & 0 \\ \sin\theta_z & \cos\theta_z & 0 \\ 0 & 0 & 1 \end{bmatrix}}_{[\pi^{0j}]} \underbrace{\begin{bmatrix} \cos\theta_y & 0 & \sin\theta_y \\ 0 & 1 & 0 \\ -\sin\theta_y & 0 & \cos\theta_y \end{bmatrix}}_{[\pi^{jk}]} \underbrace{\begin{bmatrix} 1 & 0 & 0 \\ 0 & \cos\theta_x & -\sin\theta_x \\ 0 & \sin\theta_x & \cos\theta_x \end{bmatrix}}_{[\pi^{kl}]}$$

$$= \begin{bmatrix} \alpha_x & \alpha_y & \alpha_z \\ \beta_x & \beta_y & \beta_z \\ \gamma_x & \gamma_y & \gamma_z \end{bmatrix} \qquad (6\text{-}42)$$

$$[\pi^{l0}] = \underbrace{\begin{bmatrix} 1 & 0 & 0 \\ 0 & \cos\theta_x & \sin\theta_x \\ 0 & \sin\theta_x & \cos\theta_x \end{bmatrix}}_{[\pi^{lk}]} \underbrace{\begin{bmatrix} \cos\theta_y & 0 & -\sin\theta_y \\ 0 & 1 & 0 \\ \sin\theta_y & 0 & \cos\theta_y \end{bmatrix}}_{[\pi^{kj}]} \underbrace{\begin{bmatrix} \cos\theta_z & \sin\theta_z & 0 \\ -\sin\theta_z & \cos\theta_z & 0 \\ 0 & 0 & 1 \end{bmatrix}}_{[\pi^{j0}]}$$

$$= \begin{bmatrix} \alpha_x & \beta_x & \gamma_x \\ \alpha_y & \beta_y & \gamma_y \\ \alpha_z & \beta_z & \gamma_z \end{bmatrix} \qquad (6\text{-}43)$$

where $[\pi^{0l}]$ and $[\pi^{l0}]$ are again orthogonal matrices.

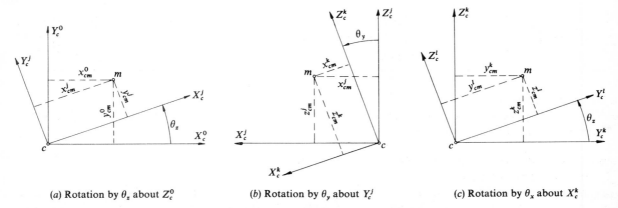

(a) Rotation by θ_z about Z_c^0 (b) Rotation by θ_y about Y_c^j (c) Rotation by θ_x about X_c^k

Fig. 6-6 Rotation of reference system.

General Motion

Once the angular transformation matrices are defined, the *general matrix equations of motion* can be written by inspection as

$$[s_{0m}^0] = [s_{0c}^0] + [\pi^{0l}][s_{cm}^l] \qquad (6\text{-}44)$$

$$[v_{0m}^0] = [\ddot{s}_{0c}^0] + [\pi^{0l}][\dot{s}_{cm}^l] + [\dot{\pi}^{0l}][s_{cm}^l] \tag{6-45}$$

$$[a_{0m}^0] = [\ddot{s}_{0c}^0] + [\pi^{0l}][\ddot{s}_{cm}^l] + 2[\dot{\pi}^{0l}][\dot{s}_{cm}^l] + [\ddot{\pi}^{0l}][s_{cm}^l] \tag{6-46}$$

where $[\dot{\pi}^{0l}]$ and $[\ddot{\pi}^{0l}]$ are the first and the second time derivatives of $[\pi^{0l}]$.
In equations (6-44)–(6-46), $[s_{cm}^l]$, $[v_{cm}^l]$, $[a_{cm}^l]$ can be written as

$$[s_{cm}^l] = [s_{cm}^l] \tag{6-47}$$

$$[v_{cm}^l] = [\dot{s}_{cm}^l] + [\Gamma][s_{cm}^l] \tag{6-48}$$

$$[a_{cm}^l] = [\ddot{s}_{cm}^l] + 2[\Gamma][\dot{s}_{cm}^l] + [\Delta][s_{cm}^l] \tag{6-49}$$

where

$$[\Gamma] = \begin{bmatrix} 0 & -\dot{\theta}_z & \dot{\theta}_y \\ \dot{\theta}_z & 0 & -\dot{\theta}_x \\ -\dot{\theta}_y & \dot{\theta}_x & 0 \end{bmatrix}, \qquad [\dot{\Gamma}] = \begin{bmatrix} 0 & -\ddot{\theta}_z & \ddot{\theta}_y \\ \ddot{\theta}_z & 0 & -\ddot{\theta}_x \\ -\ddot{\theta}_y & \ddot{\theta}_x & 0 \end{bmatrix}$$

$$[\Delta] = \begin{bmatrix} -(\dot{\theta}_y^2 + \dot{\theta}_z^2) & (\dot{\theta}_x\dot{\theta}_y - \ddot{\theta}_z) & (\dot{\theta}_x\dot{\theta}_z + \ddot{\theta}_y) \\ (\dot{\theta}_y\dot{\theta}_x + \ddot{\theta}_z) & -(\dot{\theta}_z^2 + \dot{\theta}_x^2) & (\dot{\theta}_y\dot{\theta}_z - \ddot{\theta}_x) \\ (\dot{\theta}_z\dot{\theta}_x - \ddot{\theta}_y) & (\dot{\theta}_z\dot{\theta}_y + \ddot{\theta}_x) & -(\dot{\theta}_x^2 + \dot{\theta}_y^2) \end{bmatrix}$$

The matrix-vector equivalents introduced in conjunction with (6-23) and (6-24) are also valid here (Table 6-1).

Illustrative Problems

PLANE MOTION—DERIVATIONS

6.1   Find the first time derivatives of unit vectors of the axes X_c^l, Y_c^l rotating with respect to the stationary axes X_c^0, Y_c^0.

Let $\mathbf{i}^0$, $\mathbf{j}^0$ and $\mathbf{i}^l$, $\mathbf{j}^l$ be the unit vectors in X_c^0, Y_c^0 and X_c^l, Y_c^l respectively.   From Fig. P-6.1,

$$\underbrace{\begin{bmatrix} \mathbf{i}^0 \\ \mathbf{j}^0 \end{bmatrix}}_{[e^0]} = \underbrace{\begin{bmatrix} \cos\theta_z & -\sin\theta_z \\ \sin\theta_z & \cos\theta_z \end{bmatrix}}_{[\pi^{0l}]} \underbrace{\begin{bmatrix} \mathbf{i}^l \\ \mathbf{j}^l \end{bmatrix}}_{[e^l]} \tag{1}$$

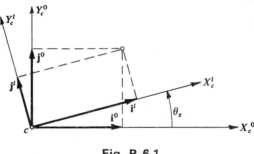

Fig. P-6.1

where θ_z is the time-dependent position angle.   Differentiating (1) with respect to t,

$$[\dot{e}^0] = [\dot{\pi}^{0l}][e^l] + [\pi^{0l}][\dot{e}^l] \tag{2}$$

where by definition, $[\dot{e}^0] = [0]$.   Then from (2),

$$[\dot{e}^l] = -[\pi^{0l}]^{-1}[\dot{\pi}^{0l}][e^l] \tag{3}$$

and since $[\pi^{0l}]^{-1} = [\pi^{0l}]^T = [\pi^{l0}]$,

$$[\dot{e}^l] = -[\pi^{l0}][\dot{\pi}^{0l}][e^l] \tag{4}$$

In full matrix form, (4) is

$$\underbrace{\begin{bmatrix} \dot{\mathbf{i}}^l \\ \dot{\mathbf{j}}^l \end{bmatrix}}_{[\dot{\mathbf{e}}^l]} = -\underbrace{\begin{bmatrix} \cos\theta_z & \sin\theta_z \\ -\sin\theta_z & \cos\theta_z \end{bmatrix}}_{[\pi^{l0}]}\underbrace{\begin{bmatrix} -\dot{\theta}_z\sin\theta_z & -\dot{\theta}_z\cos\theta_z \\ \dot{\theta}_z\cos\theta_z & -\dot{\theta}_z\sin\theta_z \end{bmatrix}}_{[\dot{\pi}^{0l}]}\begin{bmatrix} \mathbf{i}^l \\ \mathbf{j}^l \end{bmatrix} = \underbrace{\begin{bmatrix} 0 & \dot{\theta}_z \\ -\dot{\theta}_z & 0 \end{bmatrix}}_{-[\Gamma]}\underbrace{\begin{bmatrix} \mathbf{i}^l \\ \mathbf{j}^l \end{bmatrix}}_{[\mathbf{e}^l]} \tag{5}$$

which is the matrix form of (6-7). Note that the superscript *l* has been omitted in equations (6-7) since all unit vectors considered there are in the rotating axes.

6.2   Using the results of Problem 6.1, find the second time derivatives of unit vectors $\mathbf{i}^l$, $\mathbf{j}^l$.

By differentiating (5) of Problem 6.1,

$$[\ddot{\mathbf{e}}^l] = d(-[\Gamma][\mathbf{e}^l])/dt = -[\dot{\Gamma}][\mathbf{e}^l] - [\Gamma][\dot{\mathbf{e}}^l] = \left[[\Gamma]^2 - [\dot{\Gamma}]\right][\mathbf{e}^l] \tag{1}$$

In full matrix form,

$$\underbrace{\begin{bmatrix} \ddot{\mathbf{i}}^l \\ \ddot{\mathbf{j}}^l \end{bmatrix}}_{[\ddot{\mathbf{e}}^l]} = \left\{\underbrace{\begin{bmatrix} 0 & \dot{\theta}_z \\ -\dot{\theta}_z & 0 \end{bmatrix}}_{-[\Gamma]}\underbrace{\begin{bmatrix} 0 & \dot{\theta}_z \\ -\dot{\theta}_z & 0 \end{bmatrix}}_{-[\Gamma]} - \underbrace{\begin{bmatrix} 0 & -\ddot{\theta}_z \\ \ddot{\theta}_z & 0 \end{bmatrix}}_{[\dot{\Gamma}]}\right\}\underbrace{\begin{bmatrix} \mathbf{i}^l \\ \mathbf{j}^l \end{bmatrix}}_{[\mathbf{e}^l]} = \underbrace{\begin{bmatrix} -\dot{\theta}_z^2 & \ddot{\theta}_z \\ -\ddot{\theta}_z & -\dot{\theta}_z^2 \end{bmatrix}}_{[\lambda]}\underbrace{\begin{bmatrix} \mathbf{i}^l \\ \mathbf{j}^l \end{bmatrix}}_{[\mathbf{e}^l]} \tag{2}$$

which is the matrix form of (6-8). As before, the superscript *l* has been omitted in equations (6-8) since all unit vectors considered there are in the rotating axes.

6.3   Derive the velocity vector equation of plane motion of a particle *m*, given by (6-11) as $\mathbf{v}_{cm} = \dot{\mathbf{r}}_{cm} + \boldsymbol{\omega} \times \mathbf{r}_{cm}$.

Refer to Fig. 6-2, page 117, where $\mathbf{i}, \mathbf{j}$ are the unit vectors of the rotating axes and θ_z is the time-dependent position angle measured from X_c^0 to X_c^l.   Here

$$\mathbf{r}_{cm} = x_{cm}\mathbf{i} + y_{cm}\mathbf{j} \tag{1}$$

is the position vector of the particle *m* in the rotating system, and its relative and absolute time derivatives are respectively

$$\dot{\mathbf{r}}_{cm} = \dot{x}_{cm}\mathbf{i} + \dot{y}_{cm}\mathbf{j}, \qquad \mathbf{r}_{cm}^* = \dot{x}_{cm}\mathbf{i} + \dot{y}_{cm}\mathbf{j} + x_{cm}\dot{\mathbf{i}} + y_{cm}\dot{\mathbf{j}} \tag{2}, (3)$$

where $\dot{\mathbf{r}}_{cm}$ presumes $\mathbf{i}, \mathbf{j}$ are time-independent unit vectors and $\mathbf{r}_{cm}^*$ treats $\mathbf{i}, \mathbf{j}$ as functions of time.
By definition, the velocity vector is given by (3) of this problem, in which by (5) of Problem 6.1, $\dot{\mathbf{i}} = \dot{\theta}_z\mathbf{j}$, $\dot{\mathbf{j}} = -\dot{\theta}_z\mathbf{i}$.   Hence

$$\mathbf{v}_{cm} = \mathbf{r}_{cm}^* = \dot{x}_{cm}\mathbf{i} + \dot{y}_{cm}\mathbf{j} + x_{cm}\dot{\theta}_z\mathbf{j} - y_{cm}\dot{\theta}_z\mathbf{i} = (\dot{x}_{cm} - y_{cm}\dot{\theta}_z)\mathbf{i} + (\dot{y}_{cm} + x_{cm}\dot{\theta}_z)\mathbf{j} \tag{4}$$

Since in (4),

$$x_{cm}\dot{\theta}_z\mathbf{j} - y_{cm}\dot{\theta}_z\mathbf{i} = \underbrace{(\dot{\theta}_z\mathbf{k})}_{\omega} \times \underbrace{(x_{cm}\mathbf{i} + y_{cm}\mathbf{j})}_{\mathbf{r}_{cm}} = \begin{vmatrix} \mathbf{i} & \mathbf{j} & \mathbf{k} \\ 0 & 0 & \dot{\theta}_z \\ x_{cm} & y_{cm} & 0 \end{vmatrix} \tag{5}$$

equation (4) can be also written symbolically as

$$\mathbf{v}_{cm} = \mathbf{r}^*_{cm} = \dot{\mathbf{r}}_{cm} + \boldsymbol{\omega} \times \mathbf{r}_{cm} \tag{6}$$

Although form (6) of $\mathbf{v}_{cm}$ is symbolically more compact, in plane motion the expanded form (4) is frequently preferred.

6.4   Derive the acceleration vector equation of plane motion of a particle m, given by (6-12) as

$$\mathbf{a}_{cm} = \ddot{\mathbf{r}}_{cm} + \dot{\boldsymbol{\omega}} \times \mathbf{r}_{cm} + 2\boldsymbol{\omega} \times \dot{\mathbf{r}}_{cm} + \boldsymbol{\omega} \times (\boldsymbol{\omega} \times \mathbf{r}_{cm})$$

By definition,

$$\begin{aligned}
\mathbf{a}_{cm} = \mathbf{v}^*_{cm} = \mathbf{r}^{**}_{cm} &= \dot{\mathbf{r}}^*_{cm} + \boldsymbol{\omega} \times \mathbf{r}^*_{cm} + \boldsymbol{\omega}^* \times \mathbf{r}_{cm} \\
&= \ddot{\mathbf{r}}_{cm} + \boldsymbol{\omega} \times \dot{\mathbf{r}}_{cm} + \boldsymbol{\omega} \times (\dot{\mathbf{r}}_{cm} + \boldsymbol{\omega} \times \mathbf{r}_{cm}) + \dot{\boldsymbol{\omega}} \times \mathbf{r}_{cm} \\
&= \ddot{\mathbf{r}}_{cm} + \dot{\boldsymbol{\omega}} \times \mathbf{r}_{cm} + 2\boldsymbol{\omega} \times \dot{\mathbf{r}}_{cm} + \boldsymbol{\omega} \times (\boldsymbol{\omega} \times \mathbf{r}_{cm})
\end{aligned}$$

where $\dot{\boldsymbol{\omega}} = d(\dot{\theta}_z \mathbf{k})/dt = \ddot{\theta}_z \mathbf{k}$.

Note that the overdot (˙) and asterisk (*) represent differential operators requiring differentiation of the scalar components only in $\dot{\mathbf{r}}$, and differentiation of the scalar components and unit vectors in $\mathbf{r}^*$.

6.5   Derive the velocity matrix equation of plane motion of a particle m, given by (6-23) as

$$\left[v^l_{cm}\right] = \left[\dot{s}^l_{cm}\right] + \left[\Gamma\right]\left[s^l_{cm}\right]$$

By (6-19) and (6-20),

$$\left[s^0_{cm}\right] = \left[\pi^{0l}\right]\left[s^l_{cm}\right] \tag{1}$$

and

$$\left[v^0_{cm}\right] = \left[s^{0*}_{cm}\right] = \left[\pi^{0l}\right]\left[\dot{s}^l_{cm}\right] + \left[\dot{\pi}^{0l}\right]\left[s^l_{cm}\right] \tag{2}$$

Premultiplying by $\left[\pi^{l0}\right]$, equation (2) becomes

$$\left[v^l_{cm}\right] = \underbrace{\left[\pi^{l0}\right]\left[s^{0*}_{cm}\right]}_{\left[s^{l*}_{cm}\right]} = \underbrace{\left[\pi^{l0}\right]\left[\pi^{0l}\right]}_{\left[I\right]}\left[\dot{s}^l_{cm}\right] + \underbrace{\left[\pi^{l0}\right]\left[\dot{\pi}^{0l}\right]}_{\left[\Gamma\right]}\left[s^l_{cm}\right] \tag{3}$$

where

$$\left[\Gamma\right] = \left[\pi^{l0}\right]\left[\dot{\pi}^{0l}\right] = \begin{bmatrix} \cos\theta_z & \sin\theta_z \\ -\sin\theta_z & \cos\theta_z \end{bmatrix}\begin{bmatrix} -\sin\theta_z & -\cos\theta_z \\ \cos\theta_z & -\sin\theta_z \end{bmatrix}\dot{\theta}_z = \begin{bmatrix} 0 & -\dot{\theta}_z \\ \dot{\theta}_z & 0 \end{bmatrix} \tag{4}$$

6.6   Derive the acceleration matrix equation of plane motion of a particle m, given by (6-24) as

$$\left[a^l_{cm}\right] = \left[\ddot{s}^l_{cm}\right] + 2\left[\Gamma\right]\left[\dot{s}^l_{cm}\right] + \left[\Delta\right]\left[s^l_{cm}\right]$$

By (6-21),

$$\begin{aligned}
\left[a^0_m\right] = \left[v^{0*}_m\right] = \left[s^{0**}_m\right] &= \left[\pi^{0l}\right]\left[\ddot{s}^l_{cm}\right] + \left[\dot{\pi}^{0l}\right]\left[\dot{s}^l_{cm}\right] + \left[\dot{\pi}^{0l}\right]\left[\dot{s}^l_{cm}\right] + \left[\ddot{\pi}^{0l}\right]\left[s^l_{cm}\right] \\
&= \left[\pi^{0l}\right]\left[\ddot{s}^l_{cm}\right] + 2\left[\dot{\pi}^{0l}\right]\left[\dot{s}^l_{cm}\right] + \left[\ddot{\pi}^{0l}\right]\left[s^l_{cm}\right]
\end{aligned} \tag{1}$$

Premultiplying by $[\pi^{l0}]$, equation (1) becomes

$$[a_{cm}^l] = \underbrace{[\pi^{l0}][s_{cm}^{0**}]}_{[s_{cm}^{l*}]} = \underbrace{[\pi^{l0}][\pi^{0l}]}_{[I]}[\ddot{s}_{cm}^l] + \underbrace{2[\pi^{l0}][\dot{\pi}^{0l}]}_{2[\Gamma]}[\dot{s}_{cm}^l] + \underbrace{[\pi^{l0}][\ddot{\pi}^{0l}]}_{[\Delta]}[s_{cm}^l] \qquad (2)$$

where

$$[\Delta] = [\pi^{l0}][\ddot{\pi}^{0l}] = \begin{bmatrix} \cos\theta_z & \sin\theta_z \\ -\sin\theta_z & \cos\theta_z \end{bmatrix}\begin{bmatrix} -\cos\theta_z & \sin\theta_z \\ -\sin\theta_z & -\cos\theta_z \end{bmatrix}\dot{\theta}_z^2$$

$$+ \begin{bmatrix} \cos\theta_z & \sin\theta_z \\ -\sin\theta_z & \cos\theta_z \end{bmatrix}\begin{bmatrix} -\sin\theta_z & -\cos\theta_z \\ \cos\theta_z & -\sin\theta_z \end{bmatrix}\ddot{\theta}_z = \begin{bmatrix} -\dot{\theta}_z^2 & -\ddot{\theta}_z \\ \ddot{\theta}_z & -\dot{\theta}_z^2 \end{bmatrix} \qquad (3)$$

PLANE MOTION—APPLICATION

6.7 A particle m moves from c with constant relative speed v along the radius of a circular disk (Fig. P-6.7) while the disk rotates with uniform angular velocity $\omega_z = \dot{\theta}_z$. Find the apparent and true velocity and acceleration of the particle.

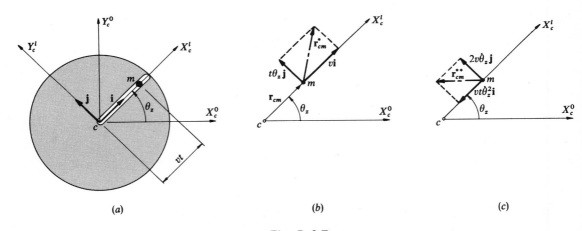

Fig. P-6.7

The equations of apparent motion of m are

$$\mathbf{r}_{cm} = vt\mathbf{i}, \qquad \dot{\mathbf{r}}_{cm} = v\mathbf{i}, \qquad \ddot{\mathbf{r}}_{cm} = 0 \qquad (1)$$

where $\mathbf{i}, \mathbf{j}$ are unit vectors in the l-system.

The equations of true motion of m are

$$\mathbf{r}_{cm} = vt\mathbf{i}, \qquad \mathbf{r}_{cm}^* = v\mathbf{i} + vt\overset{0}{\dot{\mathbf{i}}}, \qquad \mathbf{r}_{cm}^{**} = v\overset{0}{\dot{\mathbf{i}}} + 2v\dot{\mathbf{i}} + vt\ddot{\mathbf{i}}$$

where by (6-7) and (6-8), $\dot{\mathbf{i}} = \dot{\theta}_z\mathbf{j}$, $\ddot{\mathbf{i}} = -\dot{\theta}_z^2\mathbf{i} + \ddot{\overset{0}{\theta}}_z\mathbf{j}$. Hence,

$$\mathbf{r}_{cm} = vt\mathbf{i}, \qquad \mathbf{r}_{cm}^* = v(\mathbf{i} + t\dot{\theta}_z\mathbf{j}), \qquad \mathbf{r}_{cm}^{**} = -v\dot{\theta}_z(t\dot{\theta}_z\mathbf{i} - 2\mathbf{j}) \qquad (2)$$

The equations of apparent motion (1) define the motion of m referred to X_c^l, Y_c^l, Z_c^l in unit vectors of these axes, whereas the equations of true motion (2) define the motion of m referred to X_c^0, Y_c^0, Z_c^0 but in unit vectors of X_c^l, Y_c^l, Z_c^l.

6.8   Find the equations of motion of m of Problem 6.7 referred to the stationary axes X_c^0, Y_c^0, Z_c^0 and in unit vectors of these axes.

Designate the unit vectors of the stationary and rotating axes as $\mathbf{i}^0$, $\mathbf{j}^0$ and $\mathbf{i}^l$, $\mathbf{j}^l$ respectively.   Then referring to Fig. P-6.1 state their transformation relations as

$$\mathbf{i}^l = \mathbf{i}^0 \cos\theta_z + \mathbf{j}^0 \sin\theta_z, \qquad \mathbf{j}^l = -\mathbf{i}^0 \sin\theta_z + \mathbf{j}^0 \cos\theta_z \tag{1}$$

where θ_z is the position angle.

Finally insert these transformations in (2) of Problem 6.7 and rearrange as shown below.

$$\left.\begin{aligned}
\mathbf{r}_{cm} &= \mathbf{i}^0 vt \cos\theta_z + \mathbf{j}^0 vt \sin\theta_z \\
\mathbf{r}_{cm}^* &= \mathbf{i}^0 (v\cos\theta_z - vt\dot\theta_z \sin\theta_z) + \mathbf{j}^0 (v\sin\theta_z + vt\dot\theta_z \cos\theta_z) \\
\mathbf{r}_{cm}^{**} &= \mathbf{i}^0 (-v\dot\theta_z^2 t\cos\theta_z - 2v\dot\theta_z \sin\theta_z) + \mathbf{j}^0 (-v\dot\theta_z^2 t \sin\theta_z + 2v\dot\theta_z \cos\theta_z)
\end{aligned}\right\} \tag{2}$$

The comparison of (2) of this problem and (2) of Problem 6.7 shows the advantages of the rotating reference system.   Numerically, of course, both forms lead to the solution.

6.9   A particle m moves with constant relative speed v along the chord of the circular disk (Fig. P-6.9) while the disk rotates with a given angular speed $\omega_z = \dot\theta_z$ and acceleration $\dot\omega_z = \ddot\theta_z$.   Find the equations of the apparent and true motions of this particle in the rotating system with respect to the stationary system.

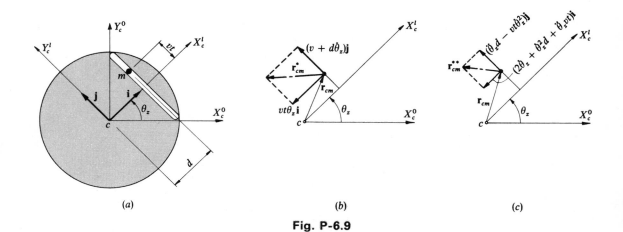

(a)   (b)   (c)

Fig. P-6.9

The matrix equations of apparent motion of m are

$$\begin{bmatrix} x_{cm}^l \\ y_{cm}^l \end{bmatrix} = \begin{bmatrix} d \\ vt \end{bmatrix}, \qquad \begin{bmatrix} \dot x_{cm}^l \\ \dot y_{cm}^l \end{bmatrix} = \begin{bmatrix} 0 \\ v \end{bmatrix}, \qquad \begin{bmatrix} \ddot x_{cm}^l \\ \ddot y_{cm}^l \end{bmatrix} = \begin{bmatrix} 0 \\ 0 \end{bmatrix} \tag{1}$$

where all components are in the rotating system and d is a given distance measured from the chord to c.

The matrix equations of the true motion [equations (6-22)–(6-24)] of m are

$$\underbrace{\begin{bmatrix} x^l_{cm} \\ y^l_{cm} \end{bmatrix}}_{[s^l_{cm}]} = \underbrace{\begin{bmatrix} d \\ vt \end{bmatrix}}_{[s^l_{cm}]}, \qquad \underbrace{\begin{bmatrix} x^{l*}_{cm} \\ y^{l*}_{cm} \end{bmatrix}}_{[s^l_{cm}]} = \underbrace{\begin{bmatrix} 0 \\ v \end{bmatrix}}_{[\dot{s}^l_{cm}]} + \underbrace{\begin{bmatrix} 0 & -\dot{\theta}_z \\ \dot{\theta}_z & 0 \end{bmatrix}}_{[\Gamma]} \underbrace{\begin{bmatrix} d \\ vt \end{bmatrix}}_{[s^l_{cm}]}$$

$$\underbrace{\begin{bmatrix} x^{l**}_{cm} \\ y^{l**}_{cm} \end{bmatrix}}_{[s^l_{cm}]} = \underbrace{\begin{bmatrix} 0 \\ 0 \end{bmatrix}}_{[\ddot{s}^l_{cm}]} + 2\underbrace{\begin{bmatrix} 0 & -\dot{\theta}_z \\ \dot{\theta}_z & 0 \end{bmatrix}}_{2[\Gamma]} \underbrace{\begin{bmatrix} 0 \\ v \end{bmatrix}}_{[\dot{s}^l_{cm}]} + \underbrace{\begin{bmatrix} -\dot{\theta}^2_z & -\ddot{\theta}_z \\ \ddot{\theta}_z & -\dot{\theta}^2_z \end{bmatrix}}_{[\Delta]} \underbrace{\begin{bmatrix} d \\ vt \end{bmatrix}}_{[s^l_{cm}]}$$

(2)

If $d = 10$ m, $v = 1$ m/sec, $\dot{\theta}_z = t$ rad/sec, $\ddot{\theta}_z = 1$ rad/sec^2,

$$x^l_{cm} = 10 \text{ m} \qquad x^{l*}_{cm} = -t \text{ m/sec} \qquad x^{l**}_{cm} = -13 \text{ m/sec}^2$$
$$y^l_{cm} = t \text{ m} \qquad y^{l*}_{cm} = 10t \text{ m/sec} \qquad y^{l**}_{cm} = 9 \text{ m/sec}^2$$

6.10 For the particle of Problem 6.9 find the matrix equations of apparent and true motion in the stationary system. Given: $d = 10$ m, $v = 1$ m/sec, $\dot{\theta}_z = t$ rad/sec, $\ddot{\theta}_z = 1$ rad/sec^2.

The matrix equations of apparent motion of m in the stationary system are equations (1) of Problem 6.9, multiplied by $[\pi^{0l}]$.

$$\underbrace{\begin{bmatrix} x^0_{cm} \\ y^0_{cm} \end{bmatrix}}_{[s^0_{cm}]} = \underbrace{\begin{bmatrix} \cos\theta_z & -\sin\theta_z \\ \sin\theta_z & \cos\theta_z \end{bmatrix}}_{[\pi^{0l}]} \underbrace{\begin{bmatrix} 10 \\ t \end{bmatrix}}_{[s^l_{cm}]}, \qquad \underbrace{\begin{bmatrix} \dot{x}^0_{cm} \\ \dot{y}^0_{cm} \end{bmatrix}}_{[\dot{s}^0_{cm}]} = \underbrace{\begin{bmatrix} \cos\theta_z & -\sin\theta_z \\ \sin\theta_z & \cos\theta_z \end{bmatrix}}_{[\pi^{0l}]} \underbrace{\begin{bmatrix} 0 \\ 1 \end{bmatrix}}_{[\dot{s}^l_{cm}]},$$

$$\underbrace{\begin{bmatrix} \ddot{x}^0_{cm} \\ \ddot{y}^0_{cm} \end{bmatrix}}_{[\ddot{s}^0_{cm}]} = \underbrace{\begin{bmatrix} \cos\theta_z & -\sin\theta_z \\ \sin\theta_z & \cos\theta_z \end{bmatrix}}_{[\pi^{0l}]} \underbrace{\begin{bmatrix} 0 \\ 0 \end{bmatrix}}_{[\ddot{s}^l_{cm}]}$$

where all vectors are related to the rotating axes but are resolved into components parallel to the stationary axes.

The matrix equations of true motion of m in the stationary system are equations (2) of Problem 6.9, multiplied by $[\pi^{0l}]$.

$$\underbrace{\begin{bmatrix} x^0_{cm} \\ y^0_{cm} \end{bmatrix}}_{[s^0_{cm}]} = \underbrace{\begin{bmatrix} \cos\theta_z & -\sin\theta_z \\ \sin\theta_z & \cos\theta_z \end{bmatrix}}_{[\pi^{0l}]} \underbrace{\begin{bmatrix} 10 \\ t \end{bmatrix}}_{[s^l_{cm}]}$$

$$\underbrace{\begin{bmatrix} x^{0*}_{cm} \\ y^{0*}_{cm} \end{bmatrix}}_{[s^{0*}_{cm}]} = \underbrace{\begin{bmatrix} \cos\theta_z & -\sin\theta_z \\ \sin\theta_z & \cos\theta_z \end{bmatrix}}_{[\pi^{0l}]} \underbrace{\begin{bmatrix} 0 \\ 1 \end{bmatrix}}_{[\dot{s}^l_{cm}]} + \underbrace{\begin{bmatrix} \cos\theta_z & -\sin\theta_z \\ \sin\theta_z & \cos\theta_z \end{bmatrix}}_{[\pi^{0l}]} \underbrace{\begin{bmatrix} 0 & -t \\ t & 0 \end{bmatrix}}_{[\Gamma]} \underbrace{\begin{bmatrix} 10 \\ t \end{bmatrix}}_{[s^l_{cm}]}$$

$$\underbrace{\begin{bmatrix} x^{0**}_{cm} \\ y^{0**}_{cm} \end{bmatrix}}_{[s^{0**}_{cm}]} = \underbrace{\begin{bmatrix} \cos\theta_z & -\sin\theta_z \\ \sin\theta_z & \cos\theta_z \end{bmatrix}}_{[\pi^{0l}]} \underbrace{\begin{bmatrix} 0 \\ 0 \end{bmatrix}}_{[\ddot{s}^l_{cm}]} + 2\underbrace{\begin{bmatrix} \cos\theta_z & -\sin\theta_z \\ \sin\theta_z & \cos\theta_z \end{bmatrix}}_{[\pi^{0l}]} \underbrace{\begin{bmatrix} 0 & -t \\ t & 0 \end{bmatrix}}_{[\Gamma]} \underbrace{\begin{bmatrix} 0 \\ 1 \end{bmatrix}}_{[\dot{s}^l_{cm}]}$$

$$+ \underbrace{\begin{bmatrix} \cos\theta_z & -\sin\theta_z \\ \sin\theta_z & \cos\theta_z \end{bmatrix}}_{[\pi^{0l}]} \underbrace{\begin{bmatrix} -t^2 & -1 \\ 1 & -t^2 \end{bmatrix}}_{[\Delta]} \underbrace{\begin{bmatrix} 10 \\ t \end{bmatrix}}_{[s^l_{cm}]}$$

6.11   A particle m moves from c with constant relative speed v along the radius R of a circular wheel while the wheel rolls (without slipping) with constant angular speed $\dot\theta_z$ on a horizontal plane, as shown in Fig. P-6.11.   Find the equations of motion of the particle with respect to 0.

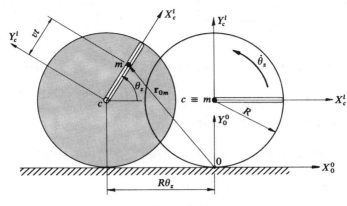

Fig. P-6.11

From Fig. P-6.11 and by *(6-44)–(6-46)*,

$$\underbrace{\begin{bmatrix} x^0_{0m} \\ y^0_{0m} \end{bmatrix}}_{[s^0_{0m}]} = \underbrace{\begin{bmatrix} -R\theta_z \\ R \end{bmatrix}}_{[s^0_{0c}]} + \underbrace{\begin{bmatrix} \cos\theta_z & -\sin\theta_z \\ \sin\theta_z & \cos\theta_z \end{bmatrix}}_{[\pi^{0l}]} \underbrace{\begin{bmatrix} vt \\ 0 \end{bmatrix}}_{[s^l_{cm}]}$$

$$\underbrace{\begin{bmatrix} x^{0*}_{0m} \\ y^{0*}_{0m} \end{bmatrix}}_{[s^{0*}_{0m}]} = \underbrace{\begin{bmatrix} -R\dot\theta_z \\ 0 \end{bmatrix}}_{[\dot s^0_{0c}]} + \underbrace{\begin{bmatrix} \cos\theta_z & -\sin\theta_z \\ \sin\theta_z & \cos\theta_z \end{bmatrix}}_{[\pi^{0l}]} \underbrace{\begin{bmatrix} v \\ 0 \end{bmatrix}}_{[\dot s^l_{cm}]} + \dot\theta_z \underbrace{\begin{bmatrix} -\sin\theta_z & -\cos\theta_z \\ \cos\theta_z & -\sin\theta_z \end{bmatrix}}_{[\dot\pi^{0l}]} \underbrace{\begin{bmatrix} vt \\ 0 \end{bmatrix}}_{[s^l_{cm}]}$$

$$\underbrace{\begin{bmatrix} x^{0**}_{0m} \\ y^{0**}_{0m} \end{bmatrix}}_{[s^{0**}_{0m}]} = \underbrace{\begin{bmatrix} 0 \\ 0 \end{bmatrix}}_{[\ddot s^0_{0c}]} + \underbrace{\begin{bmatrix} \cos\theta_z & -\sin\theta_z \\ \sin\theta_z & \cos\theta_z \end{bmatrix}}_{[\pi^{0l}]} \underbrace{\begin{bmatrix} 0 \\ 0 \end{bmatrix}}_{[\ddot s^l_{cm}]} + 2\dot\theta_z \underbrace{\begin{bmatrix} -\sin\theta_z & -\cos\theta_z \\ \cos\theta_z & -\sin\theta_z \end{bmatrix}}_{2[\pi^{0l}]} \underbrace{\begin{bmatrix} v \\ 0 \end{bmatrix}}_{[\dot s^l_{cm}]} - \dot\theta_z^2 \underbrace{\begin{bmatrix} \cos\theta_z & -\sin\theta_z \\ \sin\theta_z & \cos\theta_z \end{bmatrix}}_{[\ddot\pi^{0l}]} \underbrace{\begin{bmatrix} vt \\ 0 \end{bmatrix}}_{[s^l_{cm}]}$$

$$\begin{aligned}
x^0_{cm} &= -R\theta_z + vt\cos\theta_z, & y^0_{cm} &= R + vt\sin\theta_z \\
x^{0*}_{cm} &= -R\dot\theta_z + v(\cos\theta_z - t\dot\theta_z\sin\theta_z), & y^{0*}_{cm} &= v(\sin\theta_z + t\dot\theta_z\cos\theta_z) \\
x^{0**}_{cm} &= -v\dot\theta_z(2\sin\theta_z + t\dot\theta_z\cos\theta_z), & y^{0**}_{cm} &= v\dot\theta_z(2\cos\theta_z - t\dot\theta_z\sin\theta_z)
\end{aligned}$$

SPACE MOTION—DERIVATIONS

6.12   Find the first time derivatives of the unit vectors in the *l*-system rotating with respect to the stationary 0-system of axes.

Let $\mathbf{i}^0$, $\mathbf{j}^0$, $\mathbf{k}^0$ be the time-independent unit vectors in X^0_c, Y^0_c, Z^0_c and let $\mathbf{i}^l$, $\mathbf{j}^l$, $\mathbf{k}^l$ be the time-dependent unit vectors in X^l_c, Y^l_c, Z^l_c.

By (6-42),

$$
\begin{bmatrix} \mathbf{i}^0 \\ \mathbf{j}^0 \\ \mathbf{k}^0 \end{bmatrix} = \underbrace{\begin{bmatrix} \cos\theta_z & -\sin\theta_z & 0 \\ \sin\theta_z & \cos\theta_z & 0 \\ 0 & 0 & 1 \end{bmatrix}}_{[\pi^{0j}]} \underbrace{\begin{bmatrix} \cos\theta_y & 0 & \sin\theta_y \\ 0 & 1 & 0 \\ -\sin\theta_y & 0 & \cos\theta_y \end{bmatrix}}_{[\pi^{jk}]} \underbrace{\begin{bmatrix} 1 & 0 & 0 \\ 0 & \cos\theta_x & -\sin\theta_x \\ 0 & \sin\theta_x & \cos\theta_x \end{bmatrix}}_{[\pi^{kl}]} \underbrace{\begin{bmatrix} \mathbf{i}^l \\ \mathbf{j}^l \\ \mathbf{k}^l \end{bmatrix}}_{[\mathbf{e}^l]}
$$
$\underbrace{}_{[\mathbf{e}^0]}$
(1)

where θ_x, θ_y, θ_z are the respective rotations shown in Fig. 6-6, page 122, and

$$[\pi^{0l}] = [\pi^{0j}][\pi^{jk}][\pi^{kl}] \tag{2}$$

On differentiating (1) with respect to t,

$$[\dot{\mathbf{e}}^0] = [\dot{\pi}^{0j}][\pi^{jk}][\pi^{kl}][\mathbf{e}^l] + [\pi^{0j}][\dot{\pi}^{jk}][\pi^{kl}][\mathbf{e}^l] + [\pi^{0j}][\pi^{jk}][\dot{\pi}^{kl}][\mathbf{e}^l] + [\pi^{0j}][\pi^{jk}][\pi^{kl}][\dot{\mathbf{e}}^l] \tag{3}$$

where by definition, $[\dot{\mathbf{e}}^0] = [0]$.   Then from (3),

$$[\dot{\mathbf{e}}^l] = -[\Gamma_x][\mathbf{e}^l] - [\Gamma_y][\mathbf{e}^l] - [\Gamma_z][\mathbf{e}^l] = -[\Gamma][\mathbf{e}^l] \tag{4}$$

where for $\theta_x = 0$, $\theta_y = 0$, $\theta_z = 0$,

$$[\Gamma_z] = [\pi^{lk}][\pi^{kj}][\pi^{j0}][\dot{\pi}^{0j}][\pi^{jk}][\pi^{kl}] = \begin{bmatrix} 0 & -\dot{\theta}_z & 0 \\ \dot{\theta}_z & 0 & 0 \\ 0 & 0 & 0 \end{bmatrix} \tag{5}$$

$$[\Gamma_y] = [\pi^{lk}][\pi^{kj}][\pi^{j0}][\pi^{0j}][\dot{\pi}^{jk}][\pi^{kl}] = \begin{bmatrix} 0 & 0 & \dot{\theta}_y \\ 0 & 0 & 0 \\ -\dot{\theta}_y & 0 & 0 \end{bmatrix} \tag{6}$$

$$[\Gamma_x] = [\pi^{lk}][\pi^{kj}][\pi^{j0}][\pi^{0j}][\pi^{jk}][\dot{\pi}^{kl}] = \begin{bmatrix} 0 & 0 & 0 \\ 0 & 0 & -\dot{\theta}_x \\ 0 & \dot{\theta}_x & 0 \end{bmatrix} \tag{7}$$

With these equivalents, (4) becomes

$$
\underbrace{\begin{bmatrix} \dot{\mathbf{i}}^l \\ \dot{\mathbf{j}}^l \\ \dot{\mathbf{k}}^l \end{bmatrix}}_{[\dot{\mathbf{e}}^l]} = \underbrace{\begin{bmatrix} 0 & \dot{\theta}_z & -\dot{\theta}_y \\ -\dot{\theta}_z & 0 & \dot{\theta}_x \\ \dot{\theta}_y & -\dot{\theta}_x & 0 \end{bmatrix}}_{-[\Gamma]} \underbrace{\begin{bmatrix} \mathbf{i}^l \\ \mathbf{j}^l \\ \mathbf{k}^l \end{bmatrix}}_{[\mathbf{e}^l]}
\tag{8}
$$

which is the matrix form of (6-34).

6.13   Using the results of Problem 6.12, find the second time derivatives of unit vectors $\mathbf{i}^l$, $\mathbf{j}^l$, $\mathbf{k}^l$.

The second time derivatives of $\mathbf{i}^l$, $\mathbf{j}^l$, $\mathbf{k}^l$ obtained by differentiating (8) of Problem 6.12 are

$$[\ddot{\mathbf{e}}^l] = -[\Gamma][\dot{\mathbf{e}}^l] - [\dot{\Gamma}][\mathbf{e}^l] = [\Gamma]^2[\mathbf{e}^l] - [\dot{\Gamma}][\mathbf{e}^l] \tag{1}$$

In full matrix form,

$$
\begin{bmatrix} \ddot{\mathbf{i}}^l \\ \ddot{\mathbf{j}}^l \\ \ddot{\mathbf{k}}^l \end{bmatrix} = \left\{ \begin{bmatrix} 0 & \dot{\theta}_z & -\dot{\theta}_y \\ -\dot{\theta}_z & 0 & \dot{\theta}_x \\ \dot{\theta}_y & -\dot{\theta}_x & 0 \end{bmatrix} \begin{bmatrix} 0 & \dot{\theta}_z & -\dot{\theta}_y \\ -\dot{\theta}_z & 0 & \dot{\theta}_x \\ \dot{\theta}_y & -\dot{\theta}_x & 0 \end{bmatrix} - \begin{bmatrix} 0 & -\ddot{\theta}_z & \ddot{\theta}_y \\ \ddot{\theta}_z & 0 & -\ddot{\theta}_x \\ -\ddot{\theta}_y & \ddot{\theta}_x & 0 \end{bmatrix} \right\} \begin{bmatrix} \mathbf{i}^l \\ \mathbf{j}^l \\ \mathbf{k}^l \end{bmatrix}
$$

$$
= \underbrace{\begin{bmatrix} -(\dot{\theta}_y^2 + \dot{\theta}_z^2) & \dot{\theta}_x\dot{\theta}_y + \ddot{\theta}_z & \dot{\theta}_x\dot{\theta}_z - \ddot{\theta}_y \\ \dot{\theta}_y\dot{\theta}_x - \ddot{\theta}_z & -(\dot{\theta}_z^2 + \dot{\theta}_x^2) & \dot{\theta}_y\dot{\theta}_z + \ddot{\theta}_x \\ \dot{\theta}_z\dot{\theta}_x + \ddot{\theta}_y & \dot{\theta}_z\dot{\theta}_y - \ddot{\theta}_x & -(\dot{\theta}_x^2 + \dot{\theta}_y^2) \end{bmatrix}}_{[\lambda]} \underbrace{\begin{bmatrix} \mathbf{i}^l \\ \mathbf{j}^l \\ \mathbf{k}^l \end{bmatrix}}_{[\mathbf{e}^l]} \qquad (2)
$$

which is the matrix form of (6-35).

Note the superscript l has been omitted in (6-34) and (6-35) since in the theory section all unit vectors in these equations are in the l-system.

6.14 Derive the velocity vector equation of space motion of a particle m, given by (6-38) as

$$
\mathbf{v}_{cm} = \mathbf{r}^*_{cm} = \dot{\mathbf{r}}_{cm} + \boldsymbol{\omega} \times \mathbf{r}_{cm}
$$

First refer to Fig. 6-5, page 120, where $\mathbf{i}, \mathbf{j}, \mathbf{k}$ are the unit vectors of the rotating axes and introduce the time-dependent position angle $\theta_x, \theta_y, \theta_z$ measured as shown in Fig. 6-6. Then let

$$
\mathbf{r}_{cm} = x_{cm}\mathbf{i} + y_{cm}\mathbf{j} + z_{cm}\mathbf{k} \qquad (1)
$$

be the position vector of the particle m in the rotating system.

The relative and absolute time derivatives of $\mathbf{r}_{cm}$ are respectively

$$
\dot{\mathbf{r}}_{cm} = \dot{x}_{cm}\mathbf{i} + \dot{y}_{cm}\mathbf{i} + \dot{z}_{cm}\mathbf{k}, \qquad \mathbf{r}^*_{cm} = \dot{x}_{cm}\mathbf{i} + \dot{y}_{cm}\mathbf{j} + \dot{z}_{cm}\mathbf{k} + x_{cm}\dot{\mathbf{i}} + y_{cm}\dot{\mathbf{j}} + z_{cm}\dot{\mathbf{k}} \qquad (2),(3)
$$

where $\dot{\mathbf{r}}_{cm}$ presumes that $\mathbf{i}, \mathbf{j}, \mathbf{k}$ are time-dependent unit vectors whereas $\mathbf{r}^*_{cm}$ treats $\mathbf{i}, \mathbf{j}, \mathbf{k}$ as functions of time. By (8) of Problem 6.12,

$$
\dot{\mathbf{i}} = \dot{\theta}_z\mathbf{j} - \dot{\theta}_y\mathbf{k}, \qquad \dot{\mathbf{j}} = -\dot{\theta}_z\mathbf{i} + \dot{\theta}_x\mathbf{k}, \qquad \dot{\mathbf{k}} = \dot{\theta}_y\mathbf{i} - \dot{\theta}_x\mathbf{j}
$$

and the velocity vector (3) is

$$
\mathbf{v}_{cm} = \mathbf{r}^*_{cm} = \dot{x}_{cm}\mathbf{i} + \dot{y}_{cm}\mathbf{j} + \dot{z}_{cm}\mathbf{k} + x_{cm}(\dot{\theta}_z\mathbf{j} - \dot{\theta}_y\mathbf{k}) + y_{cm}(-\dot{\theta}_z\mathbf{i} + \dot{\theta}_x\mathbf{k}) + z_{cm}(\dot{\theta}_y\mathbf{i} - \dot{\theta}_x\mathbf{j})
$$

$$
= (\dot{x}_{cm} - y_{cm}\dot{\theta}_z + z_{cm}\dot{\theta}_y)\mathbf{i} + (\dot{y}_{cm} - z_{cm}\dot{\theta}_x + x_{cm}\dot{\theta}_z)\mathbf{j} + (\dot{z}_{cm} - x_{cm}\dot{\theta}_y + y_{cm}\dot{\theta}_x)\mathbf{k} \qquad (4)
$$

Since in (4)

$$
\mathbf{i}(-y_{cm}\dot{\theta}_z + z_{cm}\dot{\theta}_y) + \mathbf{j}(-z_{cm}\dot{\theta}_x + x_{cm}\dot{\theta}_z) + \mathbf{k}(-x_{cm}\dot{\theta}_y + y_{cm}\dot{\theta}_x)
$$

$$
= \underbrace{(\dot{\theta}_x\mathbf{i} + \dot{\theta}_y\mathbf{j} + \dot{\theta}_z\mathbf{k})}_{\boldsymbol{\omega}} \times \underbrace{(x_{cm}\mathbf{i} + y_{cm}\mathbf{j} + z_{cm}\mathbf{k})}_{\mathbf{r}_{cm}} = \begin{vmatrix} \mathbf{i} & \mathbf{j} & \mathbf{k} \\ \dot{\theta}_x & \dot{\theta}_y & \dot{\theta}_z \\ x_{cm} & y_{cm} & z_{cm} \end{vmatrix} \qquad (5)
$$

equation (4) may be also written symbolically as

$$
\mathbf{v}_{cm} = \mathbf{r}^*_{cm} = \dot{\mathbf{r}}_{cm} + \boldsymbol{\omega} \times \mathbf{r}_{cm} \qquad (6)
$$

6.15 Derive the acceleration vector equation of plane motion of a particle m, given by *(6-39)* as

$$\mathbf{a}_{cm} = \mathbf{r}_{cm}^{**} = \ddot{\mathbf{r}}_{cm} + \dot{\boldsymbol{\omega}} \times \mathbf{r}_{cm} + 2\boldsymbol{\omega} \times \dot{\mathbf{r}}_{cm} + \boldsymbol{\omega} \times (\boldsymbol{\omega} \times \mathbf{r}_{cm})$$

By definition,

$$\begin{aligned}
\mathbf{a}_{cm} = \mathbf{v}_{cm}^{*} = \mathbf{r}_{cm}^{**} &= \dot{\mathbf{r}}^{*} + \boldsymbol{\omega} \times \mathbf{r}_{cm}^{*} + \boldsymbol{\omega}^{*} \times \mathbf{r}_{cm} \\
&= \ddot{\mathbf{r}}_{cm} + \boldsymbol{\omega} \times \dot{\mathbf{r}}_{cm} + \boldsymbol{\omega} \times (\dot{\mathbf{r}}_{cm} + \boldsymbol{\omega} \times \mathbf{r}_{cm}) + (\dot{\boldsymbol{\omega}} + \boldsymbol{\omega} \times \boldsymbol{\omega}) \times \mathbf{r}_{cm} \\
&= \ddot{\mathbf{r}}_{cm} + \dot{\boldsymbol{\omega}} \times \mathbf{r}_{cm} + 2\boldsymbol{\omega} \times \dot{\mathbf{r}}_{cm} + \boldsymbol{\omega} \times (\boldsymbol{\omega} \times \mathbf{r}_{cm})
\end{aligned}$$

where $\boldsymbol{\omega}^{*} = \dot{\boldsymbol{\omega}} + \boldsymbol{\omega} \times \boldsymbol{\omega}$ and $\boldsymbol{\omega} \times \boldsymbol{\omega} = 0$.

Equation *(6-39)* is formally identical to *(6-12)* but all vectors are three dimensional and consequently the expanded vector form of *(6-39)* is more involved (Table 6-1).

6.16 Derive the velocity matrix equation of space motion of a particle m, given by *(6-48)* as

$$[v_{cm}^{l}] = [\dot{s}_{cm}^{l}] + [\Gamma][s_{cm}^{l}]$$

The derivation of *(6-48)* follows the symbolic pattern of *(1)*, *(2)*, *(3)* of Problem 6.5, where

$$[\Gamma] = [\pi^{lo}][\dot{\pi}^{ol}] = [\Gamma_x] + [\Gamma_y] + [\Gamma_z] = \begin{bmatrix} 0 & -\dot{\theta}_z & \dot{\theta}_y \\ \dot{\theta}_z & 0 & -\dot{\theta}_x \\ -\dot{\theta}_y & \dot{\theta}_x & 0 \end{bmatrix} \qquad (1)$$

is the matrix sum of *(5)*, *(6)*, *(7)* of Problem 6.12.

6.17 Derive the acceleration matrix equation of space motion of a particle m, given by *(6-49)* as

$$[a_{cm}^{l}] = [\ddot{s}_{cm}^{l}] + 2[\Gamma][\dot{s}_{cm}^{l}] + [\Delta][s_{cm}^{l}]$$

The derivation of *(6-49)* follows the symbolic pattern of *(1)*, *(2)* of Problem 6.6, but $[\Gamma]$ and $[\Delta]$ are 3×3 matrices. The coefficients of $[\Gamma]$ are already known (Problem 6.16) and those of $[\Delta]$ are computed as follows. By definition,

$$[\Delta] = [\pi^{lo}][\ddot{\pi}^{ol}] \qquad (1)$$

where

$$[\ddot{\pi}^{ol}] = d[\dot{\pi}^{ol}]/dt \qquad (2)$$

Since in *(1)* of Problem 6.16,

$$[\Gamma] = [\pi^{lo}][\dot{\pi}^{ol}] \qquad \text{or} \qquad [\pi^{ol}][\Gamma] = [\dot{\pi}^{ol}] \qquad (3)$$

the second time derivative of $[\pi^{ol}]$ can be written as

$$[\ddot{\pi}^{ol}] = d([\pi^{ol}][\Gamma])/dt = [\dot{\pi}^{ol}][\Gamma] + [\pi^{ol}][\dot{\Gamma}] = [\pi^{ol}][\Gamma][\Gamma] + [\pi^{ol}][\dot{\Gamma}] \qquad (4)$$

Putting (*4*) into (*1*) yields

$$[\Delta] = [\pi^{lo}][\ddot{\pi}^{ol}] = [\pi^{lo}][\pi^{ol}][\Gamma]^2 + [\pi^{lo}][\pi^{ol}][\dot{\Gamma}] = [\dot{\Gamma}] + [\Gamma]^2$$

$$= \begin{bmatrix} 0 & -\ddot{\theta}_z & \ddot{\theta}_y \\ \ddot{\theta}_z & 0 & -\ddot{\theta}_x \\ -\ddot{\theta}_y & \ddot{\theta}_x & 0 \end{bmatrix} + \begin{bmatrix} 0 & -\dot{\theta}_z & \dot{\theta}_y \\ \dot{\theta}_z & 0 & -\dot{\theta}_x \\ -\dot{\theta}_y & \dot{\theta}_x & 0 \end{bmatrix} \begin{bmatrix} 0 & -\dot{\theta}_z & \dot{\theta}_y \\ \dot{\theta}_z & 0 & -\dot{\theta}_x \\ -\dot{\theta}_y & \dot{\theta}_x & 0 \end{bmatrix}$$

$$= \begin{bmatrix} -(\dot{\theta}_y^2 + \dot{\theta}_z^2) & (\dot{\theta}_x\dot{\theta}_y - \ddot{\theta}_z) & (\dot{\theta}_x\dot{\theta}_z + \ddot{\theta}_y) \\ (\dot{\theta}_y\dot{\theta}_x + \ddot{\theta}_z) & -(\dot{\theta}_z^2 + \dot{\theta}_x^2) & (\dot{\theta}_y\dot{\theta}_z - \ddot{\theta}_x) \\ (\dot{\theta}_z\dot{\theta}_x - \ddot{\theta}_y) & (\dot{\theta}_z\dot{\theta}_y + \ddot{\theta}_x) & -(\dot{\theta}_x^2 + \dot{\theta}_y^2) \end{bmatrix} \quad (5)$$

SPACE MOTION—APPLICATIONS

6.18 The instantaneous position of a moving particle m is given by $\mathbf{r}_{cm}$ in the system of X_c^l, Y_c^l, Z_c^l axes, which in turn rotate with angular velocity $\boldsymbol{\omega}$ with respect to the stationary axes X_c^0, Y_c^0, Z_c^0. Find the apparent and true velocities of m at $t = 1$. Given: $\mathbf{r}_{cm} = 2t\mathbf{i} + 3t^2\mathbf{j} + 4t^3\mathbf{k}$, $\boldsymbol{\omega} = 5t\mathbf{i} + 6t\mathbf{j} + 7t\mathbf{k}$, where all unit vectors are in the *l*-system.

The apparent velocity of m is

$$\dot{\mathbf{r}}_{cm} = d\mathbf{r}_{cm}/dt = 2\mathbf{i} + 6t\mathbf{j} + 12t^2\mathbf{k}$$

For $t = 1$, $\dot{\mathbf{r}}_{cm} = 2\mathbf{i} + 6\mathbf{j} + 12\mathbf{k}$.   The true velocity of m [equation (*6-38*)] is

$$\mathbf{r}_{cm}^* = \dot{\mathbf{r}}_{cm} + \boldsymbol{\omega} \times \mathbf{r}_{cm} = 2\mathbf{i} + 6t\mathbf{j} + 12t^2\mathbf{k} + (5t\mathbf{i} + 6t\mathbf{j} + 7t\mathbf{k}) \times (2t\mathbf{i} + 3t^2\mathbf{j} + 4t^3\mathbf{k})$$

For $t = 1$, $\mathbf{r}_{cm}^* = 2\mathbf{i} + 6\mathbf{j} + 12\mathbf{k} + \begin{vmatrix} \mathbf{i} & \mathbf{j} & \mathbf{k} \\ 5 & 6 & 7 \\ 2 & 3 & 4 \end{vmatrix} = 5\mathbf{i} + 15\mathbf{k}$.

6.19 Show the matrix solution of Problem 6.18.

The apparent and true velocities (*6-48*) of m are respectively

$$\underbrace{\begin{bmatrix} \dot{x}_{cm}^l \\ \dot{y}_{cm}^l \\ \dot{z}_{cm}^l \end{bmatrix}}_{[\dot{s}_{cm}^l]} = \underbrace{\begin{bmatrix} 2 \\ 6t \\ 12t^2 \end{bmatrix}}_{[\dot{s}_{cm}^l]}, \qquad \underbrace{\begin{bmatrix} x_{cm}^{l*} \\ y_{cm}^{l*} \\ z_{cm}^{l*} \end{bmatrix}}_{[s_{cm}^{l*}]} = \underbrace{\begin{bmatrix} 2 \\ 6t \\ 12t^2 \end{bmatrix}}_{[\dot{s}_{cm}^l]} + \underbrace{\begin{bmatrix} 0 & -7t & 6t \\ 7t & 0 & -5t \\ -6t & 5t & 0 \end{bmatrix}}_{[\Gamma]} \underbrace{\begin{bmatrix} 2t \\ 3t^2 \\ 4t^3 \end{bmatrix}}_{[s_{cm}^l]}$$

For $t = 1$,

$$\begin{bmatrix} \dot{x}_{cm}^l \\ \dot{y}_{cm}^l \\ \dot{z}_{cm}^l \end{bmatrix} = \begin{bmatrix} 2 \\ 6 \\ 12 \end{bmatrix}, \qquad \begin{bmatrix} x_{cm}^* \\ y_{cm}^* \\ z_{cm}^* \end{bmatrix} = \begin{bmatrix} 2 \\ 6 \\ 12 \end{bmatrix} + \begin{bmatrix} 3 \\ -6 \\ 3 \end{bmatrix} = \begin{bmatrix} 5 \\ 0 \\ 15 \end{bmatrix}$$

6.20 Find the vector form of the apparent and true accelerations of the particle m in Problem 6.18.

The apparent acceleration of m is

$$\ddot{\mathbf{r}}_{cm} = d\dot{\mathbf{r}}_{cm}/dt = 6\mathbf{j} + 24t\mathbf{k}$$

For $t = 1$, $\ddot{\mathbf{r}}_{cm} = 6\mathbf{j} + 24\mathbf{k}$. The true acceleration of m [equation (6-39)] is

$$\mathbf{r}_{cm}^{**} = \ddot{\mathbf{r}}_{cm} + \dot{\boldsymbol{\omega}} \times \mathbf{r}_{cm} + 2\boldsymbol{\omega} \times \dot{\mathbf{r}}_{cm} + \boldsymbol{\omega} \times (\boldsymbol{\omega} \times \mathbf{r}_{cm})$$

For $t = 1$,

$$\dot{\boldsymbol{\omega}} \times \mathbf{r}_{cm} = \begin{vmatrix} \mathbf{i} & \mathbf{j} & \mathbf{k} \\ 5 & 6 & 7 \\ 2 & 3 & 4 \end{vmatrix} = 3\mathbf{i} - 6\mathbf{j} + 3\mathbf{k}$$

$$2\boldsymbol{\omega} \times \dot{\mathbf{r}}_{cm} = 2\begin{vmatrix} \mathbf{i} & \mathbf{j} & \mathbf{k} \\ 5 & 6 & 7 \\ 2 & 6 & 12 \end{vmatrix} = 60\mathbf{i} - 92\mathbf{j} + 36\mathbf{k}$$

$$\boldsymbol{\omega} \times (\boldsymbol{\omega} \times \mathbf{r}_{cm}) = \begin{vmatrix} \mathbf{i} & \mathbf{j} & \mathbf{k} \\ 5 & 6 & 7 \\ 3 & -6 & 3 \end{vmatrix} = 60\mathbf{i} + 6\mathbf{j} - 48\mathbf{k}$$

$$\mathbf{r}_{cm}^{**} = (0 + 3 + 60 + 60)\mathbf{i} + (6 - 6 - 92 + 6)\mathbf{j} + (24 + 3 + 36 - 48)\mathbf{k} = 123\mathbf{i} - 86\mathbf{j} + 15\mathbf{k}$$

6.21 Show the matrix solution of Problem 6.20.

The apparent acceleration and true acceleration (6-49) of m are respectively

$$\underbrace{\begin{bmatrix} \ddot{x}_{cm}^l \\ \ddot{y}_{cm}^l \\ \ddot{z}_{cm}^l \end{bmatrix}}_{[\ddot{s}_{cm}^l]} = \underbrace{\begin{bmatrix} 0 \\ 6 \\ 24t \end{bmatrix}}_{[\ddot{s}_{cm}^l]}$$

$$\underbrace{\begin{bmatrix} x_{cm}^{l**} \\ y_{cm}^{l**} \\ z_{cm}^{l**} \end{bmatrix}}_{[s_{cm}^{l**}]} = \underbrace{\begin{bmatrix} 0 \\ 6 \\ 24t \end{bmatrix}}_{[\ddot{s}_{cm}^l]} + \underbrace{2\begin{bmatrix} 0 & -7t & 6t \\ 7t & 0 & -5t \\ -6t & 5t & 0 \end{bmatrix}}_{2[\Gamma]}\underbrace{\begin{bmatrix} 2 \\ 6t \\ 12t^2 \end{bmatrix}}_{[\dot{s}_{cm}^l]} + \underbrace{\begin{bmatrix} -85 & 30t^2 - 7 & 35t^2 + 6 \\ 35t^2 - 6 & -74 & 42t^2 - 5 \\ 35t^2 - 6 & 42t^2 + 5 & -61 \end{bmatrix}}_{[\Delta]}\underbrace{\begin{bmatrix} 2t \\ 3t^2 \\ 4t^3 \end{bmatrix}}_{[s_{cm}^l]}$$

For $t = 1$,

$$\begin{bmatrix} \ddot{x}_{cm}^l \\ \ddot{y}_{cm}^l \\ \ddot{z}_{cm}^l \end{bmatrix} = \begin{bmatrix} 0 \\ 6 \\ 24 \end{bmatrix}, \qquad \begin{bmatrix} x_{cm}^{l**} \\ y_{cm}^{l**} \\ z_{cm}^{l**} \end{bmatrix} = \begin{bmatrix} 0 \\ 6 \\ 24 \end{bmatrix} + \begin{bmatrix} 60 \\ -92 \\ 36 \end{bmatrix} + \begin{bmatrix} 63 \\ 0 \\ -45 \end{bmatrix} = \begin{bmatrix} 123 \\ -86 \\ 15 \end{bmatrix}$$

which again show the simplicity and transparency of the matrix solution.

Problems

PLANE MOTION—DERIVATIONS

6.22   Derive the vector form of the equations of plane motion *(6-13)–(6-15)* in the polar coordinate system.

6.23   Derive the vector form of the equations of plane motion *(6-13)–(6-15)* in the curvilinear coordinate system.

6.24   Derive the matrix form of the equations of plane motion *(6-22)–(6-24)* in the polar coordinate system.

6.25   Derive the matrix form of the equations of plane motion *(6-22)–(6-24)* in the curvilinear coordinate system.

PLANE MOTION—APPLICATIONS

6.26   A particle *m* moves with relative velocity $10t$ m/sec along the circumference of a circular disk of radius $R = 10$ m while the disk rotates in the same direction with angular velocity $\omega = (5 \sin t)\mathbf{k}$ rad/sec (Fig. P-6.26).   Find the vector solution of the problem.

6.27   Show the matrix solution of Problem 6.26.

6.28   A disk of radius $R = 10$ m rolls without slipping on a stationary horizontal surface with $\omega = 10t\mathbf{k}$ rad/sec (Fig. P-6.28).   Find the velocity and acceleration of the particle *m* of the disk.

6.29   A disk of radius $R = 10$ m rolls without slipping on a stationary cylindrical surface of radius $\rho = 100$ m with $\omega = 10t\mathbf{k}$ rad/sec (Fig. P-6.29).   Find the velocity and acceleration of the particle *m* of the disk.

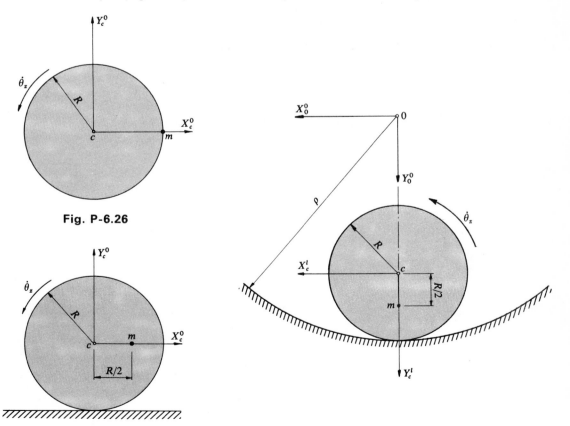

Fig. P-6.26

Fig. P-6.28   Fig. P-6.29

SPACE MOTION—DERIVATIONS

6.30 Derive the vector form of the equations of space motion (*6-38*), (*6-39*) in the cylindrical coordinate system.

6.31 Derive the vector form of the equations of space motion (*6-38*), (*6-39*) in the spherical coordinate system.

6.32 Derive the vector form of the equations of space motion (*6-38*), (*6-39*) in the curvilinear coordinate system.

6.33 Derive the matrix form of the equations of space motion (*6-38*), (*6-39*) in the cylindrical coordinate system.

6.34 Derive the matrix form of the equations of space motion (*6-38*), (*6-39*) in the spherical coordinate system.

6.35 Derive the matrix form of the equations of space motion (*6-38*), (*6-39*) in the curvilinear coordinate system.

6.36 Show that the vector forms of the Coriolis and centripetal accelerations are equivalent to their matrix counterparts given in Table 6-1.

SPACE MOTION—APPLICATIONS

Given: $\mathbf{r}_{cm} = t\mathbf{i} + t^2\mathbf{j} + t^3\mathbf{k}$, $\boldsymbol{\omega} = (\cos t)\mathbf{i} + (\sin t)\mathbf{j} + t\mathbf{k}$.

6.37 Find the vector form of the Coriolis, centripetal and centrifugal accelerations of the space motion of the particle m in terms of $\mathbf{r}_{cm}$ and $\boldsymbol{\omega}_c$ at $t = 1$.

6.38 Show the matrix solution of Problem 6.37 in the l-system.

6.39 Find the vector form of the apparent and true velocities and accelerations of the particle m in terms of $\mathbf{r}_{cm}$ and $\boldsymbol{\omega}_c$ at $t = 1$.

6.40 Show the matrix solution of Problem 6.39 in the l-system.

Chapter **7**

Kinematics of Rigid Bodies, Plane Motion

7.1 CHARACTERISTICS OF A RIGID BODY

Rigid Body

A rigid body is defined as a *system of particles* so *constrained* that the distance between any two of them is constant (fixed) and remains constant during the motion of the body. The motion of a rigid body, defined as the change of its position, is in general a space motion in which each particle of the body moves along its own path, which is related to the paths of the other particles by the condition of rigidity.

Plane Motion

If all particles of the body move parallel to a given fixed plane (reference plane), their respective paths are plane curves and the motion of the body is called *plane motion*. In such a case the body has *three degrees of freedom* and three geometrically independent coordinates (generalized coordinates) define its position.

The introduction of *external constraints* may further reduce the number of degrees of freedom. Thus four types of plane motion are possible:

(a) *Rectilinear Translation* (Fig. 7-1), in which all particles move along straight parallel paths in planes parallel to the reference plane (one linear degree of freedom).

(b) *Rotation* (Fig. 7-2), in which all particles rotate in planes parallel to the reference plane about an axis normal to this plane (one angular degree of freedom).

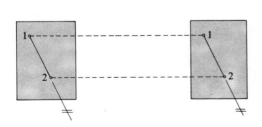

Fig. 7-1   Rectilinear translation.

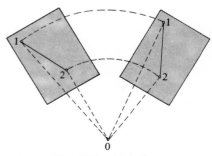

Fig. 7-2   Rotation.

(c) *Curvilinear Translation* (Fig. 7-3), in which all particles move along curvilinear parallel paths in planes parallel to the reference plane (two linear degrees of freedom).

(d) *General Motion,* in which all particles move in planes parallel to the reference plane along paths which are neither parallel nor concentric and are combinations of cases (*a*) and (*b*) or (*b*) and (*c*) (two linear and one angular degrees of freedom).

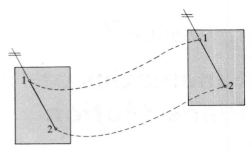

Fig. 7-3 Curvilinear translation.

Instantaneous Center and Centrode

In the motions described above, there is at any time an axis normal to the plane of motion which is instantaneously at rest.   This axis, called the *instantaneous axis*, intersects the plane of motion at a point designated as the *instantaneous center* (point of zero linear velocity).

As the body moves, the instantaneous axis also moves, generating a curvilinear cylindrical surface called the *centrodal surface*.   The intersection of this surface with the plane of motion, called the *centrode*, is the locus of instantaneous centers of motion.

In pure rotation, the centrodal surface degenerates to the axis of rotation.   In pure translation, which is rotation about the axis at infinity, the centrodal surface is this axis at infinity.

Theorems of Rigid Body Motion

The following two theorems are fundamental in the kinematics of rigid bodies.

Theorem 7.1: The *rotation of a rigid body* about a fixed point within or outside the body is equivalent to the rotation of the body about an axis through this point (*Euler's theorem*).

Theorem 7.2: The *general motion of a rigid body* may be represented as a superposition of translation and rotation about a point within or outside the body (*Chasle's theorem*).

In both cases the selection of the instantaneous axes or the centroidal axes as the reference axes of rotation offers some analytical simplifications.

7.2   ABSOLUTE PLANE MOTION

Vector Equations

The plane motion of a rigid body can be always defined by the motion of one of its laminas as shown in Fig. 7-4.

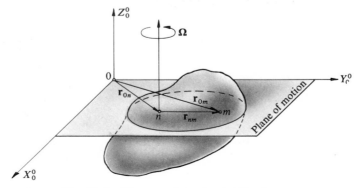

Fig. 7-4   Plane motion of a rigid body.

Since by Theorem 7.2 the motion of the lamina may be represented as *superposition* of *translation* and *rotation* about a point in its plane, the point n and the segment $\overline{nm}$ are selected for the study of this motion. The linear motion of n defines the translation, and the angular motion of radius r_{nm} defines the rotation of the body.

The *equations of plane motion* of the rigid body referred to these two points and the fixed origin 0 are

$$\mathbf{r}_{0m} = \mathbf{r}_{0n} + \mathbf{r}_{nm} \tag{7-1}$$

$$\mathbf{v}_{0m} = \mathbf{r}_{0m}^* = \dot{\mathbf{r}}_{0n} + \mathbf{\Omega} \times \mathbf{r}_{nm} \tag{7-2}$$

$$\mathbf{a}_{0m} = \mathbf{v}_{0m}^* = \mathbf{r}_{0m}^{**} = \ddot{\mathbf{r}}_{0n} + \dot{\mathbf{\Omega}} \times \mathbf{r}_{nm} + \mathbf{\Omega} \times (\mathbf{\Omega} \times \mathbf{r}_{nm}) \tag{7-3}$$

where

$$\mathbf{\Omega} = \Omega_z \mathbf{k} = \dot{\theta}_z \mathbf{k} = (d\theta_z/dt)\mathbf{k} \tag{7-4}$$

is the angular velocity of r_{nm} and consequently of the body.

As shown analytically in Problems 7.1 and 7.2, these equations can be deduced from (6-13), (6-14) and (6-15) by deleting terms involving the relative velocity and acceleration which by condition of rigidity must equal zero ($\dot{\mathbf{r}}_{nm} = 0$, $\ddot{\mathbf{r}}_{nm} = 0$, $2\mathbf{\Omega} \times \dot{\mathbf{r}}_{nm} = 0$).

Instantaneous Center

By definition, the *instantaneous center* e is the point of zero linear velocity and so its location is given by (7-2) as

$$\mathbf{r}_{0m}^* = \dot{\mathbf{r}}_{0e} + \mathbf{\Omega} \times \mathbf{r}_{em} = \mathbf{\Omega} \times \mathbf{r}_{em} \tag{7-5}$$

where the linear velocity $\dot{\mathbf{r}}_{0e}$ of e is 0.

The *coordinates of e*, computed from (7-5) and referred to m, are

$$x_{me} = -y_{0m}^*/\dot{\theta}_z, \qquad y_{me} = x_{0m}^*/\dot{\theta}_z \tag{7-6}$$

where x_{0m}^*, y_{0m}^* are the scalar components of $\mathbf{r}_{0m}^*$ in (7-2) and $x_{me} = -x_{em}$, $y_{me} = -y_{em}$.

Matrix Equations

Once the similarity of the vector equations (6-13)–(6-15) and (7-1)–(7-3) is established, the similarity of their matrix counterparts follows automatically from (6-22)–(6-24) and yields the *matrix equations of plane motion* of the rigid body:

$$\underbrace{\begin{bmatrix} x_{0m}^0 \\ y_{0m}^0 \end{bmatrix}}_{[s_{0m}^0]} = \underbrace{\begin{bmatrix} x_{0n}^0 \\ y_{0n}^0 \end{bmatrix}}_{[s_{0n}^0]} + \underbrace{\begin{bmatrix} x_{nm}^0 \\ y_{nm}^0 \end{bmatrix}}_{[s_{nm}^0]} \tag{7-7}$$

$$\underbrace{\begin{bmatrix} x_{0m}^{0*} \\ y_{0m}^{0*} \end{bmatrix}}_{[s_{0m}^{0*}]} = \underbrace{\begin{bmatrix} \dot{x}_{0n}^0 \\ \dot{y}_{0n}^0 \end{bmatrix}}_{[\dot{s}_{0n}^0]} + \underbrace{\begin{bmatrix} 0 & -\dot{\theta}_z \\ \dot{\theta}_z & 0 \end{bmatrix}}_{[\Gamma]} \underbrace{\begin{bmatrix} x_{nm}^0 \\ y_{nm}^0 \end{bmatrix}}_{[s_{nm}^0]} \tag{7-8}$$

$$\underbrace{\begin{bmatrix} x_{0m}^{0**} \\ y_{0m}^{0**} \end{bmatrix}}_{[s_{0m}^{0**}]} = \underbrace{\begin{bmatrix} \ddot{x}_{0n}^0 \\ \ddot{y}_{0n}^0 \end{bmatrix}}_{[\ddot{s}_{0n}^0]} + \underbrace{\begin{bmatrix} -\dot{\theta}_z^2 & -\ddot{\theta}_z \\ \ddot{\theta}_z & -\dot{\theta}_z^2 \end{bmatrix}}_{[\Delta]} \underbrace{\begin{bmatrix} x_{nm}^0 \\ y_{nm}^0 \end{bmatrix}}_{[s_{nm}^0]} \tag{7-9}$$

where again the terms involving the relative velocity and acceleration are deleted.

7.3 RELATIVE PLANE MOTION

Vector Equations

A more general formulation of the plane motion of a rigid body includes the rotation of the axes X_n^l, Y_n^l which are assumed to be rigidly connected to the body so that the angular velocity of the axes, ω, equals the angular velocity of the body, Ω, and furthermore the distance $\overline{nm}$ may or may not be fixed.

In such a case, the *equations of plane motion* of the rigid body are formally identical to $(6\text{-}13)$–$(6\text{-}15)$ and are respectively

$$\mathbf{r}_{Om} = \mathbf{r}_{On} + \mathbf{r}_{nm} \tag{7-10}$$

$$\mathbf{v}_{Om} = \mathbf{r}_{Om}^* = \dot{\mathbf{r}}_{On} + \dot{\mathbf{r}}_{nm} + \boldsymbol{\omega} \times \mathbf{r}_{nm} \tag{7-11}$$

$$\mathbf{a}_{Om} = \mathbf{v}_{Om}^* = \mathbf{r}_{Om}^{**} = \ddot{\mathbf{r}}_{On} + \ddot{\mathbf{r}}_{nm} + \dot{\boldsymbol{\omega}} \times \mathbf{r}_{nm} + 2\boldsymbol{\omega} \times \dot{\mathbf{r}}_{nm} + \boldsymbol{\omega} \times (\boldsymbol{\omega} \times \mathbf{r}_{nm}) \tag{7-12}$$

The completely general case which includes independent ω and Ω is rarely encountered and is not considered in this book.

Instantaneous Center

Since the velocity vectors $(7\text{-}2)$ and $(7\text{-}11)$ are identical, the location of the instantaneous center e is not affected by the rotation of X_n^l, Y_n^l; and the coordinates of e with respect to X_m^0, Y_m^0 are again given by $(7\text{-}6)$.

Matrix Equations

The matrix equivalents of $(7\text{-}10)$–$(7\text{-}12)$ are

$$\underbrace{\begin{bmatrix} x_{Om}^l \\ y_{Om}^l \end{bmatrix}}_{[s_{Om}^l]} = \underbrace{\begin{bmatrix} x_{On}^l \\ y_{On}^l \end{bmatrix}}_{[s_{On}^l]} + \underbrace{\begin{bmatrix} x_{nm}^l \\ y_{nm}^l \end{bmatrix}}_{[s_{nm}^l]} \tag{7-13}$$

$$\underbrace{\begin{bmatrix} x_{Om}^{l*} \\ y_{Om}^{l*} \end{bmatrix}}_{[s_{Om}^{l*}]} = \underbrace{\begin{bmatrix} \dot{x}_{On}^l \\ \dot{y}_{On}^l \end{bmatrix}}_{[\dot{s}_{On}^l]} + \underbrace{\begin{bmatrix} \dot{x}_{nm}^l \\ \dot{y}_{nm}^l \end{bmatrix}}_{[\dot{s}_{nm}^l]} + \underbrace{\begin{bmatrix} 0 & -\dot{\theta}_z \\ \dot{\theta}_z & 0 \end{bmatrix}}_{[\Gamma]} \underbrace{\begin{bmatrix} x_{nm}^l \\ y_{nm}^l \end{bmatrix}}_{[s_{nm}^l]} \tag{7-14}$$

$$\underbrace{\begin{bmatrix} x_{Om}^{l**} \\ y_{Om}^{l**} \end{bmatrix}}_{[s_{Om}^{l**}]} = \underbrace{\begin{bmatrix} \ddot{x}_{On}^l \\ \ddot{y}_{On}^l \end{bmatrix}}_{[\ddot{s}_{On}^l]} + \underbrace{\begin{bmatrix} \ddot{x}_{nm}^l \\ \ddot{y}_{nm}^l \end{bmatrix}}_{[\ddot{s}_{nm}^l]} + 2\underbrace{\begin{bmatrix} 0 & -\dot{\theta}_z \\ \dot{\theta}_z & 0 \end{bmatrix}}_{2[\Gamma]} \underbrace{\begin{bmatrix} \dot{x}_{nm}^l \\ \dot{y}_{nm}^l \end{bmatrix}}_{[\dot{s}_{nm}^l]} + \underbrace{\begin{bmatrix} -\dot{\theta}_z^2 & -\ddot{\theta}_z \\ \ddot{\theta}_z & -\dot{\theta}_z^2 \end{bmatrix}}_{[\Delta]} \underbrace{\begin{bmatrix} x_{nm}^l \\ y_{nm}^l \end{bmatrix}}_{[s_{nm}^l]} \tag{7-15}$$

where the position and velocity vectors are identical to $(7\text{-}7)$ and $(7\text{-}8)$ respectively.

Illustrative Problems

ABSOLUTE MOTION—DERIVATIONS

7.1 Derive the velocity vector equation $(7\text{-}2)$ of plane motion of the rigid body of Fig. P-7.1, referred to the stationary axes X_0^0, Y_0^0, Z_0^0. Given: $\mathbf{r}_{On}$, $\mathbf{r}_{nm}$, Ω.

By Theorem 7.2, the absolute plane motion of a rigid body may be represented as a superposition of translation and rotation about a point within or outside the body.

For the basic development of (7-2), three kinematic vectors must be given:

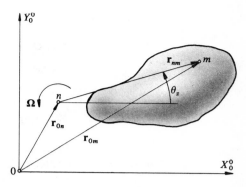

Fig. P-7.1

(a)   The absolute position vector $\mathbf{r}_{0n}$ of n (arbitrarily selected point in the plane of motion) referred to the fixed origin 0.

(b)   The angular velocity vector $\boldsymbol{\Omega}$ normal to the plane of motion (free vector).

(c)   The relative position vector $\mathbf{r}_{nm}$ of m (arbitrarily selected point in the plane of motion) referred to the moving point n.

Although n and m may lie outside or inside the body, they are always assumed to move with the body as if connected to it by rigid arms.

The position vector of m referred to the stationary axes X_0^0, Y_0^0 of Fig. P-7.1 is

$$\mathbf{r}_{0m} = \mathbf{r}_{0n} + \mathbf{r}_{nm} = x_{0n}\mathbf{i} + y_{0n}\mathbf{j} + r_{nm}[(\cos\theta_z)\mathbf{i} + (\sin\theta_z)\mathbf{j}] \qquad (1)$$

where r_{nm} is the constant radius and $\theta_z = \theta_z(t)$ is the given relative and time-dependent angular coordinate of nm (position angle).

The first total time derivatives of $\mathbf{r}_{0n}$ and $\mathbf{r}_{nm}$ are respectively

$$\mathbf{r}_{0n}^* = \dot{x}_{0n}\mathbf{i} + \dot{y}_{0n}\mathbf{j} + x_{0n}\overset{0}{\cancel{\mathbf{i}}} + y_{0n}\overset{0}{\cancel{\mathbf{j}}} = \dot{x}_{0n}\mathbf{i} + \dot{y}_{0n}\mathbf{j} = \dot{\mathbf{r}}_{0n} \qquad (2)$$

$$\begin{aligned}\mathbf{r}_{nm}^* &= r_{nm}[(-\dot{\theta}_z\sin\theta_z)\mathbf{i} + (\dot{\theta}_z\cos\theta_z)\mathbf{j}] + r_{nm}[(\cos\theta_z)\overset{0}{\cancel{\mathbf{i}}} + (\sin\theta_z)\overset{0}{\cancel{\mathbf{j}}}]\\ &= -\dot{\theta}_z y_{nm}\mathbf{i} + \dot{\theta}_z x_{nm}\mathbf{j} = \boldsymbol{\Omega} \times \mathbf{r}_{nm} \end{aligned} \qquad (3)$$

where $\boldsymbol{\Omega} = \dot{\theta}_z\mathbf{k}$.   In terms of (2) and (3), the velocity vector is

$$\mathbf{v}_{0m} = \mathbf{r}_{0m}^* = \mathbf{r}_{0n}^* + \mathbf{r}_{nm}^* = \dot{\mathbf{r}}_{0n} + \boldsymbol{\Omega} \times \mathbf{r}_{nm} \qquad (4)$$

Equation (4) can be deduced from (6-14), where $n = c$, $\dot{\mathbf{r}}_{nm} = 0$ (condition of rigidity, $r_{nm} = $ constant) and ω is replaced by $\boldsymbol{\Omega}$.

7.2   Derive the acceleration vector equation (7-3) of plane motion of the rigid body of Fig. P-7.1 referred to the stationary axes X_0^0, Y_0^0, Z_0^0.   Given: $\mathbf{r}_{0n}$, $\mathbf{r}_{nm}$, $\boldsymbol{\Omega}$.

By definition, the acceleration vector is

$$\mathbf{a}_{0m} = \mathbf{v}_{0m}^* = \mathbf{r}_{0m}^{**} = \mathbf{r}_{0n}^{**} + \mathbf{r}_{nm}^{**} \qquad (1)$$

From (2) of Problem 7.1,

$$\mathbf{r}_{0n}^{**} = \ddot{x}_{0n}\mathbf{i} + \ddot{y}_{0n}\mathbf{j} + \dot{x}_{0n}\overset{0}{\cancel{\mathbf{i}}} + \dot{y}_{0n}\overset{0}{\cancel{\mathbf{j}}} = \ddot{\mathbf{r}}_{0n} \qquad (2)$$

From (3) of Problem 7.1,

$$\mathbf{r}_{nm}^{**} = \mathbf{\Omega} \times \mathbf{r}_{nm}^{*} + \mathbf{\Omega}^{*} \times \mathbf{r}_{nm} = \mathbf{\Omega} \times (\mathbf{\Omega} \times \mathbf{r}_{nm}) + \dot{\mathbf{\Omega}} \times \mathbf{r}_{nm} \qquad (3)$$

where $\mathbf{\Omega} = \dot{\Omega}_z \mathbf{k} = \ddot{\theta}_z \mathbf{k}$.

In terms of (2) and (3), the acceleration vector (1) is

$$\mathbf{a}_{0m} = \mathbf{v}_{0m}^{*} = \mathbf{r}_{0m}^{**} = \ddot{\mathbf{r}}_{0n} + \dot{\mathbf{\Omega}} \times \mathbf{r}_{nm} + \mathbf{\Omega} \times (\mathbf{\Omega} \times \mathbf{r}_{nm}) \qquad (4)$$

Equation (4) can be deduced from (6-15), where $n = c$, $\dot{\mathbf{r}}_{nm} = 0$, $\ddot{\mathbf{r}}_{nm} = 0$ (condition of rigidity, $r_{nm} = $ constant) and ω is replaced by $\mathbf{\Omega}$.

7.3 Interpret physically and show geometrically the velocity and acceleration vectors of Problems 7.1 and 7.2.

Since the motion takes place in a plane, all linear vectors are located in this plane.

The velocity vector $\dot{\mathbf{r}}_{0n}$ defines the translatory velocity of the lamina and is tangent to the path of n.

The velocity vector $\mathbf{\Omega} \times \mathbf{r}_{nm}$ defines the tangential velocity of the lamina and is tangential to the circle of radius r_{nm}.

The acceleration vector $\ddot{\mathbf{r}}_{0n}$ defines the translatory acceleration of the lamina and in rectilinear translation is collinear to the path and in curvilinear translation deviates from the tangent of path.

The radial acceleration vector $\mathbf{\Omega} \times (\mathbf{\Omega} \times \mathbf{r}_{nm})$ defines the centripetal acceleration of the lamina and is directed from m toward n.

The tangential acceleration vector $\dot{\mathbf{\Omega}} \times \mathbf{r}_{nm}$ defines the tangential acceleration of the lamina and is tangential to the circle of radius r_{nm}.

The geometrical representation of these vectors is shown in Fig. P-7.3a, b.

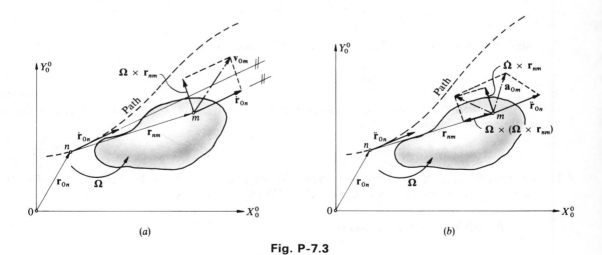

Fig. P-7.3

ABSOLUTE MOTION—APPLICATIONS

7.4 A wheel of radius $R = 10$ in. rolls without slipping with angular speed $\dot{\theta}_z = -1$ rad/sec. Find the velocity and acceleration of the point m on the circumference of the wheel (Fig. P-7.4).

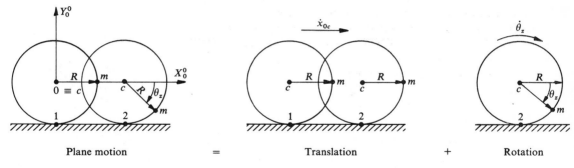

Fig. P-7.4

Since $\dot\theta_z = -1$ rad/sec, the position angle of m at t is $\theta_z = -t$ rad and the position vector of m with respect to the fixed origin 0 is

$$\mathbf{r}_{0m} = \mathbf{r}_{0c} + \mathbf{r}_{cm} = -\theta_z R\mathbf{i} + (R\cos\theta_z)\mathbf{i} + (R\sin\theta_z)\mathbf{j} = 10(t + \cos t)\mathbf{i} - (10\sin t)\mathbf{j}$$

As the unit vectors $\mathbf{i}$, $\mathbf{j}$ are stationary, the velocity and acceleration vectors are directly the respective time derivatives of $\mathbf{r}_{0m}$:

$$\mathbf{v}_{0m} = \mathbf{r}^*_{0m} = \dot{\mathbf{r}}_{0m} = 10(1 - \sin t)\mathbf{i} - (10\cos t)\mathbf{j}$$
$$\mathbf{a}_{0m} = \mathbf{r}^{**}_{0m} = \ddot{\mathbf{r}}_{0m} = (-10\cos t)\mathbf{i} + (10\sin t)\mathbf{j}$$

7.5   Using the vector equations (7-2) and (7-3), check the results of Problem 7.4.

By (7-2),

$$\mathbf{v}_{0m} = \mathbf{r}^*_{0m} = \dot{\mathbf{r}}_{0c} + \mathbf{\Omega} \times \mathbf{r}_{cm} = 10\mathbf{i} + \begin{vmatrix} \mathbf{i} & 0 & 10\cos t \\ \mathbf{j} & 0 & -10\sin t \\ \mathbf{k} & -1 & 0 \end{vmatrix}$$

$$= 10\mathbf{i} - (10\sin t)\mathbf{i} - (10\cos t)\mathbf{j}$$

By (7-3),

$$\mathbf{a}_{0m} = \mathbf{r}^{**}_{0m} = \ddot{\mathbf{r}}_{0c}^{\,0} + \dot{\mathbf{\Omega}}^{\,0} \times \mathbf{r}_{cm} + \mathbf{\Omega} \times (\mathbf{\Omega} \times \mathbf{r}_{cm})$$

$$= \begin{vmatrix} \mathbf{i} & 0 & -10\sin t \\ \mathbf{j} & 0 & 10\cos t \\ \mathbf{k} & -1 & 0 \end{vmatrix} = (-10\cos t)\mathbf{i} + (10\sin t)\mathbf{j}$$

Note that in cases where x_{cm}, y_{cm} are long algebraic expressions, the transpose of the determinant of $\mathbf{\Omega} \times \mathbf{r}_{cm}$ allows a better space utilization, i.e.

$$\begin{vmatrix} \mathbf{i} & \mathbf{j} & \mathbf{k} \\ 0 & 0 & -1 \\ 10\cos t & -10\sin t & 0 \end{vmatrix} = \begin{vmatrix} \mathbf{i} & 0 & 10\cos t \\ \mathbf{j} & 0 & -10\sin t \\ \mathbf{k} & -1 & 0 \end{vmatrix}$$

7.6 Find the angular velocity of the rigid bar $\overline{nm}$ at $t = 5$ sec if n moves with constant velocity $\mathbf{v}$ as shown in Fig. P-7.6.   Given: $a = 20$ ft, $b = 40$ ft, $v = 2$ ft/sec.

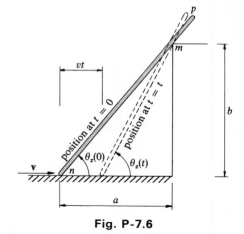

At t, the position angle of $\overline{nm}$ is

$$\theta_z = \theta_z(t) = \cot^{-1}\frac{a - vt}{b}$$

The angular velocity is then

$$\dot{\theta}_z = \frac{d}{dt}\left(\cot^{-1}\frac{a - vt}{b}\right)$$

$$= \frac{v/b}{1 + [(a - vt)/b]^2} = 0.047 \text{ rad/sec}$$

Fig. P-7.6

7.7 Find the angular velocity and acceleration of the bar $\overline{nm}$ of Fig. P-7.7 if n moves horizontally with constant linear velocity $\mathbf{v}_{0n} = -v\mathbf{i}$ along the floor and m slides vertically along the wall. Given: l, a, b, v.

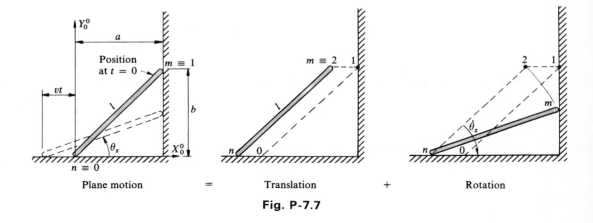

Fig. P-7.7

By inspection (Fig. P-7.7), the position angle is

$$\theta_z = \cos^{-1}\frac{a + vt}{l} \tag{1}$$

where vt is the linear displacement of n at time t.

The first time derivative of (1) is

$$\dot{\theta}_z = \frac{d}{dt}\left(\cos^{-1}\frac{a + vt}{l}\right) = -\frac{v/l}{\sqrt{1 - [(a + vt)/l]^2}} = -\frac{v}{l\sin\theta_z} \tag{2}$$

and the angular velocity is

$$\boldsymbol{\Omega} = \dot{\theta}_z \mathbf{k} = -\frac{v}{l \sin \theta_z} \mathbf{k} \tag{3}$$

The second time derivative of (1) is

$$\ddot{\theta}_z = \frac{d}{dt}\left(-\frac{v}{l \sin \theta_z}\right) = -\frac{v^2 \cos \theta_z}{l^2 \sin^3 \theta_z} \tag{4}$$

and the angular acceleration is

$$\dot{\boldsymbol{\Omega}} = \ddot{\theta}_z \mathbf{k} = -\frac{v^2 \cos \theta_z}{l^2 \sin^3 \theta_z} \mathbf{k} \tag{5}$$

7.8   Using the results of Problem 7.7, compute the velocity and acceleration of the end m of the bar of Fig. P-7.7.

Referring to Fig. P-7.7,

$$\mathbf{r}_{Om} = -vt\mathbf{i} + (l \cos \theta_z)\mathbf{i} + (l \sin \theta_z)\mathbf{j} \tag{1}$$
$$\mathbf{r}_{Om}^* = \dot{\mathbf{r}}_{Om} = -v\mathbf{i} + l\dot{\theta}_z[(-\sin \theta_z)\mathbf{i} + (\cos \theta_z)\mathbf{j}] \tag{2}$$
$$\mathbf{r}_{Om}^{**} = \ddot{\mathbf{r}}_{Om} = l\ddot{\theta}_z[(-\sin \theta_z)\mathbf{i} + (\cos \theta_z)\mathbf{j}] + l\dot{\theta}_z^2[(-\cos \theta_z)\mathbf{i} - (\sin \theta_z)\mathbf{j}] \tag{3}$$

In terms of (2) and (4) of Problem 7.7, the velocity (2) of the end m is

$$\mathbf{v}_{Om} = \dot{\mathbf{r}}_{Om} = -v\mathbf{i} + l\left(-\frac{v}{l \sin \theta_z}\right)(-\sin \theta_z)\mathbf{i} + l\left(-\frac{v}{l \sin \theta_z}\right)\cos \theta_z \mathbf{j} = (-v \cot \theta_z)\mathbf{j} \tag{4}$$

Although the calculation of $\mathbf{a}_{Om}$ may be accomplished by means of (3), the direct differentiation of (4) is more convenient.   Hence

$$\mathbf{a}_{Om} = \mathbf{v}_{Om}^* = \dot{\mathbf{v}}_{Om} = \frac{d}{dt}[(-v \cot \theta_z)\mathbf{j}] = -v\left(-\frac{\dot{\theta}_z}{\sin^2 \theta_z}\right)\mathbf{j} = -\frac{v^2}{l \sin^3 \theta_z}\mathbf{j} \tag{5}$$

If vector or matrix notation is used, the geometric interpretation of (4) and (5) is self-evident and rarely necessary.   For completeness, the velocity and acceleration triangles are shown in Fig. P-7.8a, b respectively.

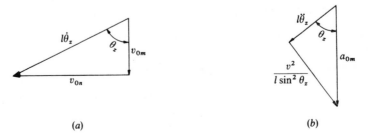

(a)   (b)

Fig. P-7.8

INSTANTANEOUS CENTER

7.9 The double gear of Fig. P-7.9 moves with constant linear velocity $\mathbf{v}_{0c} = v\mathbf{i}$ on the stationary lower rack. Find the angular velocity of the gear and the linear velocity of the upper rack. Given: R_1, R_2.

The point of contact of the gear and lower rack is the instantaneous center e.
By (7-6),

$$y_{ce} = x_{0c}^*/\dot\theta_z = \dot x_{0c}/\dot\theta_z \tag{1}$$

where $y_{ce} = -R_1$, $\dot x_{0c} = v$. The angular velocity of the gear is then $\Omega = \dot\theta_z = -v/R_1$.
With $\dot\theta_z$ known, the velocity of the upper rack is computed from (7-6), given in this case as

$$y_{me} = x_{0m}^*/\dot\theta_z = \dot x_{0m}/\dot\theta_z$$

and is

$$\dot x_{0m} = y_{me}\dot\theta_z\mathbf{i} = -(R_1+R_2)(-v/R_1)\mathbf{i} = [v(R_1+R_2)/R_1]\mathbf{i}$$

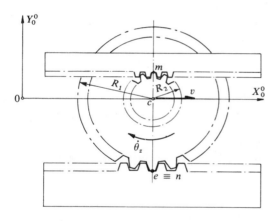

Fig. P-7.9

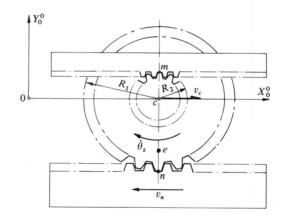

Fig. P-7.10

7.10 Consider Problem 7.9 with the gear moving with constant velocity $\mathbf{v}_{0c} = v_c\mathbf{i}$ and the lower rack moving with another constant velocity $\mathbf{v}_{0n} = -v_n\mathbf{i}$ (Fig. P-7.10).

By definition of instantaneous center [equations (7-6)],

$$y_{ne} = \dot x_{0n}/\dot\theta_z, \qquad y_{ce} = \dot x_{0c}/\dot\theta_z \tag{1}$$

The difference of these two equations gives

$$y_{ne} - y_{ce} = (\dot x_{0n} - \dot x_{0c})/\dot\theta_z \tag{2}$$

from which

$$\dot\theta_z = (\dot x_{0n} - \dot x_{0c})/(y_{ne} - y_{ce}) = (\dot x_{0n} - \dot x_{0c})/(y_{ne} + y_{ec}) = -(v_n + v_c)/R_1 \tag{3}$$

Then the vertical coordinates of e measured from n and c respectively are

$$y_{ne} = \dot{x}_{0n}/\dot{\theta}_z = -v_n/[-(v_n + v_c)/R_1] = v_n R_1/(v_n + v_c) \qquad (4)$$

$$y_{ce} = \dot{x}_{0c}/\dot{\theta}_z = v_c/[-(v_n + v_c)/R_1] = -v_c R_1/(v_n + v_c) \qquad (5)$$

which for $v_n = 0$ must verify the position of e, taken in Problem 7.9 as $y_{ne} = 0$, $y_{ce} = -R_1$.
The velocity of the upper rack is then by (7-6)

$$\mathbf{v}_{0m} = x_{0m}^* \mathbf{i} = y_{me}\dot{\theta}_z \mathbf{i} = (y_{ce} - R_2)[-(v_a + v_c)/R_1]\mathbf{i} \qquad (6)$$

where y_{ce} is given by (5) and $\dot{\theta}_z$ is given by (3).

7.11 For the rigid bar of Problem 7.7, find the location of
the instantaneous center and the equation of the centrode.

By (7-6), the coordinates of the unknown instantaneous center e are

$$x_{me} = -\dot{y}_{0m}/\dot{\theta}_z, \qquad y_{me} = \dot{x}_{0m}/\dot{\theta}_z \qquad (1)$$

where from Problem 7.7, $\dot{\theta}_z = -v/(l \sin \theta_z)$; and from
Problem 7.8, $\dot{x}_{0m} = 0$, $\dot{y}_{0m} = -v \cot \theta_z$. Hence

$$x_{me} = -l \cos \theta_z, \qquad y_{me} = 0 \qquad (2)$$

and with respect to 3,

$$x_{3e} = -l \cos \theta_z, \qquad y_{3e} = l \sin \theta_z \qquad (3)$$

Eliminating θ_z in (3), $x_{3e}^2 + y_{3e}^2 = l^2$. Thus the
centrode is a circle of radius l about 3 (Fig. P-7.11).

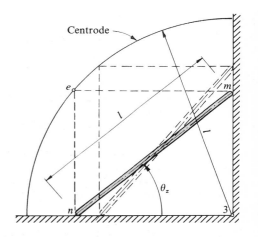

Fig. P-7.11

RELATIVE PLANE MOTION—DERIVATIONS

7.12 Derive the velocity and acceleration vector equations
(7-11) and (7-12) of plane motion of the body whose
rotation coincides with the rotation of the moving
axes X_n^l, Y_n^l, Z_n^l, and distance $\overline{nm}$ changes with time
(Fig. P-7.12).   Given: $\mathbf{r}_{0n}$, $\mathbf{r}_{nm}$, $\boldsymbol{\omega} = \boldsymbol{\Omega}$, where $\boldsymbol{\omega}$
= angular velocity of the l-system, and $\boldsymbol{\Omega}$ = angular
velocity of the rigid body.

The background of the procedure of derivation of
these equations of motion is the same as that of Problem
7.1, but the rotation of the l-system and the change in the
distance $\overline{nm}$ introduce new terms in these equations.

The position vector of m referred to the stationary
axes X_0^0, Y_0^0, Z_0^0 and the moving axes X_n^l, Y_n^l, Z_n^l is

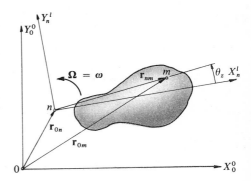

Fig. P-7.12

$$\mathbf{r}_{0m} = \mathbf{r}_{0n} + \mathbf{r}_{nm} = x_{0n}^0 \mathbf{i}^0 + y_{0n}^0 \mathbf{j}^0 + x_{nm}^l \mathbf{i}^l + y_{nm}^l \mathbf{j}^l \qquad (1)$$

where the superscripts 0 and l identify the stationary and the moving axes respectively. Differentiating,

$$\mathbf{r}^*_{0m} = \dot{x}^0_{0n}\mathbf{i}^0 + \dot{y}^0_{0n}\mathbf{j}^0 + \cancel{x^0_{0n}\dot{\mathbf{i}}^0} + \cancel{y^0_{0n}\dot{\mathbf{j}}^0} + \dot{x}^l_{nm}\mathbf{i}^l + \dot{y}^l_{nm}\mathbf{j}^l + x^l_{nm}\dot{\mathbf{i}}^l + y^l_{nm}\dot{\mathbf{j}}^l$$

where

$$\dot{x}^l_{nm}\mathbf{i}^l + \dot{y}^l_{nm}\mathbf{j}^l = \dot{x}^0_{nm}\mathbf{i}^0 + \dot{y}^0_{nm}\mathbf{j}^0 = \dot{\mathbf{r}}_{nm}$$
$$x^l_{nm}\dot{\mathbf{i}}^l + y^l_{nm}\dot{\mathbf{j}}^l = -\dot{\theta}_z y^0_{nm}\mathbf{i}^0 + \dot{\theta}_z x^0_{nm}\mathbf{j}^0 = \boldsymbol{\omega} \times \mathbf{r}_{nm}$$

are known relations.

The velocity vector is then

$$\mathbf{v}_{0m} = \mathbf{r}^*_{0m} = \dot{\mathbf{r}}_{0n} + \dot{\mathbf{r}}_{nm} + \boldsymbol{\omega} \times \mathbf{r}_{nm} \tag{2}$$

The acceleration vector is obtained from (2) by total differentiation as

$$\mathbf{r}^{**}_{0m} = \dot{\mathbf{r}}^*_{0n} + \dot{\mathbf{r}}^*_{nm} + \boldsymbol{\omega} \times \mathbf{r}^*_{nm} + \boldsymbol{\omega}^* \times \mathbf{r}_{nm}$$

where $\dot{\mathbf{r}}^*_{0n} = \ddot{\mathbf{r}}_{0n}$, $\dot{\mathbf{r}}^*_{nm} = \ddot{\mathbf{r}}_{nm} + \boldsymbol{\omega} \times \dot{\mathbf{r}}_{nm}$, $\boldsymbol{\omega} \times \mathbf{r}^*_{nm} = \boldsymbol{\omega} \times (\dot{\mathbf{r}}_{nm} + \boldsymbol{\omega} \times \mathbf{r}_{nm})$, $\boldsymbol{\omega}^* \times \mathbf{r}_{nm} = \dot{\boldsymbol{\omega}} \times \mathbf{r}_{nm}$ are known relations.

The acceleration vector is then

$$\mathbf{a}_{0m} = \mathbf{v}^*_{0m} = \mathbf{r}^{**}_{0m} = \ddot{\mathbf{r}}_{0n} + \ddot{\mathbf{r}}_{nm} + \dot{\boldsymbol{\omega}} \times \mathbf{r}_{nm} + 2\boldsymbol{\omega} \times \dot{\mathbf{r}}_{nm} + \boldsymbol{\omega} \times (\boldsymbol{\omega} \times \mathbf{r}_{nm}) \tag{3}$$

Equations (2) and (3) are formally identical to (6-14) and (6-15) and $\boldsymbol{\omega} = \boldsymbol{\Omega} = \dot{\theta}_z\mathbf{k}$ is the velocity vector of the l-system and of the body.

RELATIVE MOTIONS—APPLICATIONS

7.13 The crank $\overline{0n}$ of the slider-crank mechanism of Fig. P-7.13 has a constant angular velocity $\dot{\theta}_z$. Find the velocity and acceleration of the hinge n and of the block m. Given: a, b, $\dot{\theta}_z$.

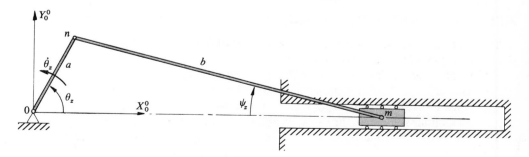

Fig. P-7.13

The vector equations of motion of the hinge n are

$$\mathbf{r}_{0n} = (a\cos\theta_z)\mathbf{i} + (a\sin\theta_z)\mathbf{j}$$
$$\mathbf{v}_{0n} = \dot{\mathbf{r}}_{0n} = (-a\dot{\theta}_z\sin\theta_z)\mathbf{i} + (a\dot{\theta}_z\cos\theta_z)\mathbf{j} \tag{1}$$
$$\mathbf{a}_{0n} = \ddot{\mathbf{r}}_{0n} = (-a\dot{\theta}_z^2\cos\theta_z)\mathbf{i} - (a\dot{\theta}_z^2\sin\theta_z)\mathbf{j}$$

where the terms involving $\ddot{\theta}_z = 0$ are omitted and $r_{0n}^* = \dot{r}_{0n}$, $r_{0n}^{**} = \ddot{r}_{0n}$.
The vector equations of motion of the block m are

$$
\begin{aligned}
\mathbf{r}_{0m} &= (a \cos \theta_z + b \cos \psi_z)\mathbf{i} \\
\mathbf{v}_{0m} = \dot{\mathbf{r}}_{0m} &= -(a\dot{\theta}_z \sin \theta_z + b\dot{\psi}_z \sin \psi_z)\mathbf{i} \\
\mathbf{a}_{0m} = \ddot{\mathbf{r}}_{0m} &= -(a\dot{\theta}_z^2 \cos \theta_z + b\dot{\psi}_z^2 \cos \psi_z + b\ddot{\psi}_z \sin \psi_z)\mathbf{i}
\end{aligned}
\tag{2}
$$

where $\ddot{\theta}_z = 0$ but $\ddot{\psi}_z \neq 0$ and $r_{0m}^* = \dot{r}_{0m}$, $r_{0m}^{**} = \ddot{r}_{0m}$.
By the law of sines in Fig. P-7.13,

$$
\frac{\sin \psi_z}{a} = \frac{\sin \theta_z}{b} \qquad \text{or} \qquad \psi_z = \sin^{-1} \frac{a \sin \theta_z}{b}
\tag{3}
$$

and by differentiating,

$$
\dot{\psi}_z = \frac{a}{b} \frac{\dot{\theta}_z \cos \theta_z}{\cos \psi_z}, \qquad \ddot{\psi}_z = (\dot{\psi}_z - \dot{\theta}_z) \tan \psi_z
\tag{4, 5}
$$

7.14   For the crank position $\theta_z = \pi/4$ in Problem 7.13, find the velocity and acceleration of the hinge n and the block m.   Given: $a = 10$ cm, $b = 30$ cm, $\dot{\theta}_z = 100$ rad/sec.

For $\theta_z = \pi/4$, equations (1) of Problem 7.13 become

$$
\begin{aligned}
\mathbf{r}_{0n} &= (10)(0.707)\mathbf{i} + (10)(0.707)\mathbf{j} = 7.07(\mathbf{i} + \mathbf{j}) \text{ cm} \\
\mathbf{v}_{0n} &= -(10)(100)(0.707)\mathbf{i} + (10)(100)(0.707)\mathbf{j} = -707(\mathbf{i} - \mathbf{j}) \text{ cm/sec} \\
\mathbf{a}_{0n} &= -(10)(100)^2(0.707)\mathbf{i} - (10)(100)^2(0.707)\mathbf{j} = -70,700(\mathbf{i} + \mathbf{j}) \text{ cm/sec}^2
\end{aligned}
$$

For $\theta_z = \pi/4$, equation (3) of Problem 7.13 gives

$$
\psi_z = \sin^{-1} \frac{0.707}{3} = 0.237 \text{ rad}
$$

and by (4) and (5) of the same problem,

$$
\dot{\psi}_z = \frac{(100)(0.707)}{(3)(0.972)} = 24.1 \text{ rad/sec}, \qquad \ddot{\psi}_z = [(24.1)^2 - (100)^2](0.242) = -2279 \text{ rad/sec}^2
$$

In terms of these values, equations (2) of Problem 7.13 yield

$$
\begin{aligned}
\mathbf{r}_{0m} &= [(10)(0.707) + (30)(0.972)]\mathbf{i} = 36.23\mathbf{i} \text{ cm} \\
\mathbf{v}_{0m} &= -[(10)(100)(0.707) + (30)(24.1)(0.235)]\mathbf{i} = -876.9\mathbf{i} \text{ cm/sec} \\
\mathbf{a}_{0m} &= -[(10)(100)^2(0.707) + (30)(24.1)^2(0.972) + (30)(-2279)(0.235)]\mathbf{i} = -71,564\mathbf{i} \text{ cm/sec}^2
\end{aligned}
$$

Although there are several semigraphical methods available for the solution of Problem 7.13, the analytical method presented above is automatic and readily applicable to computer programming.

7.15   The four-hinged bar mechanism of Fig. P-7.15 moves freely in its plane, and in the position shown the instantaneous angular speed and acceleration of the bar $\overline{0n}$ are ω_{0n}, $\dot{\omega}_{0n}$ respectively.   Find the angular speed of bars $\overline{nm}$ and $\overline{mp}$.

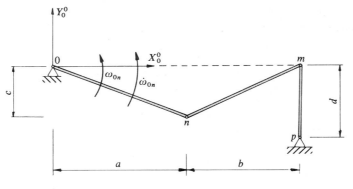

Fig. P-7.15

The velocity vector of the mechanism is

$$\mathbf{v}_{Op} = \boldsymbol{\omega}_{On} \times \mathbf{r}_{On} + \boldsymbol{\omega}_{nm} \times \mathbf{r}_{nm} + \boldsymbol{\omega}_{mp} \times \mathbf{r}_{mp} \qquad (1)$$

where $\boldsymbol{\omega}_{On} = \omega_{On}\mathbf{k}$, $\boldsymbol{\omega}_{nm} = \omega_{nm}\mathbf{k}$, $\boldsymbol{\omega}_{mp} = \omega_{mp}\mathbf{k}$ and $\mathbf{r}_{On} = a\mathbf{i} - c\mathbf{j}$, $\mathbf{r}_{nm} = b\mathbf{i} + c\mathbf{j}$, $\mathbf{r}_{mp} = -d\mathbf{j}$. Since 0 and p are stationary hinges, $\mathbf{v}_{Op} = 0$ and

$$\begin{vmatrix} \mathbf{i} & \mathbf{j} & \mathbf{k} \\ 0 & 0 & \omega_{On} \\ a & -c & 0 \end{vmatrix} + \begin{vmatrix} \mathbf{i} & \mathbf{j} & \mathbf{k} \\ 0 & 0 & \omega_{nm} \\ b & c & 0 \end{vmatrix} + \begin{vmatrix} \mathbf{i} & \mathbf{j} & \mathbf{k} \\ 0 & 0 & \omega_{mp} \\ 0 & -d & 0 \end{vmatrix} = 0$$

or

$$\omega_{On}c\mathbf{i} + \omega_{On}a\mathbf{j} - \omega_{nm}c\mathbf{i} + \omega_{nm}b\mathbf{j} + \omega_{np}\,d\mathbf{i} = 0 \qquad (2)$$

Vector equation (2) yields two algebraic equations,

$$\omega_{On}c - \omega_{nm}c + \omega_{np}\,d = 0, \qquad \omega_{On}a + \omega_{nm}b = 0 \qquad (3)$$

from which

$$\omega_{nm} = -a\omega_{On}/b, \qquad \omega_{np} = -c\omega_{On}(1 + a/b)/d$$

For $a = 10\,\text{cm}$, $b = 30\,\text{cm}$, $c = d = 10\,\text{cm}$, and $\omega_{On} = 3\,\text{rad/sec}$, the angular speeds of $\overline{nm}$ and $\overline{mp}$ are respectively

$$\omega_{nm} = -(10)(3)/30 = -1\,\text{rad/sec}, \qquad \omega_{mp} = -(10)(3)(1 + 1/3)/10 = -4\,\text{rad/sec}$$

7.16 Using the given data and results of Problem 7.15, find the angular accelerations of bars $\overline{nm}$ and $\overline{mp}$.

The acceleration vector of the mechanism is

$$\mathbf{a}_{Op} = \dot{\boldsymbol{\omega}}_{On} \times \mathbf{r}_{On} + \boldsymbol{\omega}_{On} \times (\boldsymbol{\omega}_{On} \times \mathbf{r}_{On}) + \dot{\boldsymbol{\omega}}_{nm} \times \mathbf{r}_{nm} + \boldsymbol{\omega}_{nm} \times (\boldsymbol{\omega}_{nm} \times \mathbf{r}_{nm})$$
$$+ \dot{\boldsymbol{\omega}}_{mp} \times \mathbf{r}_{mp} + \boldsymbol{\omega}_{mp} \times (\boldsymbol{\omega}_{mp} \times \mathbf{r}_{mp}) \qquad (1)$$

where

$$\omega_{0n} = \omega_{0n}\mathbf{k}, \qquad \omega_{nm} = \omega_{nm}\mathbf{k}, \qquad \omega_{mp} = \omega_{mp}\mathbf{k}$$
$$\dot{\omega}_{0n} = \dot{\omega}_{0n}\mathbf{k}, \qquad \dot{\omega}_{nm} = \dot{\omega}_{nm}\mathbf{k}, \qquad \dot{\omega}_{mp} = \dot{\omega}_{mp}\mathbf{k}$$

and

$$\mathbf{r}_{0n} = a\mathbf{i} - c\mathbf{j}, \qquad \mathbf{r}_{nm} = b\mathbf{i} + c\mathbf{j}, \qquad \mathbf{r}_{mp} = -d\mathbf{j}$$

Since 0 and p are stationary hinges, $\mathbf{a}_{0p} = 0$ and

$$\begin{vmatrix} \mathbf{i} & \mathbf{j} & \mathbf{k} \\ 0 & 0 & \dot{\omega}_{0n} \\ a & -c & 0 \end{vmatrix} + \begin{vmatrix} \mathbf{i} & \mathbf{j} & \mathbf{k} \\ 0 & 0 & \dot{\omega}_{nm} \\ b & c & 0 \end{vmatrix} + \begin{vmatrix} \mathbf{i} & \mathbf{j} & \mathbf{k} \\ 0 & 0 & \dot{\omega}_{mp} \\ 0 & -d & 0 \end{vmatrix}$$

$$+ \begin{vmatrix} \mathbf{i} & \mathbf{j} & \mathbf{k} \\ 0 & 0 & \omega_{0n} \\ \omega_{0n}c & \omega_{0n}a & 0 \end{vmatrix} + \begin{vmatrix} \mathbf{i} & \mathbf{j} & \mathbf{k} \\ 0 & 0 & \omega_{nm} \\ -\omega_{nm}c & \omega_{nm}b & 0 \end{vmatrix} + \begin{vmatrix} \mathbf{i} & \mathbf{j} & \mathbf{k} \\ 0 & 0 & \omega_{mp} \\ \omega_{mp}d & 0 & 0 \end{vmatrix} = 0$$

or

$$(\dot{\omega}_{0n}c - \dot{\omega}_{nm}c + \dot{\omega}_{mp}d - \omega_{0n}^2 a - \omega_{nm}^2 b)\mathbf{i} + (\dot{\omega}_{0n}a + \dot{\omega}_{nm}b + \omega_{0n}^2 c - \omega_{nm}^2 c + \omega_{mp}^2 d)\mathbf{j} = 0 \qquad (2)$$

Vector equation (2) yields two algebraic equations, in which ω_{0n}, $\dot{\omega}_{0n}$ are given and ω_{nm}, ω_{mp} are computed values (3) in Problem 7.15.

For $a = 10$ cm, $b = 30$ cm, $c = d = 10$ cm, $\omega_{0n} = 3$ rad/sec, $\omega_{nm} = -1$ rad/sec, $\omega_{mp} = -4$ rad/sec, and $\dot{\omega}_{0n} = 10$ rad/sec^2, the angular accelerations of $\overline{nm}$ and $\overline{mp}$, computed in reverse order from (2), are

$$\dot{\omega}_{nm} = -(\dot{\omega}_{0n}a + \omega_{0n}^2 c - \omega_{nm}^2 c + \omega_{mp}^2 d)/b$$
$$= -[(10)(10) + (3)^2(10) - (-1)^2(10) + (-4)^2(10)]/30 = -0.66 \text{ rad/sec}^2$$

$$\dot{\omega}_{mp} = -(\dot{\omega}_{0n}c + \dot{\omega}_{nm}d - \omega_{0n}^2 d - \omega_{nm}^2 b)/d$$
$$= -[(10)(10) + (-0.66)(10) - (3)^2(10) - (-1)^2(30)]/10 = 2.66 \text{ rad/sec}^2$$

7.17   Using the matrix equations and the results of Problem 7.15, determine the velocity vectors of the hinges n, m, p of the mechanism of Fig. P-7.15.   Given: $a = 10$ cm, $b = 30$ cm, $c = d = 10$ cm, $\omega_{0n} = 3$ rad/sec, $\omega_{nm} = -1$ rad/sec, $\omega_{mp} = -4$ rad/sec.

By (7-14), the velocity vectors of n, m and p in the X_0^0, Y_0^0 axes are respectively

$$\underbrace{\begin{bmatrix} x_{0n}^{0*} \\ y_{0n}^{0*} \end{bmatrix}}_{[s_{0n}^{0*}]} = \underbrace{\begin{bmatrix} 0 & -3 \\ 3 & 0 \end{bmatrix}}_{[\Gamma_{0n}]} \underbrace{\begin{bmatrix} 10 \\ -10 \end{bmatrix}}_{[s_{0n}^0]} = \begin{bmatrix} 30 \\ 30 \end{bmatrix} \text{ cm/sec} \qquad (1)$$

$$\underbrace{\begin{bmatrix} x_{0m}^{0*} \\ y_{0m}^{0*} \end{bmatrix}}_{[s_{0m}^{0*}]} = \underbrace{\begin{bmatrix} 30 \\ 30 \end{bmatrix}}_{[s_{0n}^{0*}]} + \underbrace{\begin{bmatrix} 0 & 1 \\ -1 & 0 \end{bmatrix}}_{[\Gamma_{nm}]} \underbrace{\begin{bmatrix} 30 \\ 10 \end{bmatrix}}_{[s_{nm}^0]} = \begin{bmatrix} 40 \\ 0 \end{bmatrix} \text{ cm/sec} \qquad (2)$$

$$\underbrace{\begin{bmatrix} x_{0p}^{0*} \\ y_{0p}^{0*} \end{bmatrix}}_{[s_{0p}^{0*}]} = \underbrace{\begin{bmatrix} 40 \\ 0 \end{bmatrix}}_{[s_{0m}^{0*}]} + \underbrace{\begin{bmatrix} 0 & 4 \\ -4 & 0 \end{bmatrix}}_{[\Gamma_{mp}]} \underbrace{\begin{bmatrix} 0 \\ -10 \end{bmatrix}}_{[s_{mp}^{0}]} = \begin{bmatrix} 0 \\ 0 \end{bmatrix} \text{ cm/sec} \qquad (3)$$

where (3) is the matrix equivalent of (2) of Problem 7.15, and $[\dot{s}_{0n}^{0}]$, $[\dot{s}_{nm}^{0}]$, $[\dot{s}_{mp}^{0}]$ are zero since the bars are rigid.

It should be noted that (3) written as

$$[s_{0p}^{0*}] = \underbrace{[\Gamma_{0n}]\,[s_{0n}^{0}]}_{\boldsymbol{\omega}_{0n} \times \mathbf{r}_{0n}} + \underbrace{[\Gamma_{nm}]\,[s_{nm}^{0}]}_{\boldsymbol{\omega}_{nm} \times \mathbf{r}_{nm}} + \underbrace{[\Gamma_{mp}]\,[s_{mp}^{0}]}_{\boldsymbol{\omega}_{mp} \times \mathbf{r}_{mp}} = [0] \qquad (4)$$

may also be used for the calculation of ω_{nm} and ω_{mp}.

7.18 Using the matrix equations and the results of Problems 7.15 and 7.16, determine the acceleration vectors of the hinges n, m, p of the mechanism of Fig. P-7.15. Given: $a = 10$ cm, $b = 30$ cm, $c = d = 10$ cm, $\omega_{0n} = 3$ rad/sec, $\dot{\omega}_{0n} = 10$ rad/sec^2, $\omega_{nm} = -1$ rad/sec, $\dot{\omega}_{nm} = -0.66$ rad/sec^2, $\omega_{mp} = -4$ rad/sec, $\dot{\omega}_{mp} = 2.66$ rad/sec^2.

By (7-15), the acceleration vectors of n, m and p in the X_0^0, Y_0^0 axes are respectively

$$\underbrace{\begin{bmatrix} x_{0n}^{**} \\ y_{0n}^{**} \end{bmatrix}}_{[s_{0n}^{0**}]} = \underbrace{\begin{bmatrix} -(3)^2 & -10 \\ 10 & -(3)^2 \end{bmatrix}}_{[\Delta_{0n}]} \underbrace{\begin{bmatrix} 10 \\ -10 \end{bmatrix}}_{[s_{0n}^{0}]} = \begin{bmatrix} 10 \\ 190 \end{bmatrix} \text{ cm/sec}^2 \qquad (1)$$

$$\underbrace{\begin{bmatrix} x_{0m}^{**} \\ y_{0m}^{**} \end{bmatrix}}_{[s_{0m}^{0**}]} = \underbrace{\begin{bmatrix} 10 \\ 190 \end{bmatrix}}_{[s_{0n}^{0**}]} + \underbrace{\begin{bmatrix} -(-1)^2 & -(-0.66) \\ -0.66 & -(1)^2 \end{bmatrix}}_{[\Delta_{nm}]} \underbrace{\begin{bmatrix} 30 \\ 10 \end{bmatrix}}_{[s_{nm}^{0}]} = \begin{bmatrix} -26.66 \\ 160 \end{bmatrix} \text{ cm/sec}^2 \qquad (2)$$

$$\underbrace{\begin{bmatrix} x_{0p}^{**} \\ y_{0p}^{**} \end{bmatrix}}_{[s_{0p}^{0**}]} = \underbrace{\begin{bmatrix} -26.66 \\ 160 \end{bmatrix}}_{[s_{0m}^{0**}]} + \underbrace{\begin{bmatrix} -(-4)^2 & -2.66 \\ 2.66 & -(-4)^2 \end{bmatrix}}_{[\Delta_{mp}]} \underbrace{\begin{bmatrix} 0 \\ -10 \end{bmatrix}}_{[s_{mp}^{0}]} = \begin{bmatrix} 0 \\ 0 \end{bmatrix} \text{ cm/sec}^2 \qquad (3)$$

where (3) is the matrix equivalent of (2) of Problem 7.16, and $[\ddot{s}_{0n}^{0}]$, $[\ddot{s}_{nm}^{0}]$, $[\ddot{s}_{mp}^{0}]$ are zero since the bars are rigid.

It should be noted that (3) written as

$$[s_{0p}^{0**}] = \underbrace{[\Delta_{0n}]\,[s_{0n}^{0}]}_{\boldsymbol{\omega}_{0n} \times (\boldsymbol{\omega}_{0n} \times \mathbf{r}_{0n})} + \underbrace{[\Delta_{nm}]\,[s_{nm}^{0}]}_{\boldsymbol{\omega}_{nm} \times (\boldsymbol{\omega}_{nm} \times \mathbf{r}_{nm})} + \underbrace{[\Delta_{mp}]\,[s_{mp}^{0}]}_{\boldsymbol{\omega}_{mp} \times (\boldsymbol{\omega}_{mp} \times \mathbf{r}_{mp})} = [0] \qquad (4)$$

may also be used for the calculation of $\dot{\omega}_{nm}$ and $\dot{\omega}_{mp}$.

7.19 The rigid arm $\overline{nm}$ of the slider mechanism of Fig. P-7.19 has a given angular velocity $\boldsymbol{\omega} = \dot{\theta}_z\mathbf{k}$. Find the velocity matrix equation of the sliding block m. Given: $a, \theta_z, \dot{\theta}_z$.

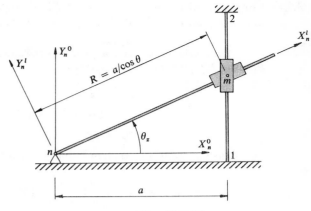

Fig. P-7.19

By (7-13), the position vector of m in the l-system is

$$[s^l_{nm}] = \begin{bmatrix} x^l_{nm} \\ y^l_{nm} \end{bmatrix} = \begin{bmatrix} \dfrac{a}{\cos\theta_z} \\ 0 \end{bmatrix} \qquad (1)$$

By (7-14), the velocity vector of m in the same system is

$$[v^l_{nm}] = \begin{bmatrix} x^{l*}_{nm} \\ y^{l*}_{nm} \end{bmatrix} = \begin{bmatrix} \dfrac{a\dot\theta_z \sin\theta_z}{\cos^2\theta_z} \\ 0 \end{bmatrix} + \begin{bmatrix} 0 & -\dot\theta_z \\ \dot\theta_z & 0 \end{bmatrix} \begin{bmatrix} \dfrac{a}{\cos\theta_z} \\ 0 \end{bmatrix} = \begin{bmatrix} \dfrac{a\dot\theta_z \sin\theta_z}{\cos^2\theta_z} \\ \dfrac{a\dot\theta_z \cos\theta_z}{\cos^2\theta_z} \end{bmatrix} \qquad (2)$$

which can be written in the 0-system as

$$[v^0_{nm}] = [\pi^{0l}][v^l_{nm}] = \begin{bmatrix} \cos\theta_z & -\sin\theta_z \\ \sin\theta_z & \cos\theta_z \end{bmatrix} \begin{bmatrix} \dfrac{a\dot\theta_z \sin\theta_z}{\cos^2\theta_z} \\ \dfrac{a\dot\theta_z \cos\theta_z}{\cos^2\theta_z} \end{bmatrix} = \begin{bmatrix} 0 \\ \dfrac{a\dot\theta_z}{\cos^2\theta_z} \end{bmatrix} \qquad (3)$$

7.20 For the slider mechanism of Fig. P-7.19 defined in Problem 7.19, find the velocity vector of the sliding block m. Given: $a, \theta_z, \dot{\theta}_z$.

The position vector of m in the X^l_n, Y^l_n axes is

$$\mathbf{r}_{nm} = \frac{a}{\cos\theta_z}\,\mathbf{i}^l \qquad (1)$$

and the velocity vector of m in the same axes is

$$\mathbf{v}_{nm} = \mathbf{r}^*_{nm} = \dot{\mathbf{r}}_{nm} + \boldsymbol{\omega}\times\mathbf{r}_{nm} = \frac{a\dot\theta_z \sin\theta_z}{\cos^2\theta_z}\,\mathbf{i}^l + (\dot\theta_z\mathbf{k}^l)\times\left(\frac{a}{\cos\theta_z}\,\mathbf{i}^l\right)$$

$$= \frac{a\dot\theta_z}{\cos^2\theta_z}[(\sin\theta_z)\mathbf{i}^l + (\cos\theta_z)\mathbf{j}^l] \qquad (2)$$

Since $\mathbf{i}^l = \mathbf{i}^0\cos\theta_z + \mathbf{j}^0\sin\theta_z$, $\mathbf{j}^l = -\mathbf{i}^0\sin\theta_z + \mathbf{j}^0\cos\theta_z$, equation (3) in the X^0_n, Y^0_n axes becomes

$$\mathbf{v}_{nm} = \frac{a\dot\theta_z}{\cos^2\theta_z}\,\mathbf{j}^0 \qquad (3)$$

which is the vector equivalent of the matrix equation (2) of Problem 7.19.

7.21   For the slider mechanism of Fig. P-7.19 defined in Problem 7.19, find the acceleration vector and matrix equation of the sliding block m.   Given: a, θ_z, $\dot{\theta}_z$, $\ddot{\theta}_z$.

The acceleration vector $\mathbf{a}_{nm}$ can be determined by (7-15), but in this case the time derivative of (3) of Problem 7.19 gives the desired vector as

$$[a^0_{nm}] = [v^{0*}_{nm}] = \begin{bmatrix} 0 \\ \dfrac{a\ddot{\theta}_z \cos\theta_z + 2a\dot{\theta}^2_z \sin\theta_z}{\cos^3\theta_z} \end{bmatrix}$$

The time derivative of (3) of Problem 7.20 is identical:

$$\mathbf{a}_{nm} = \mathbf{v}^*_{nm} = \left[\frac{d}{dt}\left(\frac{a\dot{\theta}_z}{\cos^2\theta_z}\right)\right]\mathbf{j}^0 + \frac{a\dot{\theta}_z}{\cos^2\theta_z}\dot{\mathbf{j}}^{0} = \frac{a(\ddot{\theta}_z \cos\theta_z + 2\dot{\theta}^2_z \sin\theta_z)}{\cos^3\theta_z}\mathbf{j}^0$$

Comparison of the calculations involved in Problems 7.19, 7.20 and 7.21 shows the affinity of the matrix and vector solutions of this problem.

Problems

ABSOLUTE MOTION—DERIVATIONS

7.22   Derive the velocity vector equation (7-2) of plane translation of the rigid body of Fig. P-7.1 referred to the stationary axes X^0_0, Y^0_0, Z^0_0.   Given: $\mathbf{r}_{On}$, $\mathbf{r}_{nm}$.

7.23   Derive the velocity vector equation (7-2) of plane rotation of the rigid body of Fig. P-7.1 referred to the stationary axes X^0_0, Y^0_0, Z^0_0.   Given: $\mathbf{r}_{On}$, $\mathbf{r}_{nm}$, $\boldsymbol{\Omega}$.

7.24   Derive the acceleration vector equation (7-3) of plane translation of the rigid body of Fig. P-7.1 referred to the stationary axes X^0_0, Y^0_0, Z^0_0.   Given: $\mathbf{r}_{On}$, $\mathbf{r}_{nm}$.

7.25   Derive the acceleration vector equation (7-3) of plane rotation of the rigid body of Fig. P-7.1 referred to the stationary axes X^0_0, Y^0_0, Z^0_0.   Given: $\mathbf{r}_{On}$, $\mathbf{r}_{nm}$, $\boldsymbol{\Omega}$.

7.26   Derive the velocity and acceleration matrix equations (7-8) and (7-9) of plane translation of the rigid body of Fig. P-7.1 referred to the stationary axes X^0_0, Y^0_0, Z^0_0.   Given: $[s^0_{On}]$, $[s^0_{nm}]$.

7.27   Derive the velocity and acceleration matrix equations (7-8) and (7-9) of plane rotation of the rigid body of Fig. P-7.1 referred to the stationary axes X^0_0, Y^0_0, Z^0_0.   Given: $[s^0_{On}]$, $[s^0_{nm}]$, θ_z, $\dot{\theta}_z$, $\ddot{\theta}_z$.

ABSOLUTE MOTION—APPLICATIONS

7.28   The circular cylinder of radius R_1 rolls without slipping with angular velocity $\boldsymbol{\Omega}$ and angular acceleration $\dot{\boldsymbol{\Omega}}$ along the circular cylindrical surface of radius R_2 as shown in Fig. P-7.28.   Find the velocity and acceleration of the center of the cylinder m with respect of the fixed origin e.

7.29   The rectangular rigid plate moving in slots as shown in Fig. P-7.29 has a known angular velocity $\boldsymbol{\Omega} = 2t\mathbf{k}$ rad/sec and a known angular acceleration $\dot{\boldsymbol{\Omega}} = 2\mathbf{k}$ rad/sec^2.   Find the velocity vectors of its corners 1, 2 and 3.

7.30   A straight rigid bar $\overline{nm}$ slides along the vertical and horizontal planes as shown in Fig. P-7.30.   If the linear velocity and acceleration are given as $\mathbf{v}_{On} = -2t\mathbf{i}$ m/sec, $\mathbf{a}_{On} = -2\mathbf{i}$ m/sec^2, find the velocity and acceleration vectors of the centroid c of the bar.

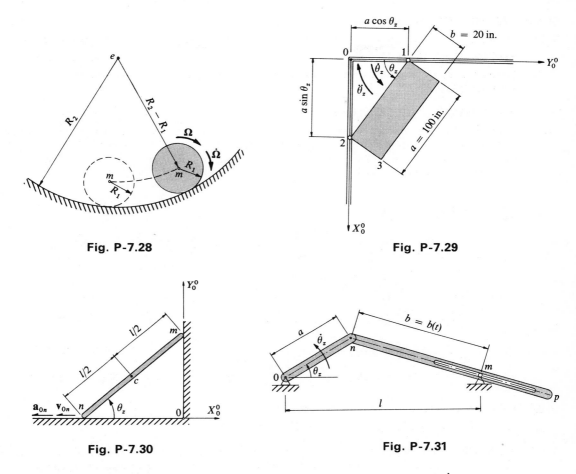

Fig. P-7.28   Fig. P-7.29

Fig. P-7.30   Fig. P-7.31

7.31   The link $\overline{0n}$ of the slide-crank mechanism of Fig. P-7.31 rotates with constant speed $\dot{\theta}_z = 1$ rad/sec.   Find the angular velocity of the link $\overline{np}$.   Given: $a, l, \theta_z, \dot{\theta}_z$.

7.32   For the mechanism of Fig. P-7.32, find the equations of motion of the free end 4.

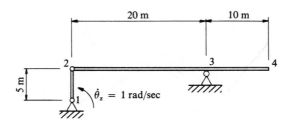

Fig. P-7.32

7.33   Using the results of Problem 7.32, determine the extreme coordinates of 4 referred to 1.

RELATIVE MOTION—DERIVATIONS

7.34 Derive the algebraic form of the equations of relative plane rigid body motion corresponding to the vector equations (7-10)–(7-12).

7.35 Derive the matrix form of the equations of relative plane rigid body motion corresponding to the vector equations (7-10)–(7-12).

RELATIVE MOTION—APPLICATIONS

7.36 A circular disk of radius R rolls without slipping in the $X_0^0 Y_0^0$ plane with given velocity and acceleration, and contains a smooth ball of mass m moving in the slot parallel to X_c^l as shown in Fig. P-7.36. Find the true velocity of m. Given: $\mathbf{v}_{0c} = 10t\mathbf{i}^0$ m/sec, $\mathbf{a}_{0c} = 10\mathbf{i}^0$ m/sec^2, $\mathbf{v}_{cm} = (2 - 3t)\mathbf{i}^l$ m/sec, $\mathbf{a}_{cm} = -3\mathbf{i}^l$ m/sec, $R = 20$ m, $r = 10$ m.

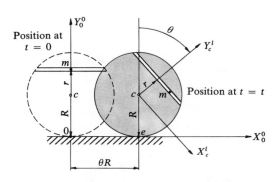
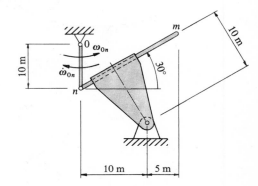

Fig. P-7.36   Fig. P-7.39

7.37 Find the true acceleration of m in Problem 7.36.

7.38 Show the matrix solution of Problems 7.36 and 7.37.

7.39 The link $\overline{0n}$ of the mechanism of Fig. P-7.39 has angular velocity $\boldsymbol{\omega}_{0n} = 2\mathbf{k}$ rad/sec and angular acceleration $\dot{\boldsymbol{\omega}}_{0n} = -10\mathbf{k}$ rad/sec^2 in the given position. Find the velocity and acceleration of the end m of bar $\overline{nm}$.

7.40 The link $\overline{0n}$ guides the pendulum $\overline{pm}$ as shown in Fig. P-7.40. If at $\theta_{pm} = 30°$ the angular velocity and acceleration of $\overline{pm}$ are respectively $\boldsymbol{\omega}_{pm} = -2\mathbf{k}$ rad/sec and $\dot{\boldsymbol{\omega}}_{pm} = 6\mathbf{k}$ rad/sec^2, compute the velocity and acceleration of $\overline{0n}$ at that position.

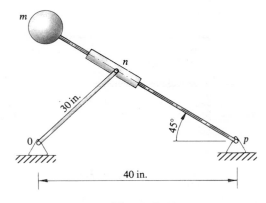

Fig. P-7.40

Chapter 8

Kinetics of Rigid Bodies, Plane Motion

8.1 CHARACTERISTICS OF A RIGID BODY

Mathematical Model

Since the number of particles forming a rigid body is assumed to be infinitely large, the body is said to be a continuum and the *distributed parameter model* defined in Section 5.1 is used as its representation. Only plane motion of this model is considered in this chapter.

The *mass of each differential element* of the distributed parameter model is given analytically as

$$dm = \gamma(x,y,z)\, dV \tag{8-1}$$

where $\gamma(x,y,z)$ is the density and dV is the volume of the element.

The *total mass of the body* is then

$$m = \int_V dm = \int_V \gamma(x,y,z)\, dV \tag{8-2}$$

where the integral is taken for the entire volume V.

If $\gamma(x,y,z) = \gamma$ is a constant, (8-2) reduces to

$$m = \gamma V \tag{8-3}$$

and the body is said to be of *constant* and *homogeneous mass*.

Mass Center

If the position of the element dm is given by the position vector $\mathbf{r}_{0m}$, then the *mass center* of the body (as in Section 5.1) is defined as the point located by the vector

$$\mathbf{r}_{0c} = \frac{\displaystyle\int_V \mathbf{r}_{0m}\gamma(x,y,z)\, dV}{\displaystyle\int_V \gamma(x,y,z)\, dV} = \frac{\displaystyle\int_m \mathbf{r}_{0m}\, dm}{\displaystyle\int_m dm} = \frac{\mathbf{Q}_0}{m} \tag{8-4}$$

where $\int_m \mathbf{r}_{0m}\, dm = \mathbf{Q}_0$ is the moment of the total mass about 0.

In the *cartesian system*,

$$\mathbf{r}_{0c} = \frac{\int_m x_{0m}\, dm}{\int_m dm}\, \mathbf{i} + \frac{\int_m y_{0m}\, dm}{\int_m dm}\, \mathbf{j} + \frac{\int_m z_{0m}\, dm}{\int_m dm}\, \mathbf{k} = x_{0c}\mathbf{i} + y_{0c}\mathbf{j} + z_{0c}\mathbf{k} \qquad (8\text{-}5)$$

where x_{0c}, y_{0c}, z_{0c} are the *coordinates of the mass center* measured from the fixed point 0.

Equations (8-4) and (8-5) are the distributed parameter model equivalents of (5-1) and (5-2). Since the rigid bodies considered in this book are assumed to be in a uniform gravitational field, their mass centers are also their *gravity centers*.

Inertia Functions

Although the inertia tensor of a three-dimensional rigid body is always defined by six inertia functions,* in the case of plane motion parallel to the $X_0 Y_0$ plane only *one inertia function*, the mass moment of inertia about the Z_0 axis normal to the plane of motion, occurs in the analysis.

By definition, this *mass moment of inertia* is

$$I_{0zz} = \int_m (x_{0m}^2 + y_{0m}^2)\, dm = \int_m r_{0m}^2\, dm \qquad (8\text{-}6)$$

which in terms of

$$x_{0m} = x_{0c} + x_{cm}, \qquad y_{0m} = y_{0c} + y_{cm} \qquad (8\text{-}7)$$

becomes

$$I_{0zz} = \underbrace{(x_{0c}^2 + y_{0c}^2)\int_m dm}_{c_{0c}^2 m} + \underbrace{\int_m (x_{cm}^2 + y_{cm}^2)\, dm}_{I_{czz}} \qquad (8\text{-}8)$$

where (from Fig. P-8.1) x_{0c}, y_{0c} are the coordinates of the mass center; x_{cm}, y_{cm} are the coordinates of *dm* with respect to the mass center; c_{0c} is the radius of the mass center with respect to 0 in the $X_0 Y_0$ plane; and I_{czz} is the mass moment of inertia of the body about the centroidal axis Z_c (axis normal to the plane of motion through the mass center).

By definition, the *radius of gyration of the total mass* with respect to Z_0 is

$$k_{0zz} = \sqrt{I_{0zz}/m} = \sqrt{c_{0c}^2 + k_{czz}^2} \qquad (8\text{-}9)$$

where

$$k_{czz} = \sqrt{I_{czz}/m} \qquad (8\text{-}10)$$

is the radius of gyration of *m* with respect to the centroidal axis Z_c.

---

*J. J. Tuma, "Statics", Quantum Publishers, New York, 1974, Chapter 8, p. 181.

Equations (8-8) and (8-9) allow the computation of the mass moment of inertia and the radius of gyration of the mass with respect to Z_0 in terms of c_{0c}, m, I_{czz}, k_{czz} and are again known as the *parallel axes theorems*.

8.2   MOTION RELATED TO THE MASS CENTER

Linear and Angular Momentum

The relationships of the preceding section applied in conjunction with the modified equations (5-8) and (5-10) allow a direct development of the analytical expressions for the *linear momentum* **G** and *angular momentum* **H** of a rigid body in plane motion.

The *linear momentum* with respect to a fixed point 0 (Problem 8.1) is

$$\mathbf{G} = \int_m \dot{\mathbf{r}}_{0m}\, dm = \int_m (\dot{\mathbf{r}}_{0c} + \mathbf{\Omega} \times \mathbf{r}_{cm})\, dm = \dot{\mathbf{r}}_{0c}m = \mathbf{G}_{0c} \tag{8-11}$$

The *angular momentum* about the same fixed point 0 (Problem 8.2) is

$$\mathbf{H} = \int_m \mathbf{r}_{0m} \times d\mathbf{G} = \int_m (\mathbf{r}_{0c} + \mathbf{r}_{cm}) \times (\dot{\mathbf{r}}_{0c} + \mathbf{\Omega} \times \mathbf{r}_{cm})\, dm$$

$$= \underbrace{\mathbf{r}_{0c} \times \dot{\mathbf{r}}_{0c}m}_{\mathbf{G}_{0c}} + \underbrace{\int_m \mathbf{r}_{cm} \times (\mathbf{\Omega} \times \mathbf{r}_{cm})\, dm}_{\mathbf{\Omega} I_{czz}} = \mathbf{H}_{0c} + \mathbf{H}_c \tag{8-12}$$

where $\mathbf{\Omega}$ is the angular velocity of the body about Z_c, I_{czz} is its mass moment of inertia about the same axes, and $\mathbf{G}_{0c}$, $\mathbf{H}_{0c}$, $\mathbf{H}_c$ have meaning similar to their equivalents in Section 5.3.

Equations of Motion

Since the position of a rigid body in plane motion is specified by three coordinates (two linear and one angular), *three independent scalar equations* (two independent vector equations) are necessary for the analytical determination of this motion.   These are the time derivatives of (8-11) and (8-12) taken in vector form as

$$\dot{\mathbf{G}} = \ddot{\mathbf{r}}_{0c}m = \dot{\mathbf{G}}_{0c} = \mathbf{F} \tag{8-13}$$

$$\dot{\mathbf{H}} = \mathbf{r}_{0c} \times \dot{\mathbf{G}}_{0c} + \dot{\mathbf{\Omega}} I_{zz} = \dot{\mathbf{H}}_{0c} + \dot{\mathbf{H}}_c = \mathbf{M} \tag{8-14}$$

where $\ddot{\mathbf{r}}_{0c}m$ is the *linear inertial function*, $\dot{\mathbf{\Omega}} I_{czz}$ is the *angular inertial function*, **F** is the *resultant force function*, and **M** is the *resultant moment function* (Problems 8.3 and 8.4).

The matrix form of these equations is

$$m \begin{bmatrix} 1 & 0 & 0 \\ 0 & 1 & 0 \\ -y_{0c} & x_{0c} & k_{czz}^2 \end{bmatrix} \begin{bmatrix} \ddot{x}_{0c} \\ \ddot{y}_{0c} \\ \ddot{\theta}_z \end{bmatrix} = \begin{bmatrix} \sum F_x \\ \sum F_y \\ \sum M_z \end{bmatrix} \tag{8-15}$$

where $\sum F_x$, $\sum F_y$ are the scalar components of the resultant force function, $\sum M_z$ is the scalar resultant moment function, $I_{czz} = k_{czz}^2 m$, and since only plane motion is involved, $\dot{\mathbf{\Omega}} = \ddot{\theta}_z$.

These equations are the distributed parametric model equivalents of the single particle equation (2-5) and this similarity allows the application of the methods of single particle kinetics in the analysis of plane motion of rigid bodies (problems of the first kind, and problems of the second kind, Section 2.2).

Conservation of Momentum

If the *resultant of forces* **F** acting on the rigid body in plane motion is *zero* (**F** = 0), then the linear momentum **G** of the body is constant.

If the *resultant of moments* **M** acting on the rigid body in plane motion is *zero* (**M** = 0), then the angular momentum **H** of the body is constant.

These two statements are the extension of the *principles of conservation of momentum* (Definitions 2.8 and 2.9) to the kinetics of rigid bodies.

D'Alambert's Principle

The physical interpretation of (8-15) reduces a problem of kinetics of rigid bodies in plane motion to an equivalent one in statics, and leads to *D'Alambert's principle of dynamic equilibrium*.

Definition 8.1: A mechanical system is in a state of dynamic equilibrium when the resultant of force functions and the resultant of moment functions equal the linear and angular inertial functions of the system respectively.

For such a state to exist in plane motion, *three conditions* must be satisfied simultaneously:

$$\sum F_x = m\ddot{x}_{0c}, \qquad \sum F_y = m\ddot{y}_{0c}, \qquad \sum M_z = -y_{0c}m\ddot{x}_{0c} + x_{0c}m\ddot{y}_{0c} + mk_{0zz}^2\ddot{\theta}_z \qquad (8\text{-}16)$$

which in the case of rest ($\ddot{x}_{0c} = 0$, $\ddot{y}_{0c} = 0$, $\ddot{\theta}_z = 0$) reduces to the *equations of static equilibrium*.

This analogy allows the application of the concept of the free-body sketch in the kinetics of rigid bodies and is of great practical importance in the visualization of many complex situations.

Special Cases

The development of (8-13) and (8-14) was based on the assumption of the condition of rigidity ($\mathbf{r}_{cm}$ = constant, $\dot{\mathbf{r}}_{cm} = 0$, $\ddot{\mathbf{r}}_{cm} = 0$). If this condition is not satisfied by some parts of the body or of the system, the introduction of the relative acceleration vectors is necessary. Conceptually this inclusion is rather simple but the resulting expressions may become quite complex.

Linear and Angular Impulse

The *linear impulse of forces* acting on a rigid body in plane motion during the time interval $t_2 - t_1$ equals the linear impulse of their resultant during the same time interval, i.e.

$$\int_{t_1}^{t_2} \mathbf{F}\, dt = \int_{t_1}^{t_2} \dot{\mathbf{G}}\, dt = \mathbf{G}_2 - \mathbf{G}_1 = (\dot{\mathbf{r}}_{0c,\,2} - \dot{\mathbf{r}}_{0c,\,1})m \qquad (8\text{-}17)$$

where $\mathbf{G}_2, \mathbf{G}_1$ are the total linear momenta (8-11) at t_2, t_1 respectively, and the total linear impulse equals the change in total linear momentum (Definition 2.10).

The *angular impulse of forces* acting on a rigid body in plane motion during the time interval $t_2 - t_1$ equals the angular impulse of their resultant during the same interval, i.e.

$$\int_{t_1}^{t_2} \mathbf{M}\, dt = \int_{t_1}^{t_2} \dot{\mathbf{H}}\, dt = \mathbf{H}_2 - \mathbf{H}_1 = (\mathbf{\Omega}_2 - \mathbf{\Omega}_1)I_{0zz} \qquad (8\text{-}18)$$

where $\mathbf{H}_2, \mathbf{H}_1$ are the total linear momenta (8-12) at t_2, t_1 respectively, and the total angular impulse equals the change in the total angular momentum (Definition 2.11).

8.3   ENERGY AND WORK

Kinetic Energy

The *total kinetic energy* T of the rigid body in plane motion referred to the fixed point 0 is

$$T = \tfrac{1}{2} \int_m \mathbf{r}^*_{0m} \cdot \mathbf{r}^*_{0m} \, dm = \tfrac{1}{2} \int_m (\dot{\mathbf{r}}_{0c} + \mathbf{\Omega} \times \mathbf{r}_{cm}) \cdot (\dot{\mathbf{r}}_{0c} + \mathbf{\Omega} \times \mathbf{r}_{cm}) \, dm$$

$$= \tfrac{1}{2}\dot{\mathbf{r}}^2_{0c} m + \tfrac{1}{2}\Omega^2 I_{czz} = T_{0c} + T_c \qquad (8\text{-}19)$$

where T_{0c} is the *translatory energy* (of the total mass concentrated at c) and T_c is the *rotary energy* (of the distributed total mass), both with respect to c.

Mechanical Work

The *total mechanical work* U done by the forces in moving a rigid body of mass m on a plane along a prescribed path from position 1 to position 2 is

$$U = \int_m \int_1^2 (\mathbf{r}^{**}_{0m} \, dm) \cdot d\mathbf{r}_{0m} = \int_m \int_1^2 (\mathbf{r}^{**}_{0c} + \mathbf{r}^{**}_{cm}) \, dm \cdot d(\mathbf{r}_{0c} + \mathbf{r}_{cm})$$

$$= \tfrac{1}{2}m(\dot{\mathbf{r}}^2_{0c,\,2} - \dot{\mathbf{r}}^2_{0c,\,1}) + \tfrac{1}{2}I_{czz}(\Omega^2_2 - \Omega^2_1)$$

$$= T_{0c,\,2} - T_{0c,\,1} + T_{c,\,2} - T_{c,\,1} = \Delta T_{0c} + \Delta T_c = U_{0c} + U_c \qquad (8\text{-}20)$$

where ΔT_{0c} and ΔT_c are the changes in the translatory and rotary energy of the body corresponding to the changes in its position.

The comparison of $(8\text{-}18)$, $(8\text{-}19)$ and $(5\text{-}26)$, $(5\text{-}27)$ shows their conceptual affinity and symbolic similarity.

Conservation of Energy

If the forces and moments acting on a rigid body are *conservative* so that the whole system has a *potential V*, then

$$T_1 + V_1 = T_2 + V_2 = \ldots = E \qquad (8\text{-}21)$$

where E is called the total energy which, as $(8\text{-}21)$ indicates, remains constant (principle of conservation of energy).

Illustrative Problems

LINEAR AND ANGULAR MOMENTUM—DERIVATIONS

8.1   Derive the linear momentum equation $(8\text{-}11)$ for the rigid body in plane motion (Fig. P-8.1).

By definition, the linear momentum of the mass element of the given body with respect to a fixed point 0 is

$$dG = \mathbf{r}^*_{0m}\, dm \qquad (1)$$

from which the total linear momentum of the body is

$$\mathbf{G} = \int_m \mathbf{r}^*_{0m}\, dm$$

where

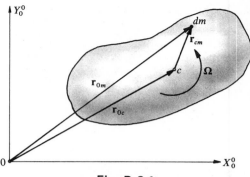

Fig. P-8.1

$$\mathbf{r}_{0m} = \mathbf{r}_{0c} + \mathbf{r}_{cm}, \qquad \mathbf{r}^*_{0m} = \mathbf{r}^*_{0c} + \mathbf{r}^*_{cm} = \dot{\mathbf{r}}_{0c} + \dot{\mathbf{r}}_{cm} + \mathbf{\Omega} \times \mathbf{r}_{cm} \qquad (2)$$

Since from the condition of rigidity $\dot{\mathbf{r}}_{cm} = 0$, then

$$\mathbf{G} = \int_m (\dot{\mathbf{r}}_{0c} + \mathbf{\Omega} \times \mathbf{r}_{cm})\, dm = \dot{\mathbf{r}}_{0c} \int_m dm + \mathbf{\Omega} \times \int_m \mathbf{r}_{cm}\, dm \qquad (3)$$

where the linear velocity $\dot{\mathbf{r}}_{0c}$ and the angular velocity $\mathbf{\Omega}$ are functions of time but otherwise are independent of the mass.   With $m = \int_m dm$ and $\int_m r_{cm}\, dm = 0$, equation (3) reduces to

$$\mathbf{G} = \dot{\mathbf{r}}_{0c} m = \mathbf{G}_{0c} \qquad (4)$$

and thus the linear momentum $\mathbf{G}$ of the rigid body equals the total mass m multiplied by the velocity of its mass center c.

8.2   Derive the angular momentum equation (8-12) for the rigid body in plane motion (Fig. P-8.1).

By definition the angular momentum of the mass element of the given body with respect to a fixed point 0 is

$$d\mathbf{H} = \mathbf{r}_{0m} \times d\mathbf{G} = \mathbf{r}_{0m} \times \mathbf{r}^*_{0m}\, dm \qquad (1)$$

where $\mathbf{r}_{0m}$ and $\mathbf{r}^*_{cm}$ have the same meaning as in (2) of Problem 8.1.

From (1), the total angular momentum of the body is

$$\mathbf{H} = \int_m (\mathbf{r}_{0c} + \mathbf{r}_{cm}) \times (\mathbf{r}^*_{0c} + \mathbf{r}^*_{cm})\, dm \qquad (2)$$

where $\mathbf{r}^*_{0c} = \dot{\mathbf{r}}_{0c}$ and $\mathbf{r}^*_{cm} = \mathbf{\Omega} \times \mathbf{r}_{cm}$ are already known from Problem 8.1.   In (2),

$$\mathbf{r}_{0c} \times \dot{\mathbf{r}}_{0c} \int_m dm = \mathbf{r}_{0c} \times \mathbf{G}_{0c} = \mathbf{H}_{0c}$$

$$\mathbf{r}_{0c} \times \left(\mathbf{\Omega} \times \int_m \mathbf{r}_{cm}\, dm \right) = 0$$

$$\int_m \mathbf{r}_{cm} \times \dot{\mathbf{r}}_{0c}\, dm = -\dot{\mathbf{r}}_{0c} \times \int_m \mathbf{r}_{cm}\, dm = 0$$

and since $\mathbf{r}_{cm}$ is normal to $\boldsymbol{\Omega}$,

$$\int_m \mathbf{r}_{cm} \times (\boldsymbol{\Omega} \times \mathbf{r}_{cm})\, dm = \boldsymbol{\Omega} \int_m r_{cm}^2\, dm = \boldsymbol{\Omega} I_{czz} = \mathbf{H}_c$$

where I_{czz} is the mass moment of inertia with respect to Z_c.   With these new equivalents, the angular momentum equation (2) becomes

$$\mathbf{H} = \mathbf{r}_{0c} \times \mathbf{G}_{0c} + \boldsymbol{\Omega} I_{czz} = \mathbf{H}_{0c} + \mathbf{H}_c$$

where $\mathbf{H}_{0c}$ is the moment of $\mathbf{G}_{0c}$ about 0, and $\mathbf{H}_c$ is the angular momentum of the body about its mass center c.

EQUATIONS OF MOTION—DERIVATIONS

8.3   Derive the vector equation (8-13) of plane motion of the rigid body of Fig. P-8.1.

The total time derivative of (8-11) is

$$\mathbf{G}^* = \int_m \mathbf{r}_{0m}^{**}\, dm = \int_m (\mathbf{r}_{0c}^{**} + \mathbf{r}_{cm}^{**})\, dm \tag{1}$$

where

$$\mathbf{r}_{0c}^{**} = \ddot{\mathbf{r}}_{0c} \tag{2}$$

$$\mathbf{r}_{cm}^{**} = \dot{\mathbf{r}}_{cm}^{*} + \boldsymbol{\Omega}^* \times \mathbf{r}_{cm} + \boldsymbol{\Omega} \times \mathbf{r}_{cm}^{*} = \ddot{\mathbf{r}}_{cm} + \boldsymbol{\Omega} \times \dot{\mathbf{r}}_{cm} + \dot{\boldsymbol{\Omega}} \times \mathbf{r}_{cm} + \boldsymbol{\Omega} \times (\dot{\mathbf{r}}_{cm} + \boldsymbol{\Omega} \times \mathbf{r}_{cm}) \tag{3}$$

Since

$$\int_m \ddot{\mathbf{r}}_{0c}\, dm = \ddot{\mathbf{r}}_{0c} m$$

$$\int_m \ddot{\mathbf{r}}_{cm}\, dm = 0, \qquad \boldsymbol{\Omega} \times \int_m \dot{\mathbf{r}}_{cm}\, dm = 0, \qquad \dot{\boldsymbol{\Omega}} \times \int_m \mathbf{r}_{cm}\, dm = 0, \qquad \boldsymbol{\Omega} \times \left(\boldsymbol{\Omega} \times \int_m \mathbf{r}_{cm}\, dm \right) = 0 \tag{4}$$

the total time derivative of $\mathbf{G}$ reduces to

$$\mathbf{G}^* = \ddot{\mathbf{r}}_{0c} m = \dot{\mathbf{G}}_{0c} = \mathbf{F} \tag{5}$$

where $\mathbf{F}$ is the resultant of all forces (surface and body forces) to which the rigid body is subjected.

This equation of motion can of course be derived directly as the first time derivative of $\mathbf{G}$ but the derivation shown above is more complete.

8.4   Derive the vector equation (8-14) of plane motion of the rigid body of Fig. P-8.1.

The total time derivative of (8-12) is

$$\mathbf{H}^* = \int_m (\mathbf{r}_{0m} \times d\mathbf{G}^* + \mathbf{r}_{0m}^* \times d\mathbf{G}) = \int_m (\mathbf{r}_{0m} \times \mathbf{r}_{0m}^{**} + \mathbf{r}_{0m}^* \times \mathbf{r}_{0m}^*)\, dm \tag{1}$$

where

$$\int_m \mathbf{r}_{0m}^* \times \mathbf{r}_{0m}^* \, dm = 0 \qquad \text{and} \qquad \int_m \mathbf{r}_{0m} \times \mathbf{r}_{0m}^{**} \, dm = \int_m (\mathbf{r}_{0c} + \mathbf{r}_{cm}) \times (\mathbf{r}_{0c}^{**} + \mathbf{r}_{cm}^{**}) \, dm \qquad (2)$$

In terms of (2) and (3) of Problem 8.3, equation (1) is

$$\mathbf{H} = \int_m (\mathbf{r}_{0c} + \mathbf{r}_{cm}) \times (\mathbf{r}_{0c}^{**} + \mathbf{r}_{cm}^{**}) \, dm$$

$$= \int_m \mathbf{r}_{0c} \times \ddot{\mathbf{r}}_{0c} \, dm + \int_m \mathbf{r}_{0c} \times [\ddot{\mathbf{r}}_{cm} + \boldsymbol{\Omega} \times \dot{\mathbf{r}}_{cm} + \dot{\boldsymbol{\Omega}} \times \mathbf{r}_{cm} + \boldsymbol{\Omega} \times (\dot{\mathbf{r}}_{cm} + \boldsymbol{\Omega} \times \mathbf{r}_{cm})] \, dm$$

$$+ \int_m \mathbf{r}_{cm} \times \ddot{\mathbf{r}}_{0c} \, dm + \int_m \mathbf{r}_{cm} \times [\ddot{\mathbf{r}}_{cm} + \boldsymbol{\Omega} \times \dot{\mathbf{r}}_{cm} + \dot{\boldsymbol{\Omega}} \times \mathbf{r}_{cm} + \boldsymbol{\Omega} \times (\dot{\mathbf{r}}_{cm} + \boldsymbol{\Omega} \times \mathbf{r}_{cm})] \, dm$$

$$= \mathbf{r}_{0c} \times \ddot{\mathbf{r}}_{0c} m + \int_m \mathbf{r}_{cm} \times (\dot{\boldsymbol{\Omega}} \times \mathbf{r}_{cm}) \, dm \qquad (3)$$

where the omitted terms are zero according to (4) of Problem 8.3.

Since $\mathbf{r}_{cm}$ is normal to $\dot{\boldsymbol{\Omega}}$, the last term in (3) reduces to $\dot{\boldsymbol{\Omega}} \int r_{cm}^2 \, dm = \dot{\boldsymbol{\Omega}} I_{czz}$ and (1) can be expressed as

$$\mathbf{H}^* = \mathbf{r}_{0c} \times \mathbf{G}_{0c} + \dot{\boldsymbol{\Omega}} I_{czz} = \mathbf{H}_{0c}^* + \mathbf{H}_c^* = \mathbf{M} \qquad (4)$$

where $\mathbf{M}$ is the resultant moment of all forces and moments to which the body is subjected.

This second vector equation of motion can again be derived directly as the first time derivative of $\mathbf{H}$ but the derivation shown above is more complete.

EQUATIONS OF MOTION—APPLICATIONS

8.5   A circular disk of radius R and weight W moves in plane along a horizontal surface as shown in Fig. P-8.5.   Derive the equations of motion of this disk. Given: initial linear velocity $\dot{\mathbf{r}}_{0c}(0) = v\mathbf{i}$, initial angular velocity $\boldsymbol{\Omega}(0) = -\omega\mathbf{k}$, coefficient of friction $\mu_k = \mu$ at the point of contact.

From Fig. P-8.5, the equations of motion (8-15) are

$$\frac{W}{g}\ddot{x}_{0c} = -\mu W \quad \text{or} \quad \ddot{x}_{0c} = -\mu g$$

$$\frac{W}{g}\ddot{y}_{0c} = -W + N \quad \text{or} \quad \ddot{y}_{0c} = 0 \text{ (since } W = N) \qquad (1)$$

$$-\frac{W}{g}k_{czz}^2\ddot{\theta}_z = -\mu W R \quad \text{or} \quad k_{czz}^2\ddot{\theta}_z = \mu g R$$

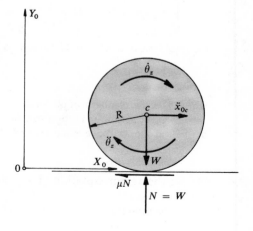

Fig. P-8.5

The integrals of the first and third equations in (1) are respectively

$$\dot{x}_{0c} = \dot{x}_{0c}(0) - \mu g t = v - \mu g t \tag{2}$$

$$\dot{\theta}_z = \dot{\theta}_z(0) + \mu g R t / k^2 = \omega + \mu g R t / k^2 \tag{3}$$

where $k^2 = k_{czz}^2$.   For no slipping, $\dot{x}_{0c} = R\dot{\theta}_z$; then $v - \mu g t = R\omega + \mu g R^2 t / k^2$ and hence

$$t = \frac{(v - R\omega)k^2}{\mu g(k^2 + R^2)} \tag{4}$$

which when put into (2) and (3) yields

$$\dot{x}_{0c} = v - \frac{v - R\omega}{k^2 + R^2}k^2, \qquad \dot{\theta}_z = \omega + \frac{v - R\omega}{k^2 + R^2}R \tag{5}$$

Beginning with the instant given by (4), the disk remains in a state of uniform rolling without sliding. Before this instant the disk rolls and slips.

8.6   A circular disk of radius R and weight W moves down an inclined plane as shown in Fig. P-8.6. Determine the angle α for which the disk will roll without slipping.   Given: initial linear velocity $\dot{\mathbf{r}}_{0c}(0) = 0$, initial angular velocity $\mathbf{\Omega}(0) = 0$, and coefficient of friction $\mu_k = \mu$ at the point of contact.

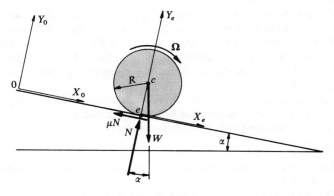

Fig. P-8.6

From Fig. P-8.6, the equations of motion (8-15) are

$$\frac{W}{g}\ddot{x}_{0c} = W \sin\alpha - \mu N \qquad \text{or} \qquad m\ddot{x}_{0c} = mg \sin\alpha - \mu N \tag{1}$$

$$\frac{W}{g}\ddot{y}_{0c} = W \cos\alpha - N \qquad \text{or} \qquad \ddot{y}_{0c} = 0 \quad (\text{since } W \cos\alpha = N) \tag{2}$$

$$-\frac{W}{g}k_{czz}^2\ddot{\theta}_z = -\mu N R \qquad \text{or} \qquad mk_{czz}^2\ddot{\theta}_z = \mu N R \tag{3}$$

For no slipping, $\dot{\theta}_z = \dot{x}_{0c}/R$, by which (3) becomes

$$mk^2\ddot{x}_{0c} = \mu N R^2 \tag{4}$$

e $k^2 = k_{czz}^2$.   Now equation (I) in terms of (4) yields

$$\left(m + \frac{mk^2}{R^2}\right)\ddot{x}_{0c} = mg \sin \alpha \tag{5}$$

from which

$$\ddot{x}_{0c} = \frac{gR^2 \sin \alpha}{k^2 + R^2} \tag{6}$$

Since from Fig. P-8.6, $N = W \cos \alpha$, equation (I) in terms of (6) is

$$\frac{mgR^2 \sin \alpha}{k^2 + R^2} = mg \sin \alpha - mg\mu \cos \alpha \qquad \text{from which} \qquad \tan \alpha < \frac{\mu(R^2 + k^2)}{k^2}$$

For a circular disk, $k^2 = R^2/2$ and $\tan \alpha < 3\mu$.

D'ALAMBERT'S PRINCIPLE

8.7   State the procedure of application of the equations of dynamic equilibrium (8-16) in the analysis of plane motion of rigid bodies.

The following general steps of application are recommended:

(1)   Select a stationary reference system of axes (cartesian, cylindrical, spherical or curvilinear) best suited for the given problem.
(2)   Replace the real mechanical system by a free-body sketch related to the selected reference system.
(3)   Show all known active forces and moments by solid line vectors acting in their given directions.
(4)   Show all unknown forces and moments by solid line vectors acting in the positive direction.
(5)   Show all known inertial forces and moments by broken line vectors acting in their given directions.
(6)   Show all unknown inertial forces and moments by broken line vectors acting in the positive direction.
(7)   Apply equations of dynamic equilibrium by equating the respective sum of inertial forces or moments to the corresponding sum of acting forces or moments.
(8)   Solve the resulting differential equations of motion.

Note that:

(a)   Each degree of freedom provides one condition of dynamic equilibrium (one differential equation of motion).
(b)   The integral of each differential equation of motion has two constants of integration to be determined from two given special conditions (initial, intermediate or terminal conditions).
(c)   Each constraint provides one condition of static equilibrium (one algebraic or transcendental equation of rest).

8.8   A four-wheel drive vehicle of weight W accelerates on a horizontal road from rest to speed v.   Its wheel base is l and its center of gravity is given by coordinates a, b, c shown in Fig. P-8.8.   Find the forces associated with this motion.

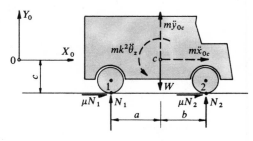

First select the cartesian axes X_0, Y_0, Z_0 as the reference system and show the active and inertial forces and moments (Fig. P-8.8).   Then by (8-16),

Fig. P-8.8

$$m\ddot{x}_{0c} = \mu N_1 + \mu N_2 \tag{1}$$

$$m\ddot{y}_{0c} = N_1 + N_2 - mg \tag{2}$$

$$mk^2\ddot{\theta}_z + x_{0c}m\ddot{y}_{0c} = c\mu N_1 + c\mu N_2 + (x_{0c} - a)N_1 - x_{0c}mg + (x_{0c} + b)N_2 \tag{3}$$

Since the vehicle is assumed to be in contact with the road, it has one linear degree of freedom ($x_{0c} > 0$), one linear constraint ($y_{0c} = 0$) and one angular constraint ($\theta_z = 0$). Thus (1) is the equation of dynamic equilibrium ($\ddot{x}_{0c} > 0$), and (2) and (3) are equations of static equilibrium ($\ddot{y}_{0c} = 0$, $\ddot{\theta}_z = 0$), i.e.

$$m\ddot{x}_{0c} = \mu(N_1 + N_2) \tag{4}$$

$$0 = N_1 + N_2 - mg \tag{5}$$

$$0 = c\mu(N_1 + N_2) + x_{0c}(N_1 - mg + N_2) - aN_1 + bN_2 \tag{6}$$

These three equations solved for $\ddot{x}_{0c}, N_1, N_2$ give respectively

$$\ddot{x}_{0c} = \mu g, \qquad N_1 = mg(b + c\mu)/l, \qquad N_2 = mg(a - \mu c)/l \tag{7}, (8), (9)$$

The integrals of (7) for $x_{0c}(0) = 0$, $\dot{x}_{0c}(0) = 0$, are

$$\dot{x}_{0c} = \mu g t, \qquad x_{0c} = \mu g t^2/2 \tag{10}, (11)$$

The time required to attain the speed v is, from (10), $t = v/\mu g$; and the corresponding distance is, from (11), $s = \mu g(v/\mu g)^2/2 = v^2/2\mu g$.

Note that the assumption that all four wheels remain in contact with the road requires that in (9), $a - \mu c \neq 0$.

Finally it must be remarked that (1)–(3) can be written more conveniently with respect to the translating centroidal axes X_c, Y_c, Z_c and so (3) reduces to

$$mk^2\ddot{\theta}_z = (\mu c - a)N_1 + (\mu c + b)N_2$$

The equations (1)–(3) give however a more general approach, which is necessary in some cases.

8.9 State the procedure of application of the equations of dynamic equilibrium (8-16) in the analysis of plane motion of systems of rigid bodies.

The procedure of Problem 8.7 requires the following modifications:

(1) Select a stationary reference system of axes common to the entire assembly and if necessary a specific moving reference system of axes for each body of the assembly.
(2) Replace the real mechanical system by a set of free bodies, each corresponding to one body or several bodies of the assembly (as convenient).
(3) Repeat steps 3 through 8 of Problem 8.7 for each free-body sketch.

Note that the free bodies are related by:

(a) The conditions of stress compatibility, i.e. the corresponding active forces and moments at the respective cut must be equal in magnitude but of opposite direction (same as in statics).
(b) The conditions of kinematic compatibility, i.e. the corresponding kinematic vectors at the respective cut must be equal in magnitude and of the same direction.

8.10 A block of weight W_2 is suspended on a cable wound around a frictionless pulley of weight W_1 and radius r (Fig. P-8.10a). If the block is allowed to fall freely from a position of rest, determine the acceleration of the pulley, the tension in the cable and the reactions on the bearing of the pulley. Given: W_1, W_2, r, g.

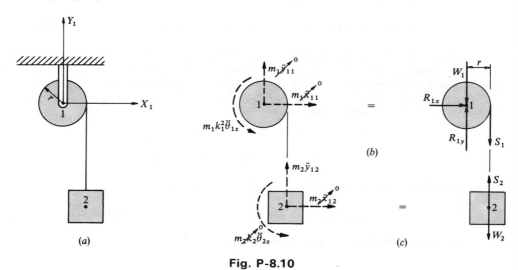

Fig. P-8.10

Since the pulley is stationary (but free to rotate), its centroidal axes X_1, Y_1, Z_1 are selected as the reference system and each body is isolated as a free body (Fig. P-8.10b, c), each represented by two sketches. The left sketch represents the inertial forces and moments and is equal to the right sketch subjected to the active forces.

From Fig. P-8.10b,

$$m\ddot{x}_{11} = R_{1x}, \qquad m\ddot{y}_{11} = R_{1y} - W_1 - S_1, \qquad mk_1^2\ddot{\theta}_{1z} = -Sr \qquad (1),(2),(3)$$

where $\ddot{x}_{11}$, $\ddot{y}_{11}$, $\ddot{\theta}_{1z}$ are the components of the acceleration of the pulley with respect to 1; R_{1x}, R_{1y} are the reactions of the pulley; S_1 is the tensile force in the cable, and k_1 is the radius of gyration of the pulley.

By the conditions of constraint (stationary pulley), (1) and (2) are equations of static equilibrium ($\ddot{x}_{11} = 0$, $\ddot{y}_{11} = 0$) and (3) is an equation of dynamic equilibrium ($\ddot{\theta}_{1z} \neq 0$).   Therefore

$$0 = R_{1x}, \qquad 0 = R_{1y} - W_1 - S_1, \qquad mk_1^2\ddot{\theta}_{1z} = -S_1 r \qquad (4),(5),(6)$$

From Fig. P-8.10c,

$$m\ddot{x}_{12} = 0, \qquad m\ddot{y}_{12} = S_2 - W_2, \qquad mk_2^2\ddot{\theta}_{2z} = 0 \qquad (7),(8),(9)$$

where $\ddot{x}_{12}$, $\ddot{y}_{12}$, $\ddot{\theta}_{2z}$ are the components of the acceleration of the block, S_2 is the tension in the cable, and k_2 is the radius of gyration of the block.

By the definition of motion (free fall), $\ddot{x}_{12} = 0$, $\ddot{\theta}_{2z} = 0$ and $\ddot{y}_{12} \neq 0$.   Therefore

$$m\ddot{y}_{12} = S_2 - W_2 \qquad (10)$$

From the stress compatibility of these two free bodies, $S_1 = S_2$; and from the kinematic compatibility, $r\dot{\theta}_{1z} = \dot{y}_{12}$, since the speed of the cable on the pulley and at the block must be the same.   Differentiating, $r\ddot{\theta}_{1z} = \ddot{y}_{12}$, and the solution of (6) and (10) gives

$$\ddot{y}_{12} = \frac{-g}{1 + m_1 k_1^2/m_2 r^2} = \frac{-g}{1 + m_1/2m_2} \qquad (11)$$

$$\ddot{\theta}_{1z} = \frac{\ddot{y}_{12}}{r} = \frac{-g/r}{1 + m_1/2m_2} \tag{12}$$

$$S_1 = \frac{W_2}{1 + m_2 r^2/m_1 k^2} = \frac{W_2}{1 + 2m_2/m_1} \tag{13}$$

where m_1, m_2 are the masses of the pulley and block respectively. Substituting (13) into (5),

$$R_{1y} = W_1 + \frac{W_2}{1 + 2m_2/m_1}$$

For large m_2 and small m_1,

$$\ddot{y}_{12} \cong -g, \qquad \dot{y}_{12} \cong -gt, \qquad \ddot{\theta}_{1z} \cong -g/r, \qquad S_1 \cong 0, \qquad R_{1y} \cong W_1$$

and the motion approaches a free fall of the block.
For $m_1 = m_2$,

$$\ddot{y}_{12} = -2g/3, \qquad \dot{y}_{12} = -2gt/3, \qquad \ddot{\theta}_{1z} = -2gr/3r, \qquad \dot{\theta}_{1z} = -2grt/3r$$

$$R_{1x} = 0, \qquad R_{1y} = 4W_1/3, \qquad S_1 = W_1/3$$

which shows the appreciable effect of the mass of the pulley on the motion of the block, and the motion is a retarded free fall.

LINEAR AND ANGULAR MOMENTUM

8.11 A rigid, straight bar of mass m and length l is displaced from its stationary position $\theta_z = 0$ with initial angular velocity Ω_1, and due to gravity slides along a frictionless vertical wall and horizontal floor in a plane normal to both (Fig. P-8.11). Find the equations of its motion. Given: l, m, Ω_1.

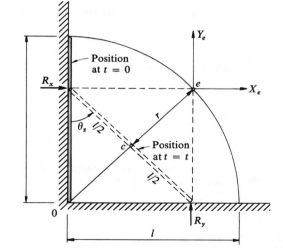

Fig. P-8.11

Since the centrode of motion (Problem 7.11) is a circle of radius l about 0, it is convenient to refer the motion of the bar to the translating cartesian axes X_e, Y_e, Z_e whose origin is the instantaneous center e. With these axes (Fig. P-8.11),

$$\mathbf{r}_{ec} = (-r \sin \theta_z)\mathbf{i} - (r \cos \theta_z)\mathbf{j} \tag{1}$$

$$\dot{\mathbf{r}}_{ec} = (-r\dot{\theta}_z \cos \theta_z)\mathbf{i} + (r\dot{\theta}_z \sin \theta_z)\mathbf{j} \tag{2}$$

where $\dot{\theta}_z = \Omega$ and $r = l/2$.

The angular momentum of the bar about e is by (8-12)

$$\mathbf{H}_e = \mathbf{r}_{ec} \times \dot{\mathbf{r}}_{ec}m + \Omega I_{czz} \tag{3}$$

which in terms of (1) and (2) becomes

$$\mathbf{H}_e = \Omega r^2 m + \Omega I_{czz} = \Omega I_{ezz} = \dot{\theta}_z (ml^2/3)\mathbf{k} \tag{4}$$

where $I_{ezz} = mr^2 + ml^2/12 = ml^2/3$ (parallel axes theorem).

By (8-14), the time derivative of $\mathbf{H}_e$ is

$$\dot{\mathbf{H}}_e = \mathbf{M}_e \qquad\qquad (5)$$

where

$$\dot{\mathbf{H}}_e = \ddot{\theta}_z(ml^2/3)\mathbf{k} \qquad \text{and} \qquad \mathbf{M}_e = (mgl/2)(\sin\theta_z)\mathbf{k} \qquad\qquad (6), (7)$$

Then from (5),

$$\ddot{\theta}_z = \frac{3g\sin\theta_z}{2l} \qquad\qquad (8)$$

where $\ddot{\theta}_z = \dfrac{d\Omega}{d\theta_z}\dfrac{d\theta_z}{dt} = \dfrac{d\Omega}{d\theta_z}\Omega.$ Integrating and solving for Ω,

$$\Omega = \dot{\theta}_z = \sqrt{(3g/l)(1 - \cos\theta_z) + 2C} \qquad\qquad (9)$$

where at $\theta_z = 0$, $\Omega = \Omega_1$ and $2C = \Omega_1^2$. The angular speed of the bar is then

$$\Omega = \sqrt{(3g/l)(1 - \cos\theta_z) + \Omega_1^2} \qquad\qquad (10)$$

which is valid for all θ_z as long as $R_x \geq 0$.

8.12 Find the angle θ_z at which the bar of Problem 8.11 leaves the wall.

By (8-13), the horizontal reaction of the bar is

$$R_x = \dot{G}_x \qquad\qquad (1)$$

where by (2) of Problem 8.11,

$$G_x = \dot{x}_{ec}m = -r\dot{\theta}_z(\cos\theta_z)m \qquad\qquad (2)$$

and

$$\dot{G}_x = -(r\ddot{\theta}_z\cos\theta_z - r\dot{\theta}_z^2\sin\theta_z)m \qquad\qquad (3)$$

As the bar slides downward, R_x decreases. When R_x becomes zero, the bar leaves the wall; at this instant, $\dot{G}_x = 0$, and from (3),

$$\frac{\sin\theta_z}{\cos\theta_z} = \frac{\ddot{\theta}_z}{\dot{\theta}_z^2} \qquad\qquad (4)$$

where by (8) and (9) of Problem 8.11,

$$\ddot{\theta}_z = \frac{3g\sin\theta_z}{2l}, \qquad \dot{\theta}_z^2 = \frac{3g(1 - \cos\theta_z) + l\Omega_1^2}{l} \qquad\qquad (5), (6)$$

Then from (4) the position of departure is given by

$$\theta_z = \cos^{-1}(2/3 + 2l\Omega_1^2/9g)$$

which for $\Omega_1 = 0$ reduces to $\theta_z = \cos^{-1}(2/3) = 48.2°$.

8.13 A solid sphere of mass m and radius b rests on the top of another fixed sphere of radius a as shown in Fig. P-8.13.   If the free sphere rolls from 1 with initial angular speed $\dot{\phi}_{1z}$, determine its angular speed at time t.   Given: $a, b, m, \dot{\phi}_{1z}$.

Since the circumference of the fixed sphere is the centrode of rolling of the free sphere, the angular momentum of the free sphere with respect to the point of contact e (instantaneous center) is

$$\mathbf{H}_e = -\dot{\phi}_z I_{ezz} = -\dot{\phi}_z(7mb^2/5)\mathbf{k} \qquad (1)$$

where $\dot{\phi}_z$ is the angular speed of the free sphere.
The condition of rolling requires that the velocity vector of the centroid c of the free sphere with respect to 0 must be equal to its velocity with respect to e, i.e.

$$\underbrace{-(a+b)\dot{\theta}_z}_{\mathbf{v}_{0c}} = \underbrace{-b\dot{\phi}_z}_{\mathbf{v}_{ec}} \qquad (2)$$

by which (1) becomes

$$\mathbf{H}_e = -\dot{\theta}_z(R/b)I_{ezz}\mathbf{k} = -\dot{\theta}_z(7mRb/5)\mathbf{k} \qquad (3)$$

where $R = a + b$.   According to (8-14),

$$\underbrace{-\ddot{\theta}_z(7mRb/5)\mathbf{k}}_{\dot{\mathbf{H}}_e} = \underbrace{-mgb(\sin\theta_z)\mathbf{k}}_{\mathbf{M}_e} \qquad (4)$$

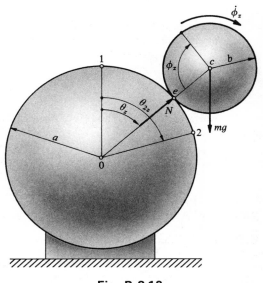

Fig. P-8.13

where $\dot{\mathbf{H}}_e$ is the time derivative of (3) and $\mathbf{M}_e$ is the moment of the weight of the free sphere about e.   Then from (4),

$$\ddot{\theta}_z = \frac{5g\sin\theta_z}{7R}$$

where (as in Problem 8.11) $\ddot{\theta}_z = \dfrac{d\Omega}{d\theta_z}\dfrac{d\theta_z}{dt} = \dfrac{d\Omega}{d\theta_z}\Omega.$ On integrating and solving for Ω,

$$\Omega = \dot{\theta}_z = \sqrt{(10g/7R)(1-\cos\theta_z)+2C} \qquad (5)$$

where at $t = 0$, $\theta_z = 0$ and $2C = \dot{\theta}_{1z}^2$.
The angular speed of the radius R is then

$$\dot{\theta}_z = \sqrt{(10g/7R)(1-\cos\theta_z)+\dot{\theta}_{1z}^2} \qquad (6)$$

and the angular speed of the free sphere is

$$\dot{\phi}_z = \sqrt{(10gR/7b^2)(1-\cos\theta_z)+\dot{\phi}_{1z}^2} \qquad (7)$$

where $\dot{\phi}_{1z}$ is the angular speed at $t = 0$.

8.14 Find the angle θ_{2z} at which the free sphere of Problem 8.13 leaves the surface of the fixed sphere.

As in Problem 8.13, the contact force between these two spheres is

$$N = \dot{G}_n + mg \cos \theta_z = -\frac{mv^2}{R} + mg \cos \theta_z \qquad (1)$$

where $\dot{G}_n$ is the time derivative of the normal component of the linear momentum, v is the speed (circular motion) and $mg \cos \theta_z$ is the normal component of the weight of the free sphere.

At departure, $N = 0$ and so

$$0 = -\frac{m(R\dot{\theta}_z)^2}{R} + mg \cos \theta_z \qquad (2)$$

which in terms of (2) and (7) of Problem 8.13 yields

$$\theta_{2z} = \cos^{-1}(10/17 + 7b\dot{\phi}_{1z}^2/17g) \qquad (3)$$

For $\dot{\phi}_{1z} = 0$, $\theta_{2z} = \cos^{-1}(10/17) = 53.97°$.

ENERGY AND WORK

8.15 Derive the work-energy equation (8-20) for the rigid body in plane motion (Fig. P-8.1).

By definition and in terms of the derivations introduced before (Problems 8.1–8.4), the total mechanical work done by forces moving a rigid body of mass m along a prescribed path from position 1 to position 2 is

$$U = \int_m \int_1^2 (\mathbf{r}_{0m}^{**} \, dm) \cdot d\mathbf{r}_{0m} = \int_m \int_{t_1}^{t_2} (\mathbf{r}_{0m}^{**} \cdot \mathbf{r}_{0m}^{*} \, dm) \, dt$$

$$= \int_m dm \int_{t_1}^{t_2} \frac{d}{2\,dt} (\mathbf{r}_{0m}^{*} \cdot \mathbf{r}_{0m}^{*}) \, dt = \tfrac{1}{2} \int_m \left[\mathbf{r}_{0m}^{*} \cdot \mathbf{r}_{0m}^{*} \right]_{t_1}^{t_2} dm$$

where by (2) of Problem 8.1 $\mathbf{r}_{0m}^{*} = \dot{\mathbf{r}}_{0c} + \mathbf{\Omega} \times \mathbf{r}_{cm}$, and $\mathbf{r}_{0m}^{*} \cdot \mathbf{r}_{0m}^{*} = \dot{r}_{0c}^2 + 2\dot{\mathbf{r}}_{0c} \cdot (\mathbf{\Omega} \times \mathbf{r}_{cm}) + \Omega^2 r_{cm}^2$. Then

$$U = \tfrac{1}{2} \int_m \left[\dot{r}_{0c}^2 \right]_{t_1}^{t_2} dm + \tfrac{1}{2} \int_m \left[\dot{\mathbf{r}}_{0c} \cdot (\mathbf{\Omega} \times \mathbf{r}_{cm}) \right]_{t_1}^{t_2} dm + \tfrac{1}{2} \int_m \left[\Omega^2 r_{cm}^2 \right]_{t_1}^{t_2} dm$$

$$= \tfrac{1}{2} m(\dot{r}_{0c,\,1}^2 - \dot{r}_{0c,\,1}^2) + \tfrac{1}{2} \left[\dot{\mathbf{r}}_{0c} \cdot \left(\mathbf{\Omega} \times \overset{0}{\overbrace{\int_m \mathbf{r}_{om} \, dm}} \right) \right]_{t_1}^{t_2} + \tfrac{1}{2} I_{czz}(\Omega_2^2 - \Omega_1^2)$$

which is a rigid body generalization of Problem 5.13.

8.16 Using the principle of conservation of energy, solve Problem 8.11.

Selecting 0 as the datum, the potential and kinetic energies at 1 and 2 are respectively

$$V_1 = mgr \qquad\qquad T_1 = \tfrac{1}{2}mv_1^2 + \tfrac{1}{2}I_{czz}\Omega_1^2 \qquad (1)$$

$$V_2 = mgr \cos \theta_z \qquad\qquad T_2 = \tfrac{1}{2}mv_2^2 + \tfrac{1}{2}I_{czz}\Omega_2^2 \qquad (2)$$

where $v_1 = r\Omega_1$, $v_2 = r\Omega_2$, $I_{czz} = \frac{1}{3}mr^2$. In terms of ($1$) and ($2$), equation ($8$-$21$) is

$$\tfrac{1}{2}mr^2\Omega_1^2 + \tfrac{1}{6}mr^2\Omega_1^2 + mgr = \tfrac{1}{2}mr^2\Omega_2^2 + \tfrac{1}{6}mr^2\Omega_2^2 + mgr\cos\theta_z \qquad (3)$$

from which

$$\Omega_2 = \sqrt{(3g/l)(1 - \cos\theta_z) + \Omega_1^2} \qquad (4)$$

This equation is identical to (10) of Problem 8.11 and is valid for all θ_z as long as $R_x \geq 0$.

8.17 Using the principle of conservation of energy, solve Problem 8.13.

Note that although the geometry of this problem is different from that of Problem 8.16, the energy method of solution for both problems is the same.

Selecting 0 as the datum, the potential and kinetic energies at 1 and 2 are respectively

$$V_1 = Rmg \qquad\qquad T_1 = \tfrac{1}{2}mv_1^2 + \tfrac{1}{2}I_{czz}\dot\phi_{1z}^2 \qquad (1)$$

$$V_2 = Rmg\cos\theta_z \qquad\qquad T_2 = \tfrac{1}{2}mv_2^2 + \tfrac{1}{2}I_{czz}\dot\phi_{2z}^2 \qquad (2)$$

where $R = a + b$, $v_1 = b\dot\phi_{1z}$, $v_2 = b\dot\phi_{2z}$, $I_{czz} = 2mb^2/5$, and by (2) of Problem 8.13,

$$R\dot\theta_z = b\dot\phi_z \qquad (3)$$

In terms of (3),

$$T_1 = \tfrac{7}{10}mR^2\dot\theta_{1z}^2, \qquad T_2 = \tfrac{7}{10}mR^2\dot\theta_{2z}^2 \qquad (4)$$

and (8-21) becomes

$$\tfrac{7}{10}mR^2\dot\theta_{1z}^2 + Rmg = \tfrac{7}{10}mR^2\dot\theta_{2z}^2 + Rmg\cos\theta_z \qquad (5)$$

from which

$$\dot\theta_{2z} = \sqrt{(10g/7R)(1 - \cos\theta_z) + \dot\theta_{1z}^2}$$

This equation is again identical to (6) of Problem 8.13 and is valid for all θ_z as long as $N \geq 0$.

8.18 A rectangular block is moving on a horizontal plane with a constant velocity $\mathbf{v}$ until it strikes a cleat. Find the velocity $\mathbf{v}$ required to turn the block 90° as shown in Fig. P-8.18. Given: a, b, m and $e = \sqrt{a^2 + b^2}$.

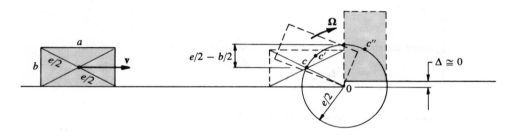

Fig. P-8.18

At impact, the moment of the linear momentum about 0 must equal the angular momentum about 0, i.e.

$$\mathbf{r}_{0c} \times \mathbf{G}_{0c} = \Omega I_{0zz} \tag{1}$$

where $\mathbf{r}_{0c} = -(a/2)\mathbf{i} + (b/2)\mathbf{j}$, $\mathbf{G}_{0c} = mv\mathbf{i}$, $I_{0zz} = me^2/3$, and Ω is the angular velocity of the block. From (1),

$$\Omega = -\frac{3vb}{2e^2}\mathbf{k} \tag{2}$$

To complete its rotation from the horizontal to the vertical position, the kinetic energy of rotation must equal the change in potential energy, i.e.

$$\underbrace{\tfrac{1}{2}\Omega^2 I_{0zz}}_{\Delta T} = \underbrace{mg(e/2 - b/2)}_{-\Delta V} \tag{3}$$

Applying (2),

$$v = 2(e/b)\sqrt{g(e - b)/3} \tag{4}$$

If $v < 2(e/b)\sqrt{g(e - b)/3}$, the block will stop before reaching the top and return back.   If $v > 2(e/b)\sqrt{g(e - b)/3}$, the block will tip over.   In this case as in all impact cases, a loss of energy occurs and can be estimated as

$$\frac{\tfrac{1}{2}I_{0zz}\Omega^2}{\tfrac{1}{2}mv^2} = 3\left(\frac{b}{2e}\right)^2 \tag{5}$$

which for $a = b$ is 37.5%.

Problems

EQUATIONS OF MOTION

8.19   A slender bar of weight W and length l is supported in a horizontal position as shown in Fig. P-8.19.   Define the motion of the mass center c of the bar produced by a sudden removal of the right support.   Given: W, l.

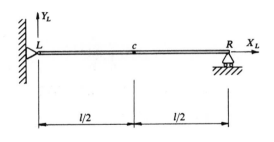

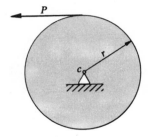

Fig. P-8.19   **Fig. P-8.20**

8.20   A flywheel of radius r and mass m is free to rotate about a fixed axis normal to its plane and passing through its center (Fig. P-8.20).   Find the angular velocity and acceleration of the flywheel produced by a tangential force of constant magnitude P.   Given: r, m, P.

8.21   A solid cylinder and a solid sphere of identical radius r and of identical weight W roll without slipping down an inclined plane (Fig. P-8.21).   Compare their equations of motion.   Assume they both start from rest at 0.   Given: r, W, b, h.

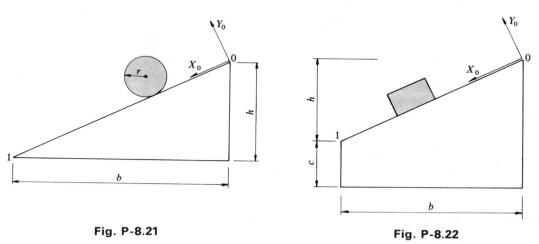

Fig. P-8.21   Fig. P-8.22

8.22   A block of weight W slides down an inclined plane with initial velocity v_0 (Fig. P-8.22).   If the coefficient of kinetic friction between the block and the plane is μ, what is the velocity of the block as it leaves the plane at 1?   Given: W, v_0, μ, b, c, h.

D'ALAMBERT'S PRINCIPLE

8.23   Determine the left end reaction of the bar in Problem 8.19 at rest and during the motion.

8.24   Determine the reactions of the flywheel of Problem 8.20.

8.25   A block of weight W_3 is connected to an inextensible cord of negligible mass which passes over a fixed pulley of weight W_2 and radius r_2, and a free pulley of weight W_1 and radius r_1 (Fig. P-8.25).   Neglecting friction between cord and pulleys, find the acceleration of the falling block.   Given: W_1, W_2, W_3, r_1, r_2.

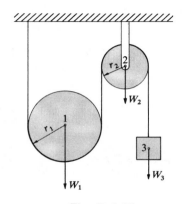

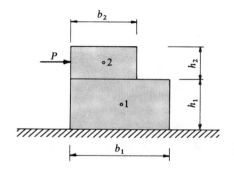

Fig. P-8.25   Fig. P-8.26

8.26 Two blocks of weights W_1 and W_2 respectively, are at rest when a horizontal force of constant magnitude P is applied as shown in Fig. P-8.26. If the coefficients of kinetic friction between the blocks and between the lower block and the base are μ_2 and μ_1 respectively, what is the acceleration of each block? Given: $W_1, W_2, b_1, b_2, h_1, h_2, \mu_1, \mu_2, P$.

8.27 A slender bar of weight W_2 and length l is attached by a hinge to a circular disk of weight W_1 and radius r as shown in Fig. P-8.27. The disk is free to rotate about a fixed axis normal to its plane and passing through its center 0. Neglecting friction, find the angular acceleration of the disk and of the bar produced by a moment of constant magnitude Q applied on the disk. Given: W_1, W_2, r, l, Q.

8.28 Consider the system of Problem 8.27 acted upon by a horizontal force of constant magnitude P as shown in Fig. P-8.28. Neglecting friction, find the angular acceleration of the bar and of the disk produced by this force. Given: W_1, W_2, r, l, P.

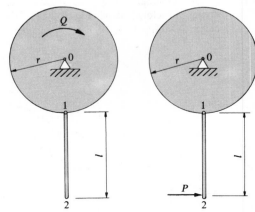

Fig. P-8.27   Fig. P-8.28

LINEAR AND ANGULAR MOMENTUM

8.29 A slender, straight bar of weight W and length l rests on the edge of a fixed block as shown in Fig. P-8.29. If the bar is given an initial angular speed $\dot\theta_{0z}$, what is its angular speed at time t, before leaving the edge of the block? Given: $W, l, \dot\theta_{0z}$.

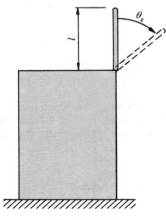

Fig. P-8.29

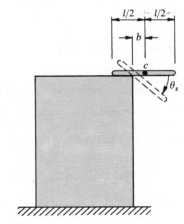

Fig. P-8.32

8.30 Find the angle θ_{2z} at which the bar of Problem 8.29 leaves the edge of the block.

8.31 Using the results of Problem 8.30, derive the equations of motion of the bar of Problem 8.29 after leaving the edge of the block.

8.32 A slender, straight bar of weight W and length l is held in a horizontal position on the top of a fixed block as shown in Fig. P-8.32. If the bar is released, what is its angular speed at time t before leaving the edge of the block? Given: W, l, b.

8.33 Find the angle θ_{2z} at which the bar of Problem 8.32 leaves the edge of the block.

WORK AND ENERGY

8.34 Using the principle of conservation of energy, solve Problem 8.25.

8.35 Using the principle of conservation of energy, solve Problem 8.29.

8.36 Using the principle of conservation of energy, solve Problem 8.32.

8.37 A slender, straight bar of weight W and length l is hinged at 0 and attached to a linear spring of stiffness κ as shown in Fig. P-8.37. For the position shown, the spring is unstretched and the angular speed of the bar is $\dot{\theta}_{0z}$. Determine the angular velocity of the bar after it has rotated through $\theta_z = \pi/2$. Given: $W, l, b, \kappa, \dot{\theta}_{0z}$.

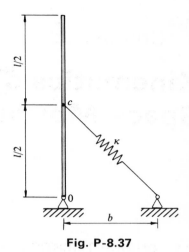

Fig. P-8.37

Chapter 9

Kinematics of Rigid Bodies, Space Motion

9.1 CHARACTERISTICS OF A RIGID BODY

Degrees of Freedom

When some or all particles of a rigid body move along space paths, the motion of the body is called *space motion*. In such a case, the position of the body (Fig. 9-1) is given at any instant t by *six displacements* (coordinates), measured from an arbitrarily selected datum (origin) and designated as

$$x_{0n} = x_{0n}(t), \qquad y_{0n} = y_{0n}(t), \qquad z_{0n} = z_{0n}(t) \tag{9-1}$$

$$\theta_{nx} = \theta_{nx}(t), \qquad \theta_{ny} = \theta_{ny}(t), \qquad \theta_{nz} = \theta_{nz}(t) \tag{9-2}$$

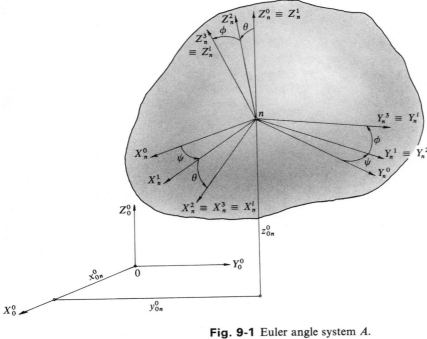

Sequence of rotations:
ψ about Z_n^1
θ about Y_n^2
ϕ about X_n^3

Fig. 9-1 Euler angle system A.

178

where x_{0n}, y_{0n}, z_{0n} are the *linear position coordinates* of an arbitrarily selected point n in the body and θ_{nx}, θ_{ny}, θ_{nz} are the *angular position coordinates* of the body, which have the same meaning as those introduced in (6-42) and (6-43).

If the motion of the body is subjected to r *constraints*, the number of possible and independent displacements reduces to

$$n = 6 - r \qquad (9\text{-}3)$$

where n is the *number of degrees of freedom* of the body.

Generalized Coordinates

These *independent displacements* are called *generalized coordinates*; and although their number is fixed by (9-3), many different sets of such coordinates are admissible.

Note that the linear coordinates are always directed segments, allowing vector representation, whereas the angular coordinates do not have all the properties required of vectors and do not permit vector representation.

Instantaneous Axis and Centrodal Surface

In space motion of a rigid body there is at any time an axis about which the body rotates and along which the body translates. This axis is called the *instantaneous axis* (line of zero transverse velocity), and the motion of the body referred to this axis is called the *screw motion*.

As the body moves, the instantaneous axis also moves, generating a warped surface called the *centrodal surface*. For a body which rotates about a fixed point, the centrodal surface becomes a *centrodal cone*.

Theorems of Rigid Body Motion

The fundamental theorems of rigid body motion introduced in Chapter 7 and designated as *Euler's theorem* and *Chasle's theorem*, are general and apply also in the kinematics of space motion.

9.2   EULER ANGLES

Geometry of Rotation

The position angles of a rigid body in space motion (Fig. 9-1) given by (9-2) are frequently called *Euler angles* and denoted by

$$\theta_{nz} = \psi, \qquad \theta_{ny} = \theta, \qquad \theta_{nx} = \phi \qquad (9\text{-}4)$$

where θ_{nz}, θ_{ny}, θ_{nx} are the successive rotations of the cartesian axes discussed in Section 6.4, page 121.

Three different types of *Euler angle systems* are in common use; their relationships are shown in Table 9-1 below and their constructions are given in Problems 9.1–9.3. System A (Fig. 9-1) has been adopted in aeronautical engineering and more recently in the analysis of space vehicles. Systems B and C are being used in the analysis of gyroscopic motion.

If these angles are limited to the range

$$0 \leq \psi < 2\pi, \qquad -\pi/2 \leq \theta \leq \pi/2, \qquad 0 \leq \phi < 2\pi \qquad (9\text{-}5)$$

any position of the body can be attained by performing successively the prescribed rotations (Table 9-1).

Table 9.1 Euler Angle Systems

	A	B	C
Sequence of rotations	ψ_A about $Z_n^0 \equiv Z_n^1$ θ_A about $Y_n^1 \equiv Y_n^2$ ϕ_A about $X_n^2 \equiv X_n^3$	ϕ_B about $Z_n^0 \equiv Z_n^1$ θ_B about $X_n^1 \equiv X_n^4$ ψ_B about $Z_n^4 \equiv Z_n^5$	ψ_C about $Z_n^0 \equiv Z^1$ θ_C about $Y_n^1 \equiv Y_n^2$ ϕ_C about $Z_n^2 \equiv Z_n^6$
Relation of angles	$\psi_A = \psi$ $\theta_A = \theta$ $\phi_A = \phi$	$\phi_B = -\psi$ $\theta_B = \pi/2 - \theta$ $\psi_B = \phi$	$\psi_C = -\psi$ $\theta_C = \pi/2 - \theta$ $\phi_C = \phi$
Relations of unit vectors	$\mathbf{i}_A^0 = \mathbf{i}^0$ $\mathbf{j}_A^0 = \mathbf{j}^0$ $\mathbf{k}_A^0 = \mathbf{k}^0$	$\mathbf{i}_B^0 = -\mathbf{j}^0$ $\mathbf{j}_B^0 = -\mathbf{i}^0$ $\mathbf{k}_B^0 = -\mathbf{k}^0$	$\mathbf{i}_C^0 = \mathbf{i}^0$ $\mathbf{j}_C^0 = -\mathbf{j}^0$ $\mathbf{k}_C^0 = -\mathbf{k}^0$
	$\mathbf{i}_A^l = \mathbf{i}^3$ $\mathbf{j}_A^l = \mathbf{j}^3$ $\mathbf{k}_A^l = \mathbf{k}^3$	$\mathbf{i}_B^l = \mathbf{i}^5 = -\mathbf{j}^3$ $\mathbf{j}_B^l = \mathbf{j}^5 = -\mathbf{k}^3$ $\mathbf{k}_B^l = \mathbf{k}^5 = \mathbf{i}^3$	$\mathbf{i}_C^l = \mathbf{i}^6 = \mathbf{k}^3$ $\mathbf{j}_C^l = \mathbf{j}^6 = -\mathbf{j}^3$ $\mathbf{k}_C^l = \mathbf{k}^6 = \mathbf{i}^3$
	Problem 9.1	Problem 9.2	Problem 9.3

Euler Matrices $[\pi^{0l}]$, $[\pi^{l0}]$

The *angular transformation matrices* relating the cartesian components of vector $\mathbf{r}_{nm}$ in the 0-system (stationary axes) to their counterparts in the l-system (rotating axes), and vice versa, are the already known π-matrices (Section 6.4, page 121) expressed *in terms of Euler angles* (9-4),

$$
\underbrace{\begin{bmatrix} x_{nm}^l \\ y_{nm}^l \\ z_{nm}^l \end{bmatrix}}_{[s_{nm}^l]} = \underbrace{\begin{bmatrix} \cos\psi\cos\theta & \sin\psi\cos\theta & -\sin\theta \\ \begin{matrix}(-\sin\psi\cos\phi \\ +\cos\psi\sin\theta\sin\phi)\end{matrix} & \begin{matrix}(\cos\psi\cos\phi \\ +\sin\psi\sin\theta\sin\phi)\end{matrix} & \cos\theta\sin\phi \\ \begin{matrix}(\sin\psi\sin\phi \\ +\cos\psi\sin\theta\cos\phi)\end{matrix} & \begin{matrix}(-\cos\psi\sin\phi \\ +\sin\psi\sin\theta\cos\phi)\end{matrix} & \cos\theta\cos\phi \end{bmatrix}}_{[\pi^{l0}]} \underbrace{\begin{bmatrix} x_{nm}^0 \\ y_{nm}^0 \\ z_{nm}^0 \end{bmatrix}}_{[s_{nm}^0]}
$$

(9-6)

$$
\begin{bmatrix} x^0_{nm} \\ \\ y^0_{nm} \\ \\ z^0_{nm} \end{bmatrix} = \begin{bmatrix} \cos\psi\cos\theta & \begin{pmatrix} -\sin\psi\cos\phi \\ +\cos\psi\sin\theta\sin\phi \end{pmatrix} & \begin{pmatrix} \sin\psi\sin\phi \\ +\cos\psi\sin\theta\cos\phi \end{pmatrix} \\ \sin\psi\cos\theta & \begin{pmatrix} \cos\psi\cos\phi \\ +\sin\psi\sin\theta\sin\phi \end{pmatrix} & \begin{pmatrix} -\cos\psi\sin\phi \\ +\sin\psi\sin\theta\cos\phi \end{pmatrix} \\ -\sin\theta & \cos\theta\sin\phi & \cos\theta\cos\phi \end{bmatrix} \begin{bmatrix} x^l_{nm} \\ \\ y^l_{nm} \\ \\ z^l_{nm} \end{bmatrix} \tag{9-7}
$$

$$\underbrace{}_{[s^0_{nm}]} \qquad\qquad \underbrace{}_{[\pi^{0l}]} \qquad\qquad \underbrace{}_{[s^l_{nm}]}$$

where $[\pi^{0l}]$ and $[\pi^{l0}]$ are orthogonal matrices constructed by matrix multiplication indicated in (6-42) and (6-43).

Euler Matrices $[\Gamma^l]$, $[\Gamma^0]$

The *generalizations of* $[\Gamma]$ introduced in (6-48) are the Euler matrices $[\Gamma^l]$ and $[\Gamma^0]$:

$$
[\Gamma^l] = [\pi^{l0}][\dot\pi^{0l}] = \begin{bmatrix} 0 & -\Omega^l_z & \Omega^l_y \\ \Omega^l_z & 0 & -\Omega^l_x \\ -\Omega^l_y & \Omega^l_x & 0 \end{bmatrix} \tag{9-8}
$$

$$
[\Gamma^0] = [\pi^{0l}][\dot\pi^{l0}] = \begin{bmatrix} 0 & -\Omega^0_z & \Omega^0_y \\ \Omega^0_z & 0 & -\Omega^0_x \\ -\Omega^0_y & \Omega^0_x & 0 \end{bmatrix} \tag{9-9}
$$

where

$$
\begin{aligned}
\Omega^l_x &= \dot\phi - \dot\psi\sin\theta \\
\Omega^l_y &= \dot\theta\cos\phi + \dot\psi\cos\theta\sin\phi \\
\Omega^l_z &= \dot\psi\cos\theta\cos\phi - \dot\theta\sin\phi
\end{aligned} \tag{9-10}
$$

are the *angular velocities of the body in the l-system* (Fig. 9-2) and $\dot\phi$, $\dot\theta$, $\dot\psi$ are the nonorthogonal *angular velocities of the Euler angle system A* (Fig. 9-3).

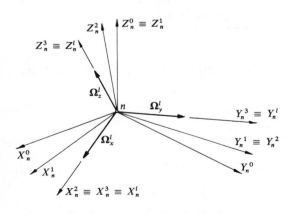

Fig. 9-2 Angular velocities in the *l*-system.

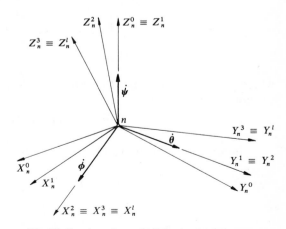

Fig. 9-3 Angular velocities in the *e*-system.

The *angular velocities of the body in the 0-system* (Fig. 9-4) are then

$$[\Omega^0] = [\pi^{0l}][\Omega^l] \qquad (9\text{-}11)$$

where $[\pi^{0l}]$ and $[\Omega^l]$ are given by *(9-7)* and *(9-10)* respectively.

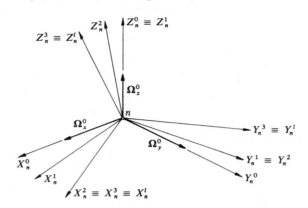

Fig. 9-4   Angular velocities in the 0-system.

Euler Matrices $[\tau^{le}]$, $[\tau^{el}]$, $[\tau^{0e}]$, $[\tau^{e0}]$

The most typical matrix based on the system of Euler angles is the *τ-matrix*, which provides the relationship of the *cartesian angular velocity vector* $[\Omega^l]$ to the *Eulerian angular velocity vector* $[\Omega^e]$.

From *(9-10)*,

$$\underbrace{\begin{bmatrix} \Omega_x^l \\ \Omega_y^l \\ \Omega_z^l \end{bmatrix}}_{[\Omega^l]} = \underbrace{\begin{bmatrix} 1 & 0 & -\sin\theta \\ 0 & \cos\phi & \cos\theta\sin\phi \\ 0 & -\sin\phi & \cos\theta\cos\phi \end{bmatrix}}_{[\tau^{le}]} \underbrace{\begin{bmatrix} \dot{\phi} \\ \dot{\theta} \\ \dot{\psi} \end{bmatrix}}_{[\Omega^e]} \qquad (9\text{-}12)$$

and inversely,

$$\underbrace{\begin{bmatrix} \dot{\phi} \\ \dot{\theta} \\ \dot{\psi} \end{bmatrix}}_{[\Omega^e]} = \underbrace{\begin{bmatrix} 1 & \sin\phi\tan\theta & \cos\phi\tan\theta \\ 0 & \cos\phi & -\sin\phi \\ 0 & (\sin\phi)/(\cos\theta) & (\cos\phi)/(\cos\theta) \end{bmatrix}}_{[\tau^{el}]} \underbrace{\begin{bmatrix} \Omega_x^l \\ \Omega_y^l \\ \Omega_z^l \end{bmatrix}}_{[\Omega^l]} \qquad (9\text{-}13)$$

where $[\tau^{le}][\tau^{el}] = [I]$, but they are *not orthogonal matrices* since $[\Omega^e]$ is in the X_n^3, Y_n^2, Z_n^1 axes which are not orthogonal, i.e.

$$[\tau^{le}]^T \neq [\tau^{el}], \qquad [\tau^{le}]^T \neq [\tau^{le}]$$

In terms of *(9-6)*, *(9-7)* and *(9-12)*, *(9-13)*, the remaining relations are

$$[\Omega^0] = \underbrace{[\pi^{0l}][\tau^{le}]}_{[\tau^{0e}]}[\Omega^e], \qquad [\Omega^e] = \underbrace{[\tau^{el}][\pi^{l0}]}_{[\tau^{l0}]}[\Omega^0] \qquad (9\text{-}14),\,(9\text{-}15)$$

where $[\tau^{0e}][\tau^{e0}] = [I]$, but as before they are *not orthogonal*.

9.3   ABSOLUTE SPACE MOTION

Vector Equations

Since according to Chasle's theorem (Theorem 7.2, page 138) the motion of a rigid body can always be represented as superposition of translation and rotation about an arbitrarily selected point, as before, the point n and the segment $\overline{nm}$ are selected for the study of this motion (Fig. 9-5).   Then the linear motion of n defines the translation and the angular motion of radius r_{nm} defines the rotation of the body.

The *equations of space motion* of the rigid body referred to these two points and the fixed origin 0, are

$$\mathbf{r}_{0m} = \mathbf{r}_{0n} + \mathbf{r}_{nm} \tag{9-16}$$

$$\mathbf{v}_{0m} = \mathbf{r}^*_{0m} = \dot{\mathbf{r}}_{0n} + \boldsymbol{\Omega} \times \mathbf{r}_{nm} \tag{9-17}$$

$$\mathbf{a}_{0m} = \mathbf{v}^*_{0m} = \mathbf{r}^{**}_{0m} = \ddot{\mathbf{r}}_{0n} + \dot{\boldsymbol{\Omega}} \times \mathbf{r}_{nm} + \boldsymbol{\Omega} \times (\boldsymbol{\Omega} \times \mathbf{r}_{nm}) \tag{9-18}$$

In these equations,

$$\mathbf{r}_{0n} = x^0_{0n}\mathbf{i}^0 + y^0_{0n}\mathbf{j}^0 + z^0_{0n}\mathbf{k}^0 \tag{9-19}$$

$$\mathbf{r}_{nm} = x^l_{nm}\mathbf{i}^l + y^l_{nm}\mathbf{j}^l + z^l_{nm}\mathbf{k}^l = x^0_{nm}\mathbf{i}^0 + y^0_{nm}\mathbf{j}^0 + z^0_{nm}\mathbf{k}^0 \tag{9-20}$$

$$\boldsymbol{\Omega} = \Omega^l_x\mathbf{i}^l + \Omega^l_y\mathbf{j}^l + \Omega^l_z\mathbf{k}^l = \Omega^0_x\mathbf{i}^0 + \Omega^0_y\mathbf{j}^0 + \Omega^0_z\mathbf{k}^0 \tag{9-21}$$

$$\dot{\boldsymbol{\Omega}} = \dot{\Omega}^l_x\mathbf{i}^l + \dot{\Omega}^l_y\mathbf{j}^l + \dot{\Omega}^l_z\mathbf{k}^l = \dot{\Omega}^0_x\mathbf{i}^0 + \dot{\Omega}^0_y\mathbf{j}^0 + \dot{\Omega}^0_z\mathbf{k}^0 \tag{9-22}$$

where the superscripts 0 and l designate the stationary and rotating systems respectively.

These equations can be deduced from (6-31), (6-38), (6-39) by deleting $\dot{\mathbf{r}}_{nm}$, $\ddot{\mathbf{r}}_{nm}$ and $2\boldsymbol{\Omega} \times \dot{\mathbf{r}}_{nm}$, which by condition of rigidity must equal zero.   The inclusion of Euler angles in (9-20)–(9-22) can be accomplished by means of (9-12) as shown in Problems 9.10 and 9.11.

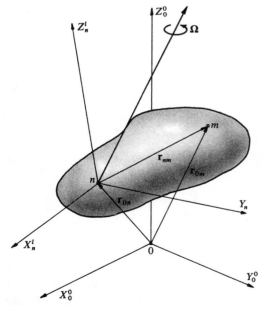

Fig. 9-5   Space motion of a rigid body.

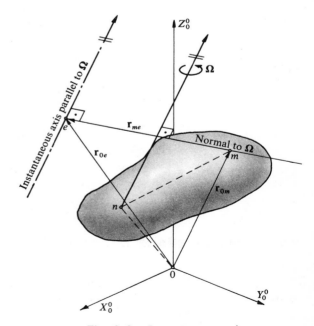

Fig. 9-6   Instantaneous axis.

Instantaneous Axis

By definition, the *instantaneous axis* is the line of zero transverse velocity and its location is given by

$$\mathbf{r}_{me} = (\mathbf{\Omega} \times \mathbf{r}_{0m}^*)/\Omega^2 \qquad (9\text{-}23)$$

where $\mathbf{r}_{me} = -\mathbf{r}_{em}$ is normal to the instantaneous axis and also to $\mathbf{\Omega}$ (Fig. 9-6).

In matrix form,

$$\underbrace{\begin{bmatrix} x_{me}^l \\ y_{me}^l \\ z_{me}^l \end{bmatrix}}_{[s_{me}^l]} = \frac{1}{\Omega^2} \underbrace{\begin{bmatrix} 0 & -\Omega_z^l & \Omega_y^l \\ \Omega_z^l & 0 & -\Omega_x^l \\ -\Omega_y^l & \Omega_x^l & 0 \end{bmatrix}}_{[\Gamma^l]} \underbrace{\begin{bmatrix} x_{0m}^{l*} \\ y_{0m}^{l*} \\ z_{0m}^{l*} \end{bmatrix}}_{[s_{0m}^{l*}]} \qquad (9\text{-}24)$$

which in the case of plane motion reduces to (7-6).

The instantaneous axis passes through e, and its direction cosines

$$\alpha_e = \Omega_x/\Omega, \qquad \beta_e = \Omega_y/\Omega, \qquad \gamma_e = \Omega_z/\Omega \qquad (9\text{-}25)$$

are the direction cosines of $\mathbf{\Omega}$.

Matrix Equations

The matrix equations of space motion follow the pattern of (7-7)–(7-9) and can be written in either system of axes. In the 0-system,

$$[s_{0m}^0] = [s_{0n}^0] + [s_{nm}^0] \qquad (9\text{-}26)$$

$$[s_{0m}^{0*}] = [\dot{s}_{0n}^0] + [\Gamma^0][s_{nm}^0] \qquad (9\text{-}27)$$

$$[s_{0m}^{0**}] = [\ddot{s}_{0n}^0] + [\Delta^0][s_{nm}^0] \qquad (9\text{-}28)$$

where again the terms involving the relative velocity and acceleration are deleted and

$$[\Gamma^0] = \begin{bmatrix} 0 & -\Omega_z^0 & \Omega_y^0 \\ \Omega_z^0 & 0 & -\Omega_x^0 \\ -\Omega_y^0 & \Omega_x^0 & 0 \end{bmatrix} \qquad (9\text{-}29)$$

$$[\Delta^0] = \begin{bmatrix} -[(\Omega_y^0)^2 + (\Omega_z^0)^2] & \Omega_x^0\Omega_y^0 - \dot{\Omega}_z^0 & \Omega_x^0\Omega_z^0 + \dot{\Omega}_y^0 \\ \Omega_x^0\Omega_y^0 + \dot{\Omega}_z^0 & -[(\Omega_z^0)^2 + (\Omega_x^0)^2] & \Omega_y^0\Omega_z^0 - \dot{\Omega}_x^0 \\ \Omega_z^0\Omega_x^0 - \dot{\Omega}_y^0 & \Omega_z^0\Omega_y^0 + \dot{\Omega}_x^0 & -[(\Omega_x^0)^2 + (\Omega_y^0)^2] \end{bmatrix} \qquad (9\text{-}30)$$

9.4   RELATIVE SPACE MOTION

Vector Equations

The general case of space motion of a rigid body includes the rotating axes X^l, Y^l, Z^l which are assumed to be rigidly connected to the body, so that the angular velocity of the axes, ω, equals the angular velocity of the body, $\mathbf{\Omega}$, and furthermore, the distance $\overline{nm}$ may or may not be fixed. Formally, they are identical to (7-10)–(7-12), but include three-dimensional vectors.

The completely general case, which includes independent ω and Ω, is rarely encountered and as such is not considered in this book.

Instantaneous Axis

Since the velocity vector (9-17) is not affected by the rotation of $\omega = \Omega$, the location and direction of the instantaneous axis are given again by (9-23) and (9-24).

Matrix Equations

The matrix equations of relative space motion of a rigid body are three-dimensional generalizations of (7-13)–(7-15), which can be written in either system of axes.   In the 0-system,

$$[s_{0m}^0] = [s_{0n}^0] + [s_{nm}^0] \qquad (9\text{-}31)$$

$$[s_{0m}^{0*}] = [\dot{s}_{0n}^0] + [\dot{s}_{nm}^0] + [\Gamma^0][s_{nm}^0] \qquad (9\text{-}32)$$

$$[s_{0m}^{0**}] = [\ddot{s}_{0n}^0] + [\ddot{s}_{nm}^0] + 2[\Gamma^0][\dot{s}_{nm}^0] + [\Delta^0][s_{nm}^0] \qquad (9\text{-}33)$$

where Γ^0 and Δ^0 are given by (9-29) and (9-30) respectively.

Illustrative Problems

EULER ANGLES

9.1 Construct the angular transformation matrices for the Euler angle system A (case A, Table 9-1, page 180).

By definition, the Euler angle system A is obtained by successive rotations of the initial axes X^0, Y^0, Z^0 through the Euler angles ψ, θ, ϕ as shown in Table P-9.1.

These three rotations are:

(a) Rotation of the 0-system about $Z^0 \equiv Z^1$ through angle ψ into the 1-system (Table P-9.1a).
(b) Rotation of the 1-system about $Y^1 \equiv Y^2$ through angle θ into the 2-system (Table P-9.1b).
(c) Rotation of the 2-system about $X^2 \equiv X^3$ through angle ϕ into the 3-system (Table P-9.1c).

The final system of axes, designated as the l-system, is in this case the 3-system.

The matrix relations of the unit vectors in each system of axes are given below the respective rotation in Table P-9.1.

By direct successive substitutions (Table P-9.1a, b, c),

$$[\mathbf{e}^0] = [\pi^{01}][\mathbf{e}^1] = [\pi^{01}][\pi^{12}][\mathbf{e}^2] = \underbrace{[\pi^{01}][\pi^{12}][\pi^{23}]}_{[\pi^{03}]}[\mathbf{e}^3] \qquad (1)$$

where $[\pi^{03}]$ is the Euler angular transformation matrix $[\pi^{0l}]$ given in (9-7).

By inverse successive substitutions (Table P-9.1c, b, a),

$$[\mathbf{e}^3] = [\pi^{32}][\mathbf{e}^2] = [\pi^{32}][\pi^{21}][\mathbf{e}^1] = \underbrace{[\pi^{32}][\pi^{21}][\pi^{10}]}_{[\pi^{30}]}[\mathbf{e}^0] \qquad (2)$$

Table P-9.1   Euler Angle System A

$$
\begin{bmatrix} i^0 \\ j^0 \\ k^0 \end{bmatrix} = \begin{bmatrix} \cos\psi & -\sin\psi & 0 \\ \sin\psi & \cos\psi & 0 \\ 0 & 0 & 1 \end{bmatrix} \begin{bmatrix} i^1 \\ j^1 \\ k^1 \end{bmatrix}
$$
$$[\mathbf{e}^0] \qquad\quad [\pi^{01}] \qquad\quad [\mathbf{e}^1]$$

$$
\begin{bmatrix} i^1 \\ j^1 \\ k^1 \end{bmatrix} = \begin{bmatrix} \cos\theta & 0 & \sin\theta \\ 0 & 1 & 0 \\ -\sin\theta & 0 & \cos\theta \end{bmatrix} \begin{bmatrix} i^2 \\ j^2 \\ k^2 \end{bmatrix}
$$
$$[\mathbf{e}^1] \qquad\quad [\pi^{12}] \qquad\quad [\mathbf{e}^2]$$

$$
\begin{bmatrix} i^2 \\ j^2 \\ k^2 \end{bmatrix} = \begin{bmatrix} 1 & 0 & 0 \\ 0 & \cos\phi & -\sin\phi \\ 0 & \sin\phi & \cos\phi \end{bmatrix} \begin{bmatrix} i^3 \\ j^3 \\ k^3 \end{bmatrix}
$$
$$[\mathbf{e}^2] \qquad\quad [\pi^{23}] \qquad\quad [\mathbf{e}^3]$$

$$
\begin{bmatrix} i^1 \\ j^1 \\ k^1 \end{bmatrix} = \begin{bmatrix} \cos\psi & \sin\psi & 0 \\ -\sin\psi & \cos\psi & 0 \\ 0 & 0 & 1 \end{bmatrix} \begin{bmatrix} i^0 \\ j^0 \\ k^0 \end{bmatrix}
$$
$$[\mathbf{e}^1] \qquad\quad [\pi^{10}] \qquad\quad [\mathbf{e}^0]$$

$$
\begin{bmatrix} i^2 \\ j^2 \\ k^2 \end{bmatrix} = \begin{bmatrix} \cos\theta & 0 & -\sin\theta \\ 0 & 1 & 0 \\ \sin\theta & 0 & \cos\theta \end{bmatrix} \begin{bmatrix} i^1 \\ j^1 \\ k^1 \end{bmatrix}
$$
$$[\mathbf{e}^2] \qquad\quad [\pi^{21}] \qquad\quad [\mathbf{e}^1]$$

$$
\begin{bmatrix} i^3 \\ j^3 \\ k^3 \end{bmatrix} = \begin{bmatrix} 1 & 0 & 0 \\ 0 & \cos\phi & \sin\phi \\ 0 & -\sin\phi & \cos\phi \end{bmatrix} \begin{bmatrix} i^2 \\ j^2 \\ k^2 \end{bmatrix}
$$
$$[\mathbf{e}^3] \qquad\quad [\pi^{32}] \qquad\quad [\mathbf{e}^2]$$

where $[\pi^{30}]$ is the Euler angular transformation matrix $[\pi^{l0}]$ given in (9-6).

Since the determinants of $[\pi^{0l}]$ and $[\pi^{l0}]$ equal $+1$, these matrices are orthogonal so that

$$[\pi^{l0}] = [\pi^{0l}]^T \qquad \text{and} \qquad [\pi^{0l}] = [\pi^{l0}]^T \qquad (3),(4)$$

9.2   Construct the angular transformation matrices for the Euler angle system B (case B, Table 9-1, page 180).

Again, the three successive rotations shown in Table P-9.2 are required.   The final system of axes desig-nated as the l-system in this case is the 5-system.   Contrary to Problem 9.1, the sequence of angles is ϕ, θ, ψ.   By direct successive substitutions (Table P-9.2a, b, c),

$$[\mathbf{e}^0] = [\pi^{01}][\mathbf{e}^1] = [\pi^{01}][\pi^{14}][\mathbf{e}^4] = \underbrace{[\pi^{01}][\pi^{14}][\pi^{45}]}_{[\pi^{05}]}[\mathbf{e}^5] \qquad (1)$$

where

$$[\pi^{05}] = \left[\begin{array}{c|c|c} \cos\phi\cos\psi - \sin\phi\cos\theta\sin\psi & -\cos\phi\sin\psi - \sin\phi\cos\theta\cos\psi & \sin\phi\sin\theta \\ \hline \sin\phi\cos\psi - \cos\phi\cos\theta\sin\psi & -\sin\phi\sin\psi + \cos\phi\cos\theta\cos\psi & -\cos\phi\sin\theta \\ \hline \sin\theta\sin\psi & \sin\theta\cos\psi & \cos\theta \end{array}\right] \qquad (2)$$

is the Euler angular transformation matrix $[\pi^{0l}]$ in the angle system B.

From the orthogonality condition,

$$[\pi^{50}] = [\pi^{05}]^T \qquad (3)$$

which is the Euler angular transformation matrix $[\pi^{l0}]$ in the angle system B.

Table P-9.2   Euler Angle System B

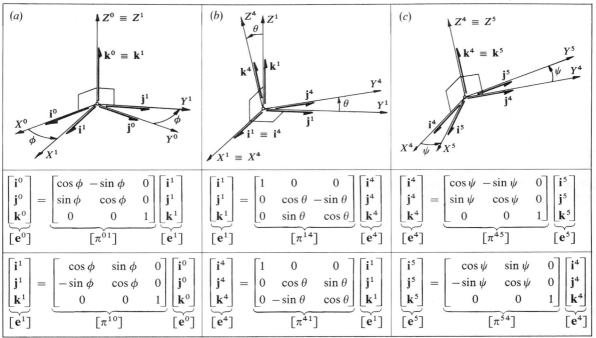

9.3 Construct the angular transformation matrices for the Euler angle system C (case C, Table 9-1, page 180).

The three successive rotations defining the system C are shown in Table P-9.3, and the final system of axes designated as the l-system is in this case the 6-system.

By direct successive substitutions (Table P-9.3a, b, c),

$$[e^0] = [\pi^{01}][e^1] = [\pi^{01}][\pi^{12}][e^2] = \underbrace{[\pi^{01}][\pi^{12}][\pi^{26}]}_{[\pi^{06}]}[e^6] \tag{1}$$

where

$$[\pi^{06}] = \left[\begin{array}{cc|cc|c} \cos\psi\cos\theta\cos\phi - \sin\psi\sin\phi & & -\cos\psi\cos\theta\sin\phi - \sin\psi\cos\phi & & \cos\psi\sin\theta \\ \hline \sin\psi\cos\theta\cos\phi - \cos\psi\sin\phi & & -\sin\psi\cos\theta\sin\phi + \cos\psi\cos\phi & & \sin\psi\sin\theta \\ \hline -\sin\theta\cos\phi & & \sin\theta\sin\phi & & \cos\theta \end{array}\right] \tag{2}$$

is the Euler angular transformation matrix $[\pi^{0l}]$ in the angle system C.

From the orthogonality condition,

$$[\pi^{60}] = [\pi^{06}]^T \tag{3}$$

which is the Euler angular transformation matrix $[\pi^{l0}]$ in the angle system C.

Table P-9.3   Euler Angle System C

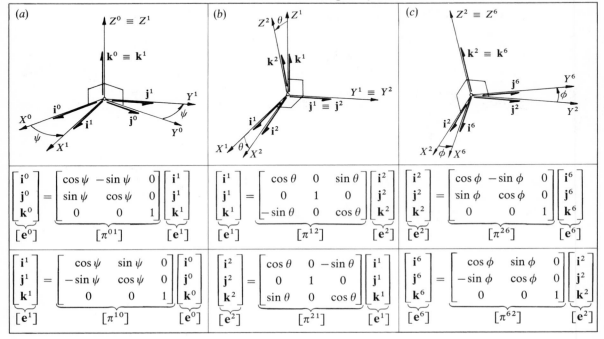

9.4   Show that finite rotations cannot be represented by vectors.

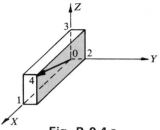

Fig. P-9.4 a

The ice block of Fig. P-9.4a undergoes three rotations,

$$\theta_x = \pi/2, \qquad \theta_y = \pi/2, \qquad \theta_z = \pi/2$$

about the respective axes X, Y, Z, executed in direct and inverse order as shown in Fig. P-9.4b and c, respectively.

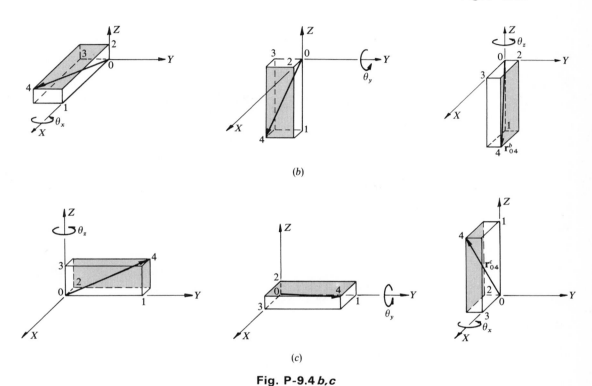

(b)

(c)

Fig. P-9.4 b,c

The comparison of the final positions of vector $\mathbf{r}_{04}^b$ in Fig. P-9.4b and of vector $\mathbf{r}_{04}^c$ in Fig. P-9.4c, reveals that although the angles of rotation used were of the same magnitude and direction, the final positions of $\mathbf{r}_{04}$ in each case are different,

$$\mathbf{r}_{04}^b \neq \mathbf{r}_{04}^c$$

and therefore

$$\boldsymbol{\theta}_x + \boldsymbol{\theta}_y + \boldsymbol{\theta}_z \neq \boldsymbol{\theta}_z + \boldsymbol{\theta}_y + \boldsymbol{\theta}_x$$

For the same reason the sequence of matrices forming the matrix product of $[\pi^{0l}]$ and $[\pi^{l0}]$ cannot be interchanged.

9.5 Find the time derivatives of unit vectors $\mathbf{i}^l$, $\mathbf{j}^l$, $\mathbf{k}^l$ in terms of the Euler angle system A.

By (9-7),

$$[\mathbf{e}^o] = [\pi^{ol}][\mathbf{e}^l] \tag{1}$$

where $[\mathbf{e}^o]$ is the column matrix of unit vectors in the stationary axes, $[\mathbf{e}^l]$ is the column matrix of unit vectors in the rotating axes, and $[\pi^{ol}]$ is their transformation matrix.

The time derivative of (1) is

$$[\dot{\mathbf{e}}^o] = [\dot{\pi}^{ol}][\mathbf{e}^l] + [\pi^{ol}][\dot{\mathbf{e}}^l] \tag{2}$$

where $[\dot{\mathbf{e}}^o] = 0$ (time-independent unit vectors). Then from (2),

$$[\dot{\mathbf{e}}^l] = -[\pi^{lo}][\dot{\pi}^{ol}][\mathbf{e}] = -[\Gamma^l][\mathbf{e}^l] \tag{3}$$

where

$$[\Gamma^l] = [\pi^{lo}][\dot{\pi}^{ol}] = \left[\begin{array}{c|c|c} 0 & \dot{\theta}\sin\phi - \dot{\psi}\cos\theta\cos\phi & \dot{\psi}\cos\theta\sin\phi + \dot{\theta}\cos\phi \\ \hline \dot{\psi}\cos\theta\cos\phi - \dot{\theta}\sin\phi & 0 & \dot{\psi}\sin\theta - \dot{\phi} \\ \hline -\dot{\psi}\cos\theta\sin\phi - \dot{\theta}\cos\phi & \dot{\phi} - \dot{\psi}\sin\theta & 0 \end{array} \right] \tag{4}$$

or symbolically,

$$[\Gamma^l] = [\pi^{lo}][\dot{\pi}^{ol}] = \begin{bmatrix} 0 & -\Omega_z^l & \Omega_y^l \\ \Omega_z^l & 0 & -\Omega_x^l \\ -\Omega_y^l & \Omega_x^l & 0 \end{bmatrix} \tag{5}$$

By inspection,

$$\begin{aligned} \Omega_x^l &= \dot{\phi} - \dot{\psi}\sin\theta \\ \Omega_y^l &= \dot{\theta}\cos\phi + \dot{\psi}\cos\theta\sin\phi \\ \Omega_z^l &= \dot{\psi}\cos\theta\cos\phi - \dot{\theta}\sin\phi \end{aligned} \tag{6}$$

9.6 Express the unit vectors $\mathbf{e}^\psi$, $\mathbf{e}^\theta$, $\mathbf{e}^\phi$ of angular velocities $\dot{\psi}, \dot{\theta}, \dot{\phi}$ of the Euler angle system A in terms of unit vectors $\mathbf{i}^l$, $\mathbf{j}^l$, $\mathbf{k}^l$.

From Table P-9.1b, c the unit vector $\mathbf{e}^\psi$ is the unit vector along the Z^1 axis,

$$\mathbf{e}^\psi = \mathbf{k}^1 = [-\sin\theta \quad 0 \quad \cos\theta] \begin{bmatrix} 1 & 0 & 0 \\ 0 & \cos\phi & -\sin\phi \\ 0 & \sin\phi & \cos\phi \end{bmatrix} \begin{bmatrix} \mathbf{i}^l \\ \mathbf{j}^l \\ \mathbf{k}^l \end{bmatrix} \tag{1}$$

$$= (-\sin\theta)\mathbf{i}^l + (\cos\theta\sin\phi)\mathbf{j}^l + (\cos\theta\cos\phi)\mathbf{k}^l$$

From Table P-9.1c the unit vector $\mathbf{e}^\theta$ is the unit vector along the Y^2 axis,

$$\mathbf{e}^\theta = \mathbf{j}^2 = \begin{bmatrix} 0 & \cos\phi & -\sin\phi \end{bmatrix} \begin{bmatrix} \mathbf{i}^l \\ \mathbf{j}^l \\ \mathbf{k}^l \end{bmatrix} = (\cos\phi)\mathbf{j}^l - (\sin\phi)\mathbf{k}^l \tag{2}$$

Finally, the unit vector $\mathbf{e}^\phi$ is the unit vector along the X^3 axis,

$$\mathbf{e}^\phi = \mathbf{i}^3 = \mathbf{i}^l \tag{3}$$

9.7   Express the angular velocity vector $\boldsymbol{\Omega}$ of a rigid body in terms of the Euler angle system A in the unit vectors $\mathbf{i}^l$, $\mathbf{j}^l$, $\mathbf{k}^l$ (Table P-9.1).

In the Euler angle system A,

$$\boldsymbol{\Omega} = \dot{\psi}\mathbf{e}^\psi + \dot{\theta}\mathbf{e}^\theta + \dot{\phi}\mathbf{e}^\phi \tag{1}$$

which in terms of the relations of Problem 9.6 becomes

$$\boldsymbol{\Omega} = \underbrace{(\dot{\phi} - \dot{\psi}\sin\theta)\mathbf{i}^l}_{\Omega_x^l} + \underbrace{(\dot{\theta}\cos\phi + \dot{\psi}\cos\theta\sin\phi)\mathbf{j}^l}_{\Omega_y^l} + \underbrace{(\dot{\psi}\cos\theta\cos\phi - \dot{\theta}\sin\phi)\mathbf{k}^l}_{\Omega_z^l} \tag{2}$$

and gives an alternative derivation of $(9\text{-}10)$.

9.8   Express the unit vectors $\mathbf{e}^\phi$, $\mathbf{e}^\theta$, $\mathbf{e}^\psi$ of the angular velocities $\dot{\phi}$, $\dot{\theta}$, $\dot{\psi}$ of the Euler angle system B in terms of the unit vectors $\mathbf{i}^l$, $\mathbf{j}^l$, $\mathbf{k}^l$ (Table P-9.2).

From Table P-9.2b,c the unit vector $\mathbf{e}^\phi$ is the unit vector along the Z^1 axis,

$$\mathbf{e}^\phi = \mathbf{k}^1 = \begin{bmatrix} 0 & \sin\theta & \cos\theta \end{bmatrix} \begin{bmatrix} \cos\psi & -\sin\psi & 0 \\ \sin\psi & \cos\psi & 0 \\ 0 & 0 & 1 \end{bmatrix} \begin{bmatrix} \mathbf{i}^l \\ \mathbf{j}^l \\ \mathbf{k}^l \end{bmatrix}$$

$$= (\sin\theta\sin\psi)\mathbf{i}^l + (\sin\theta\cos\psi)\mathbf{j}^l + (\cos\theta)\mathbf{k}^l \tag{1}$$

From Table P-9.2c the unit vector $\mathbf{e}^\theta$ is the unit vector along the X^4 axis,

$$\mathbf{e}^\theta = \mathbf{i}^4 = \begin{bmatrix} \cos\psi & -\sin\psi & 0 \end{bmatrix} \begin{bmatrix} \mathbf{i}^l \\ \mathbf{j}^l \\ \mathbf{k}^l \end{bmatrix} = (\cos\psi)\mathbf{i}^l - (\sin\psi)\mathbf{j}^l \tag{2}$$

Finally, the unit vector $\mathbf{e}^\psi$ is the unit vector along the Z^5 axis,

$$\mathbf{e}^\psi = \mathbf{k}^5 = \mathbf{k}^l \tag{3}$$

9.9   Express the angular velocity vector $\boldsymbol{\Omega}$ of a rigid body in terms of the Euler angle system B in the unit vectors $\mathbf{i}^l$, $\mathbf{j}^l$, $\mathbf{k}^l$ (Table P-9.2).

In the Euler angle system B,

$$\boldsymbol{\Omega} = \dot{\phi}\mathbf{e}^\phi + \dot{\theta}\mathbf{e}^\theta + \dot{\psi}\mathbf{e}^\psi \tag{1}$$

which in terms of the relations of Problem 9.8 becomes

$$\boldsymbol{\Omega} = \underbrace{(\dot{\phi}\sin\theta\sin\psi + \dot{\theta}\cos\psi)\mathbf{i}^l}_{\Omega_x^l} + \underbrace{(\dot{\phi}\sin\theta\cos\psi - \dot{\theta}\sin\psi)\mathbf{j}^l}_{\Omega_y^l} + \underbrace{(\dot{\phi}\cos\theta + \dot{\psi})\mathbf{k}^l}_{\Omega_z^l} \tag{2}$$

and gives the equivalent of (9-10) in the Euler angle system B.

ABSOLUTE SPACE MOTION

9.10   The circular cone in Fig. P-9.10 rolls without slipping on a horizontal plane about the fixed point 0 so that its axis has angular velocity $\dot{\psi}$ with respect to Z_0^0.   Determine its angular velocity about X_0^l.   Given: l, $\alpha = \pi/6$, $\dot{\psi} = 2\pi$ rad/sec.

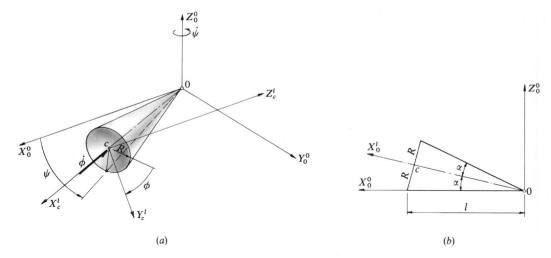

(a)   (b)

Fig. P-9.10

The motion of the cone is referred to the Euler angle system A (Fig. P-9.10), and the respective angles are

$$\psi = \psi(t), \qquad \theta = -\alpha, \qquad \phi = \phi(t) \tag{1}$$

From the geometry of the cone, $l\psi = -R\phi = -(l\sin\alpha)\phi$ and

$$\phi = -\psi/\sin\alpha, \qquad \dot{\phi} = -\dot{\psi}/\sin\alpha \tag{2}$$

By (9-10),

$$\Omega_x^l = \dot{\phi} - \dot{\psi}\sin\theta = -\dot{\psi}/(\sin\alpha) + \dot{\psi}\sin\alpha = -1.5\pi \text{ rad/sec} \tag{3}$$

9.11 Find the coordinates of point m on the node line of Fig. P-9.11.   Given: l, R, ϕ, θ, ψ.

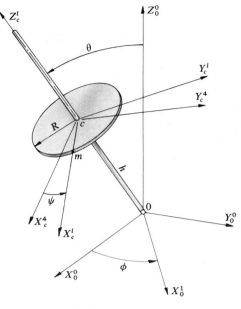

The angles of Fig. P-9.11 form the Euler angle system B (Table P-9.2).
In the l-system,

$$x^l_{0m} = R, \qquad y^l_{0m} = 0, \qquad z^l_{0m} = h \qquad (1)$$

In the 0-system,

$$[s^0_{0m}] = [\pi^{0l}][s^l_{0m}] \qquad (2)$$

where $[s^l_{0m}]$ is given by (1) and $[\pi^{0l}]$ equals $[\pi^{05}]$ of Problem 9.2.

$$
\left.
\begin{aligned}
x^0_{0m} &= (\cos \phi \cos \psi - \sin \phi \cos \theta \sin \psi)R \\
&\quad + (\sin \phi \sin \theta)h \\
y^0_{0m} &= (\sin \phi \cos \psi - \cos \phi \cos \theta \sin \psi)R \\
&\quad - (\cos \phi \sin \theta)h \\
z^0_{0m} &= (\sin \theta \sin \psi)R + (\cos \theta)h
\end{aligned}
\right\} \qquad (3)
$$

Fig. P-9.11

9.12 Find the angular velocity vector $\mathbf{\Omega}$ and the linear velocity vector $\mathbf{r}^*_{0m}$ of the point m in Problem 9.11.

The components of $\mathbf{\Omega}$ in the l-system are given by (2) of Problem 9.9.
For $\theta = \alpha = $ constant, they are

$$\Omega^l_x = \dot{\phi} \sin \alpha \sin \psi, \qquad \Omega^l_y = \dot{\phi} \sin \alpha \cos \psi, \qquad \Omega^l_z = \dot{\phi} \cos \alpha + \dot{\psi}$$

Since the position vector of m, $\mathbf{r}_{0m}$, is already known [Problem 9.11, equation (1)], the linear velocity vector of m in the l-system is

$$
\mathbf{r}^*_{0m} = \mathbf{\Omega} \times \mathbf{r}_{0m} =
\begin{vmatrix}
\mathbf{i}^l & \mathbf{j}^l & \mathbf{k}^l \\
\Omega^l_x & \Omega^l_y & \Omega^l_z \\
x^l_{0m} & y^l_{0m} & z^l_{0m}
\end{vmatrix}
$$

$$= (h\dot{\phi} \sin \alpha \cos \psi)\mathbf{i}^l - (h\dot{\phi} \sin \alpha \sin \psi - R\dot{\phi} \cos \alpha - R\dot{\psi})\mathbf{j}^l - (R\dot{\phi} \sin \alpha \cos \psi)\mathbf{k}^l$$

INSTANTANEOUS AXIS

9.13 Derive equation $(9\text{-}23)$, which defines the location of the instantaneous axis of rotation.

The velocity vector of a point in a rigid body is by $(9\text{-}17)$,

$$\mathbf{r}^*_{0m} = \dot{\mathbf{r}}_{0e} + \mathbf{\Omega} \times \mathbf{r}_{em} \qquad (1)$$

where e is the point of intersection of the instantaneous axis with the plane through m normal to that axis (Fig. 9.6, page 183).

By definition, the instantaneous axis is parallel to $\mathbf{\Omega}$ and its transverse velocity is zero.

After multiplication by $\boldsymbol{\Omega}$, (1) becomes

$$\boldsymbol{\Omega} \times \mathbf{r}_{0m}^* = \boldsymbol{\Omega} \times \dot{\mathbf{r}}_{0e} + \boldsymbol{\Omega} \times (\boldsymbol{\Omega} \times \mathbf{r}_{em}) = \boldsymbol{\Omega} \times \mathbf{r}_{0e} + (\boldsymbol{\Omega} \cdot \mathbf{r}_{em})\boldsymbol{\Omega} - (\boldsymbol{\Omega} \cdot \boldsymbol{\Omega})\mathbf{r}_{em} \qquad (2)$$

where $\boldsymbol{\Omega} \times \dot{\mathbf{r}}_{0e} = 0$ (parallel vectors), $\boldsymbol{\Omega} \cdot \mathbf{r}_{0e} = 0$ (normal vectors), $\boldsymbol{\Omega} \cdot \boldsymbol{\Omega} = \Omega^2$ (collinear vectors). Hence

$$\boldsymbol{\Omega} \times \mathbf{r}_{0m}^* = -\Omega^2 \mathbf{r}_{em} \qquad (3)$$

and with $\mathbf{r}_{me} = -\mathbf{r}_{em}$,

$$\mathbf{r}_{me} = (\boldsymbol{\Omega} \times \mathbf{r}_{0m}^*)/\Omega^2 \qquad (4)$$

9.14 Find by inspection the instantaneous axis of rotation in Problem 9.10.

The angular velocity vector (Fig. P-9.14)

$$\boldsymbol{\Omega} = (\dot{\phi} \cos \alpha)\mathbf{i}^i + (\dot{\psi} + \dot{\phi} \sin \alpha)\mathbf{k}^i$$

where from (2) of Problem 9.8,

$$\dot{\phi} = -\dot{\psi}/\sin \alpha$$

and $\mathbf{i}^i$, $\mathbf{k}^i$ are unit vectors rotating with the plane X_c^l, Z_0^0. Then

$$\boldsymbol{\Omega} = (-\dot{\psi} \cot \alpha)\mathbf{i}^i$$

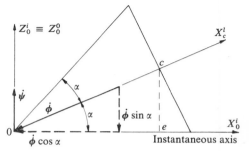

Fig. P-9.14

which indicates that the vector $\boldsymbol{\Omega}$ is in the horizontal plane and rotates about 0.

Since the instantaneous line of action of $\boldsymbol{\Omega}$ is the only line which satisfies the definition of the instantaneous axis of rotation, the rotating axis X_0^i is the instantaneous axis.

9.15 Locate analytically the instantaneous axis of rotation in Problem 9.10.

The angular velocity vector of the cone in Fig. P-9.10a is by (2) of Problem 9.7,

$$\boldsymbol{\Omega} = (\dot{\phi} - \dot{\psi} \sin \theta)\mathbf{i}^l + (\dot{\theta} \cos \phi + \dot{\psi} \cos \theta \sin \phi)\mathbf{j}^l + (\dot{\psi} \cos \theta \cos \phi - \dot{\theta} \sin \phi)\mathbf{k}^l \qquad (1)$$

where from Problem 9.10, $\theta = -\pi/6$, $\dot{\theta} = 0$, $\phi = -2\psi$, $\dot{\phi} = -2\dot{\psi}$. Hence

$$\boldsymbol{\Omega} = -1.5\dot{\psi}\mathbf{i}^l - (0.866\dot{\psi} \sin 2\psi)\mathbf{j}^l + (0.866\dot{\psi} \cos 2\psi)\mathbf{k}^l \qquad (2)$$

Since the center c of the base has the simplest position vector, c is selected as the reference point. By $(9\text{-}24)$,

$$[s_{ce}^l] = \frac{1}{\Omega^2} [\Gamma^l] [s_{0c}^{l*}] = \frac{1}{\Omega^2} [\Gamma^l] [\Gamma^l] [s_{0c}^l] \qquad (3)$$

and in full matrix form

$$
\begin{bmatrix} x_{ce}^l \\ y_{ce}^l \\ z_{ce}^l \end{bmatrix} = \frac{1}{\Omega^2} \underbrace{\begin{bmatrix} 0 & -\Omega_z^l & \Omega_y^l \\ \Omega_z^l & 0 & -\Omega_x^l \\ -\Omega_y^l & \Omega_x^l & 0 \end{bmatrix}}_{[\Gamma^l]} \underbrace{\begin{bmatrix} 0 & -\Omega_z^l & \Omega_y^l \\ \Omega_z^l & 0 & -\Omega_x^l \\ -\Omega_y^l & \Omega_x^l & 0 \end{bmatrix}}_{[\Gamma^l]} \underbrace{\begin{bmatrix} l\cos\alpha \\ 0 \\ 0 \end{bmatrix}}_{[s_{0c}^l]}
$$
$$\underbrace{\phantom{\begin{bmatrix} x \\ y \\ z \end{bmatrix}}}_{[s_{ce}^l]} \tag{4}$$

where Ω_x^l, Ω_y^l, Ω_z^l are given by (2) and $\Omega^2 = 3\dot{\psi}^2$ is known from Problem 9.14.   Equation (4) yields

$$x_{ce}^l = -0.216l, \qquad y_{ce}^l = 0.375l\sin 2\psi, \qquad z_{ce}^l = -0.375l\cos 2\psi$$

which places e on the X_0^i axis directly below c (Fig. P-9.14), thus identifying X_0^i as the instantaneous axis.

RELATIVE SPACE MOTION

9.16   The governor in Fig. P-9.16 consists of rigid
bars $\overline{12}$, $\overline{13}$, $\overline{45}$, $\overline{46}$, two balls of equal mass and
a collar free to slide along the vertical shaft.
As the governor rotates with constant angular
velocity of magnitude $\dot\psi$, the balls 2 and 3 move
outward.   Find the velocity and acceleration
of these balls.   Given: $\overline{12} = \overline{13} = l$, $\overline{01} = h$,
$\psi = at$, $\theta = \pi/2 - bt$.

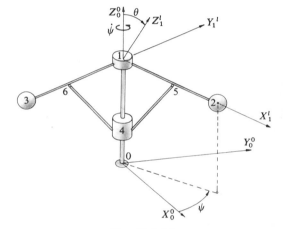

Fig. P-9.16

In terms of Euler angle system A ($\phi = 0$,
$\dot\phi = 0$), the angular velocities (9-10) are

$$\begin{aligned}
\Omega_x^l &= \dot\phi - \dot\psi\sin\theta = -a\cos bt \\
\Omega_y^l &= \dot\theta\cos\phi + \dot\psi\cos\theta\sin\phi = -b \qquad (1) \\
\Omega_z^l &= \dot\psi\cos\theta\cos\phi - \dot\theta\sin\phi = a\sin bt
\end{aligned}$$

The position and velocity vectors of ball 2 are respectively,

$$\mathbf{r}_{12} = l\mathbf{i}^l, \qquad \mathbf{r}_{12}^* = \dot{\mathbf{r}}_{12} + \mathbf{\Omega}\times\mathbf{r}_{12} = \begin{vmatrix} \mathbf{i}^l & -a\cos bt & l \\ \mathbf{j}^l & -b & 0 \\ \mathbf{k}^l & a\sin bt & 0 \end{vmatrix} = (al\sin bt)\mathbf{j}^l + bl\mathbf{k}^l \tag{2}$$

The acceleration vector of ball 2 is

$$\mathbf{r}_{12}^{**} = \ddot{\mathbf{r}}_{12} + \dot{\mathbf{\Omega}}\times\mathbf{r}_{12} + \mathbf{\Omega}\times(\mathbf{\Omega}\times\mathbf{r}_{12}) \tag{3}$$

and can be also computed as the second total derivative of (2), i.e.

$$\mathbf{r}_{12}^{**} = (abl\cos bt)\mathbf{j}^l + (al\sin bt)\dot{\mathbf{j}}^l + bl\dot{\mathbf{k}}^l \tag{4}$$

where by (5) of Problem 9.5 and in terms of (1),

$$\begin{aligned}
\dot{\mathbf{j}}^l &= -\Omega_z^l\mathbf{i}^l + \Omega_x^l\mathbf{k}^l = (-a\sin bt)\mathbf{i}^l - (a\cos bt)\mathbf{k}^l \\
\dot{\mathbf{k}}^l &= \Omega_y^l\mathbf{i}^l - \Omega_x^l\mathbf{j}^l = -b\mathbf{i}^l + (a\cos bt)\mathbf{j}^l
\end{aligned} \tag{5}$$

Hence

$$\mathbf{r}_{12}^{**} = -l(b^2 + a^2 \sin^2 bt)\mathbf{i}^l + (2abl \cos bt)\mathbf{j}^l - (a^2 l \sin bt \cos bt)\mathbf{k}^l \qquad (6)$$

which can be expressed in terms of $\mathbf{i}^0$, $\mathbf{j}^0$, $\mathbf{k}^0$ by means of $[\pi^{l0}]$ given in (9-6).

9.17 Find the effects of the earth's rotation on the winds blowing parallel to the surface at height h and latitude γ (Fig. P-9.17). Given: R = earth's radius, γ = latitude, $\dot{\psi}$ = constant angular velocity of the earth; wind velocity = $v_0[(\cos \alpha)\mathbf{i}^l + (\sin \alpha)\mathbf{j}^l]$ where α = constant, h = altitude of wind center.

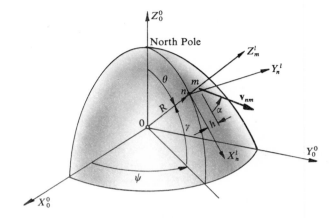

Fig. P-9.17

In the Euler angle system A (Fig. P-9.17),

$$\psi = \psi(t), \quad \theta = \pi/2 - \gamma, \quad \phi = 0 \qquad (1)$$

the kinematic vectors of the wind are

$$\mathbf{r}_{0m} = \mathbf{r}_{0n} + \mathbf{r}_{nm} \qquad (2)$$
$$\mathbf{r}_{0m}^* = \dot{\mathbf{r}}_{0n} + \dot{\mathbf{r}}_{nm} + \mathbf{\Omega} \times (\mathbf{r}_{0n} + \mathbf{r}_{nm}) \qquad (3)$$
$$\mathbf{r}_{0m}^{**} = \ddot{\mathbf{r}}_{0n} + \ddot{\mathbf{r}}_{nm} + \dot{\mathbf{\Omega}} \times (\mathbf{r}_{0n} + \mathbf{r}_{nm}) + 2\mathbf{\Omega} \times (\dot{\mathbf{r}}_{0n} + \dot{\mathbf{r}}_{nm}) + \mathbf{\Omega} \times [\mathbf{\Omega} \times (\mathbf{r}_{0n} + \mathbf{r}_{nm})] \qquad (4)$$

where

$$\mathbf{r}_{0n} = R\mathbf{k}^l, \qquad \mathbf{r}_{nm} = (v_0 t \cos \alpha)\mathbf{i}^l + (v_0 t \sin \alpha)\mathbf{j}^l + h\mathbf{k}^l \qquad (5)$$

By (9-10),

$$\mathbf{\Omega} = (-\dot{\psi} \cos \gamma)\mathbf{i}^l + (\dot{\psi}\sin \gamma)\mathbf{k}^l, \qquad \dot{\psi} = \text{constant} \qquad (6)$$
$$\dot{\mathbf{\Omega}} = (-\ddot{\psi} \cos \gamma)\mathbf{i}^l + (\ddot{\psi} \sin \gamma)\mathbf{k}^l = 0, \qquad \ddot{\psi} = 0 \qquad (7)$$

The velocity vector (3) is

$$\mathbf{r}_{0m}^* = (v_0 \cos \alpha)\mathbf{i}^l + (v_0 \sin \alpha)\mathbf{j}^l + \begin{vmatrix} \mathbf{i}^l & -\dot{\psi} \cos \gamma & v_0 t \cos \alpha \\ \mathbf{j}^l & 0 & v_0 t \sin \alpha \\ \mathbf{k}^l & \dot{\psi} \sin \gamma & R + h \end{vmatrix}$$

$$= (v_0 \cos \alpha - \dot{\psi} v_0 t \sin \alpha \sin \gamma)\mathbf{i}^l + [v_0 \sin \alpha + \dot{\psi}(R + h) \cos \gamma + \dot{\psi} v_0 t \cos \alpha \sin \gamma]\mathbf{j}^l$$
$$- (\dot{\psi} v_0 t \sin \alpha \cos \gamma)\mathbf{k}^l \qquad (8)$$

which for $h = 0$ and $t = 0$ reduces to

$$\mathbf{r}_{0m}^* = (v_0 \cos \alpha)\mathbf{i}^l + (v_0 \sin \alpha + \dot{\psi} R \cos \gamma)\mathbf{j}^l \qquad (9)$$

Finally, the acceleration (4) is

$$\mathbf{r}_{Om}^{**} = 2 \begin{vmatrix} \mathbf{i}^l & -\dot{\psi}\cos\gamma & v_0\cos\alpha \\ \mathbf{j}^l & 0 & v_0\sin\alpha \\ \mathbf{k}^l & \dot{\psi}\sin\gamma & 0 \end{vmatrix} + \begin{vmatrix} \mathbf{i}^l & -\dot{\psi}\cos\gamma & -\dot{\psi}v_0 t\sin\alpha\sin\gamma \\ \mathbf{j}^l & 0 & \dot{\psi}(R+h)\cos\gamma + \dot{\psi}v_0 t\cos\alpha\sin\gamma \\ \mathbf{k}^l & \dot{\psi}\sin\gamma & -\dot{\psi}v_0 t\sin\alpha\cos\gamma \end{vmatrix}$$

$$\begin{aligned} = & (-2\dot{\psi}v_0\sin\alpha\sin\gamma)\mathbf{i}^l + (2\dot{\psi}v_0\cos\alpha\sin\gamma)\mathbf{j}^l - (2\dot{\psi}v_0\sin\alpha\cos\gamma)\mathbf{k}^l \\ & - \dot{\psi}^2\sin\gamma[(R+h)\cos\alpha - v_0 t\cos\alpha\sin\gamma]\mathbf{i}^l + (\dot{\psi}^2 v_0 t\sin\alpha)\mathbf{j}^l \\ & - \dot{\psi}^2\cos\gamma[(R+h)\cos\gamma - v_0 t\cos\alpha\sin\gamma]\mathbf{k}^l \end{aligned} \qquad (10)$$

which for $h = 0$ and $t = 0$ reduces to

$$\begin{aligned} \mathbf{r}_{Om}^{**} = & -\dot{\psi}(2v_0\sin\alpha\sin\gamma + \dot{\psi}R\sin\gamma\cos\alpha)\mathbf{i}^l + 2\dot{\psi}(v_0\cos\alpha\sin\gamma)\mathbf{j}^l \\ & - \dot{\psi}(2v_0\sin\alpha\cos\gamma + \dot{\psi}R\cos^2\gamma)\mathbf{k}^l \end{aligned}$$

Since for $t = 0$, $\mathbf{\Omega} \times (\mathbf{\Omega} \times \mathbf{r}_{0m})$ represents the centripetal acceleration in the $X_n^l Z_n^l$ plane, it does not affect the wind blowing.   In turn, the Coriolis acceleration $2\mathbf{\Omega} \times \dot{\mathbf{r}}_{0m}$ has two components in the $X_m^l Y_m^l$ plane which form a tangential vector,

$$2\dot{\psi}v_0\sin\gamma[(-\sin\alpha)\mathbf{i}^l + (\cos\alpha)\mathbf{j}^l]$$

and affects the wind blowing.

At the equator the effect vanishes, but increases positively toward the North Pole and negatively toward the South Pole.   Thus winds blowing south on the Northern Hemisphere accelerate to the east, and on the Southern Hemisphere they accelerate to the west.

Problems

EULER ANGLES

9.18 Find the time derivatives of unit vectors $\mathbf{i}^l$, $\mathbf{j}^l$, $\mathbf{k}^l$ in terms of the Euler angle system C (Table 9-1, page 180, and Table P-9.3, page 188).

9.19 Express the unit vectors $\mathbf{e}^\psi$, $\mathbf{e}^\theta$, $\mathbf{e}^\phi$ of the angular velocities $\dot{\psi}$, $\dot{\theta}$, $\dot{\phi}$ of the Euler angle system C (Table 9-1 and Table P-9.3) in terms of unit vectors $\mathbf{i}^l$, $\mathbf{j}^l$, $\mathbf{k}^l$.

9.20 Express the angular velocity vector $\mathbf{\Omega}$ in terms of the Euler angle system C in the unit vectors $\mathbf{i}^l$, $\mathbf{j}^l$, $\mathbf{k}^l$ (use results of Problem 9.19).

9.21 Construct the Euler matrices $[\tau^{le}]$ and $[\tau^{el}]$ relating the angular velocity vector $[\mathbf{\Omega}^e]$ of the Euler angle system C to the angular velocity vector $[\mathbf{\Omega}^l]$ of the rotating cartesian system.

ABSOLUTE SPACE MOTION

9.22 A rigid body with a fixed point 0 rotates with $\Omega_x^0 = 10\pi/\text{sec}$ about the X_0^0 axis. Find the velocity vector of m (Fig. P-9.22) given by $\mathbf{r}_{0m} = (2\mathbf{i}^0 + 3\mathbf{j}^0 + 4\mathbf{k}^0)m$.

9.23 Find the acceleration vector of the point m in Problem 9.22.

9.24 Show the matrix solution of Problems 9.22 and 9.23.

9.25 The circular disk of Fig. P-9.25 rotates with $\dot{\phi} = 6\pi/\text{sec}$ about a horizontal shaft attached rigidly to a vertical shaft which rotates with $\dot{\psi} = 2\pi/\text{sec}$. Find the velocity vector of the point m on the circumference of the disk. Given: $a, R, \dot{\phi}, \dot{\psi}$.

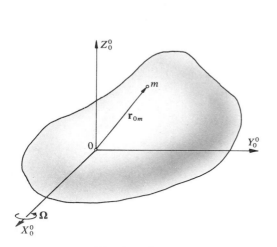

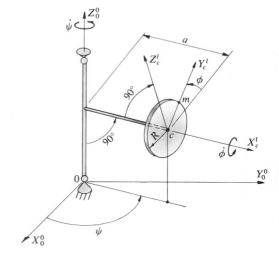

Fig. P-9.22   **Fig. P-9.25**

9.26 Find the matrix solution of Problem 9.12 in the 0-system and also in the l-system.

9.27 A circular right cone rotates without slipping on a fixed circular right cone about their common top 0 with $\dot{\psi} = 6\pi/\text{sec}$ (Fig. P-9.27). Find its angular velocity vector in the 0-system and also in the l-system. Given: $\alpha, \beta, l, \dot{\psi}$.

9.28 An axially symmetrical satellite has two constant angular velocities $\dot{\phi}$, $\dot{\psi}$ shown symbolically in Fig. P-9.28. Find the absolute velocity of point m on the equator of the satellite. Given: $\dot{\phi}, \theta, \dot{\psi}, R$, all constant.

9.29 Find the absolute acceleration of point m in Problem P-9.28.

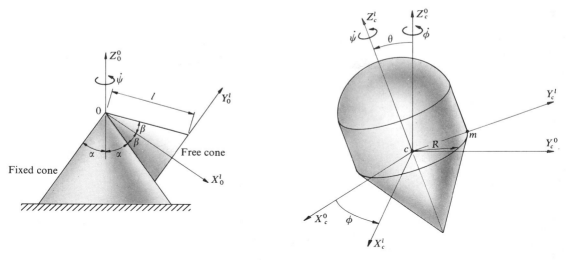

Fig. P-9.27   Fig. P-9.28

RELATIVE SPACE MOTION

9.30 A straight rod rotates along a conical surface about the Z_0^0 axis as shown in Fig. P-9.30, and a ring slides along the rod with constant linear speed v. Find the absolute velocity and acceleration of the ring as it leaves the free end of the rod. Given: $\dot\phi, \theta, l, v$, all constant.

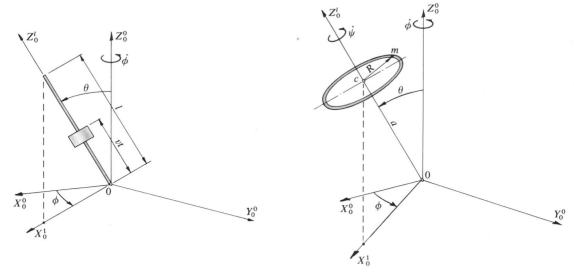

Fig. P-9.30   Fig. P-9.31

9.31 A circular tube-ring of radius R rotates with constant angular speed $\dot\phi$ about the Z_0^0 axis in an inclined position of constant slope, and rotates about Z_0^l with a speed $\dot\psi$ (Fig. P-9.31). Find the absolute velocity of a ball of negligible radius which moves within the tube with speed v. Given: $\dot\phi, \dot\psi, \theta, v, a, R$, all constant.

9.32 An automobile travels in a westerly direction with constant speed along a level road at a latitude of 45°. Find the effect of the earth's rotation on its speed and acceleration.

Chapter 10

Kinetics of Rigid Bodies, Space Motion

10.1 CHARACTERISTICS OF A RIGID BODY

Inertia Functions*

In addition to the concept of mass m and of the position vector of the mass center $\mathbf{r}_{0c}$ defined by (8-2) and (8-4) respectively, ten *mass inertia functions* occur in the dynamics of rigid bodies. They are:

$$I_{0xx} = \int_m (y_{0m}^2 + z_{0m}^2)\, dm \qquad I_{0xy} = \int_m x_{0m} y_{0m}\, dm \qquad I_{0xz} = \int_m x_{0m} z_{0m}\, dm$$

$$I_{0yx} = \int_m y_{0m} x_{0m}\, dm \qquad I_{0yy} = \int_m (z_{0m}^2 + x_{0m}^2)\, dm \qquad I_{0yz} = \int_m y_{0m} z_{0m}\, dm \qquad (10\text{-}1)$$

$$I_{0zx} = \int_m z_{0m} x_{0m}\, dm \qquad I_{0zy} = \int_m z_{0m} y_{0m}\, dm \qquad I_{0zz} = \int_m (x_{0m}^2 + y_{0m}^2)\, dm$$

$$J_0 = \int_m \underbrace{(x_{0m}^2 + y_{0m}^2 + z_{0m}^2)}_{r_{0m}^2}\, dm \qquad (10\text{-}2)$$

where $I_{0xx}, I_{0yy}, I_{0zz}$ are the *moments of inertia*, I_{0xy}, $I_{0xz}, I_{0yx}, I_{0yz}, I_{0zx}, I_{0zy}$ are the *products of inertia* and J_0 is the *polar moment of inertia* in the stationary reference system X_0, Y_0, Z_0 (Fig. 10-1).

By inspection,

$$I_{0xy} = I_{0yx}, \quad I_{0yz} = I_{0zy}, \quad I_{0zx} = I_{0xz} \qquad (10\text{-}3)$$

and

$$J_0 = \tfrac{1}{2}(I_{0xx} + I_{0yy} + I_{0zz}) \qquad (10\text{-}4)$$

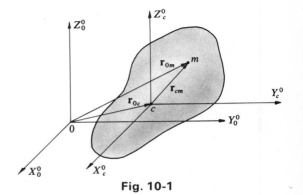

Fig. 10-1

*J. J. Tuma, "Statics", Quantum Publishers, New York, 1974, Chapter 8, pp. 179–183.

The functions (10-1) and (10-2) define the mass distribution with respect to the chosen axes and as such appear in the equations of motion of rigid bodies (Section 10.2).

Inertia Tensor

The array of inertia functions is called the *inertia tensor* $[T_0]$, which can be conveniently constructed as

$$[T_0] = \int_m \underbrace{\begin{bmatrix} 0 & z_{0m} & -y_{0m} \\ -z_{0m} & 0 & x_{0m} \\ y_{0m} & -x_{0m} & 0 \end{bmatrix}}_{[r_{0m}]^T} \underbrace{\begin{bmatrix} dm & & \\ & dm & \\ & & dm \end{bmatrix}}_{[dm]} \underbrace{\begin{bmatrix} 0 & -z_{0m} & y_{0m} \\ z_{0m} & 0 & -x_{0m} \\ -y_{0m} & x_{0m} & 0 \end{bmatrix}}_{[r_{0m}]}$$

$$= \begin{bmatrix} I_{0xx} & -I_{0xy} & -I_{0xz} \\ -I_{0yx} & I_{0yy} & -I_{0yz} \\ -I_{0zx} & -I_{0zy} & I_{0zz} \end{bmatrix} \tag{10-5}$$

The relationships (10-3) indicate that the inertia tensor is *symmetrical* and only six functions, $I_{0xx}, I_{0yy}, I_{0zz}, I_{0xy}, I_{0yz}, I_{0zx}$, are necessary for its construction.

Translation of Axes

In terms of

$$[r_{0m}] = [r_{0c}] + [r_{cm}] \tag{10-6}$$

the inertia tensor (10-5) becomes

$$[T_0] = \int_m [r_{0c}]^T [dm] [r_{0c}] + \int_m [r_{cm}]^T [dm] [r_{cm}] = [T_{0c}] + [T_c] \tag{10-7}$$

where

$$[T_{0c}] = \int_m \begin{bmatrix} y_{0c}^2 + z_{0c}^2 & -x_{0c}y_{0c} & -x_{0c}z_{0c} \\ -y_{0c}x_{0c} & z_{0c}^2 + x_{0c}^2 & -y_{0c}z_{0c} \\ -z_{0c}x_{0c} & -z_{0c}y_{0c} & x_{0c}^2 + y_{0c}^2 \end{bmatrix} dm = \begin{bmatrix} I_{0cxx} & -I_{0cxy} & -I_{0cxz} \\ -I_{0cyx} & I_{0cyy} & -I_{0cyz} \\ -I_{0czx} & -I_{0czy} & I_{0czz} \end{bmatrix} \tag{10-8}$$

is the inertia tensor of the mass m concentrated at the mass center c, with respect to the stationary axes X_0, Y_0, Z_0; and

$$[T_c] = \int_m \begin{bmatrix} y_{cm}^2 + z_{cm}^2 & -x_{cm}y_{cm} & -x_{cm}z_{cm} \\ -y_{cm}x_{cm} & z_{cm}^2 + x_{cm}^2 & -y_{cm}z_{cm} \\ -z_{cm}x_{cm} & -z_{cm}y_{cm} & x_{cm}^2 + y_{cm}^2 \end{bmatrix} dm = \begin{bmatrix} I_{cxx} & -I_{cxy} & -I_{cxz} \\ -I_{cyx} & I_{cyy} & -I_{cyz} \\ -I_{czx} & -I_{czy} & I_{czz} \end{bmatrix} \tag{10-9}$$

is the inertia tensor of the distributed mass m with respect to the centroidal axes X_c, Y_c, Z_c, which are parallel to the respective reference axes X_0, Y_0, Z_0.

The relationships defined by (*10-7*) are sometimes called the *parallel axes inertia theorems* and offer the possibility of expressing the inertia tensor $[T_0]$ in terms of the time-dependent $[T_{0c}]$ and the time-independent $[T_c]$.   Since the elements of $[T_c]$ are frequently known tabular values, (*10-7*) allows a rapid and convenient construction of $[T_0]$.

Rotation of Axes

The relationships of two inertia tensors $[T_0^0]$ and $[T_0^l]$ related to X_0^0, Y_0^0, Z_0^0 and X_0^l, Y_0^l, Z_0^l respectively (Fig. 10-2) are

$$[T_0^0] = [\pi^{0l}][T_0^l][\pi^{l0}] \qquad (10\text{-}10)$$

$$[T_0^l] = [\pi^{l0}][T_0^0][\pi^{0l}] \qquad (10\text{-}11)$$

where

$$[\pi^{0l}] = \begin{bmatrix} \alpha_x & \alpha_y & \alpha_z \\ \beta_x & \beta_y & \beta_z \\ \gamma_x & \gamma_y & \gamma_z \end{bmatrix} \qquad (10\text{-}12)$$

$$[\pi^{l0}] = \begin{bmatrix} \alpha_x & \beta_x & \gamma_x \\ \alpha_y & \beta_y & \gamma_y \\ \alpha_z & \beta_z & \gamma_z \end{bmatrix} \qquad (10\text{-}13)$$

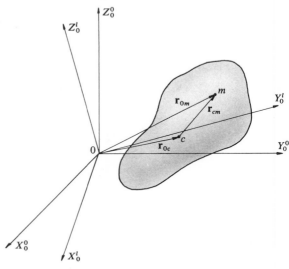

Fig. 10-2

are the orthogonal *angular transformation matrices*, the coefficients of which are the direction cosines of the respective Euler angle system (Tables P-9.1, P-9.2, P-9.3).

Principal Functions of Inertia

For any point 0 there exist three mutually perpendicular axes X_0^p, Y_0^p, Z_0^p about which the products of inertia of the mass of the body vanish.   Such axes are called the *principal axes* and the moments of inertia about these axes are called the *principal inertia functions*, $I_{0,1}^p$, $I_{0,2}^p$, $I_{0,3}^p$, obtained as the roots of the determinant equation given below and derived in Problem 10.5.

$$\begin{vmatrix} I_{0xx}^0 - I_{0,i}^p & -I_{0xy}^0 & -I_{0xz}^0 \\ -I_{0yx}^0 & I_{0yy}^0 - I_{0,i}^p & -I_{0yz}^0 \\ -I_{0zx}^0 & -I_{0zy}^0 & I_{0zz}^0 - I_{0,i}^p \end{vmatrix} = 0 \qquad (i = 1,2,3) \qquad (10\text{-}14)$$

where the superscripts 0 and p identify the reference and the principal axes respectively, and 0 is c, n or any point in or off the body.

Position of Principal Axes

The *direction cosines* of the principal axes X_0^p, Y_0^p, Z_0^p with respect to X_0^0, Y_0^0, Z_0^0 form the respective angular transformation matrix given below and derived in Problem 10.6,

$$[\pi^{0p}] = \begin{bmatrix} \cos(X_0^0, X_0^p) & \cos(X_0^0, Y_0^p) & \cos(X_0^0, Z_0^p) \\ \cos(Y_0^0, X_0^p) & \cos(Y_0^0, Y_0^p) & \cos(Y_0^0, Z_0^p) \\ \cos(Z_0^0, X_0^p) & \cos(Z_0^0, Y_0^p) & \cos(Z_0^0, Z_0^p) \end{bmatrix} = \pm \begin{bmatrix} \sqrt{a_1/d_1} & \sqrt{a_2/d_2} & \sqrt{a_3/d_3} \\ \sqrt{b_1/d_1} & \sqrt{b_2/d_2} & \sqrt{b_3/d_3} \\ \sqrt{c_1/d_1} & \sqrt{c_2/d_2} & \sqrt{c_3/d_3} \end{bmatrix} \qquad (10\text{-}15)$$

where

$$a_i = \begin{vmatrix} I^0_{0yy} - I^p_{n,i} & -I^0_{0yz} \\ -I^0_{0zy} & I^0_{0zz} - I^p_{0,i} \end{vmatrix} = (I^0_{0yy} - I^p_{0,i})(I^0_{0zz} - I^p_{0,i}) - (I^0_{0yz})^2$$

$$b_i = \begin{vmatrix} I^0_{0zz} - I^p_{0,i} & -I^0_{0zx} \\ -I^0_{0xz} & I^0_{0xx} - I^p_{0,i} \end{vmatrix} = (I^0_{0zz} - I^p_{0,i})(I^0_{0xx} - I^p_{0,i}) - (I^0_{0zx})^2$$

$$c_i = \begin{vmatrix} I^0_{0xx} - I^p_{0,i} & -I^0_{0xy} \\ -I^0_{0yx} & I^0_{0yy} - I^p_{0,i} \end{vmatrix} = (I^0_{0xx} - I^p_{0,i})(I^0_{0yy} - I^p_{0,i}) - (I^0_{0xy})^2$$

$$d_i = a_i + b_i + c_i \qquad (i = 1, 2, 3)$$

(10-16)

and $I^p_{0,1}, I^p_{0,2}, I^p_{0,3}$ are the roots of (10-14).

The relations (10-16) show clearly that a_i, b_i, c_i are the *principal minors of the determinant* in (10-14) and d_i is their sum.   This structural relationship indicates a direct construction of $[\pi^{0p}]$ from (10-14).

Radii of Gyration

By definition, the radii of gyration of a rigid body of mass m in the X_c, Y_c, Z_c system are

$$k_{cxx} = \sqrt{I_{cxx}/m} \qquad k_{cxy} = \sqrt{I_{cxy}/m} \qquad k_{cxz} = \sqrt{I_{cxz}/m}$$
$$k_{cyx} = \sqrt{I_{cyx}/m} \qquad k_{cyy} = \sqrt{I_{cyy}/m} \qquad k_{cyz} = \sqrt{I_{cyz}/m} \qquad (10\text{-}17)$$
$$k_{czx} = \sqrt{I_{czx}/m} \qquad k_{czy} = \sqrt{I_{czy}/m} \qquad k_{czz} = \sqrt{I_{czz}/m}$$

where c is the centroid.   By the parallel axes theorems (10-7), the radii of gyration of the same body in the X_0, Y_0, Z_0 system are

$$k_{0xx} = \sqrt{y^2_{0c} + z^2_{0c} + k^2_{cxx}} \qquad k_{0xy} = \sqrt{x_{0c}y_{0c} + k^2_{cxy}} \qquad k_{0xz} = \sqrt{x_{0c}z_{0c} + k^2_{cxz}}$$
$$k_{0yx} = \sqrt{y_{0c}x_{0c} + k^2_{cyx}} \qquad k_{0yy} = \sqrt{z^2_{0c} + x^2_{0c} + k^2_{cyy}} \qquad k_{0yz} = \sqrt{y_{0c}z_{0c} + k^2_{cyz}} \qquad (10\text{-}18)$$
$$k_{0zx} = \sqrt{z_{0c}x_{0c} + k^2_{czx}} \qquad k_{0zy} = \sqrt{z_{0c}y_{0c} + k^2_{czy}} \qquad k_{0zz} = \sqrt{x^2_{0c} + y^2_{0c} + k^2_{czz}}$$

where 0 is the fixed origin.

10.2   MOTION RELATED TO THE MASS CENTER

Linear and Angular Momentum

The relationships of the preceding section, when applied in conjunction with modified (5-8) and (5-10), allow a direct development of the analytical expressions for the linear momentum **G** and the angular momentum **M** of a rigid body in space motion.

The *linear momentum* with respect to a fixed point 0 (Problem 10.1) is

$$\mathbf{G} = \int_m \mathbf{r}^*_{0m} \, dm = \int_m (\dot{\mathbf{r}}_{0c} + \boldsymbol{\Omega} \times \mathbf{r}_{cm}) \, dm = \dot{\mathbf{r}}_{0c}m = \mathbf{G}_{0c} \qquad (10\text{-}19)$$

which is formally identical to (8-11).

The *angular momentum* about the same fixed point 0 (Problem 10.2) is

$$\mathbf{H} = \int_m \mathbf{r}_{0m} \times d\mathbf{G} = \int_m (\mathbf{r}_{0c} + \mathbf{r}_{cm}) \times (\dot{\mathbf{r}}_{0c} + \mathbf{\Omega} \times \mathbf{r}_{cm})\, dm$$

$$= \mathbf{r}_{0c} \times \underbrace{\dot{\mathbf{r}}_{0c}m}_{\mathbf{G}_{0c}} + \int_m \mathbf{r}_{cm} \times (\mathbf{\Omega} \times \mathbf{r}_{cm})\, dm = \mathbf{H}_{0c} + \mathbf{H}_c \qquad (10\text{-}20)$$

where $\mathbf{G}_{0c}$ is the linear momentum of the total mass concentrated at c with respect to 0, $\mathbf{H}_{0c}$ is the angular momentum of the total mass concentrated at c about 0, $\mathbf{H}_c$ is the angular momentum of the distributed mass about c, and they are similar to their counterparts in Section 5.3.

The evaluation of (10-20) gives the *physical origin to the inertia functions* (10-9) and can be conveniently written in the compact matrix form (Problem 10.3) as

$$\underbrace{\begin{bmatrix} H_x^0 \\ H_y^0 \\ H_z^0 \end{bmatrix}}_{[H^0]} = \underbrace{\begin{bmatrix} 0 & -z_{0c}^0 & y_{0c}^0 \\ z_{0c}^0 & 0 & -x_{0c}^0 \\ -y_{0c}^0 & x_{0c}^0 & 0 \end{bmatrix}}_{[r_{0c}^0]} \underbrace{\begin{bmatrix} G_{0cx}^0 \\ G_{0cy}^0 \\ G_{0cz}^0 \end{bmatrix}}_{[G_{0c}^0]} + \underbrace{\begin{bmatrix} I_{cxx}^0 & -I_{cxy}^0 & -I_{cxz}^0 \\ -I_{cyx}^0 & I_{cyy}^0 & -I_{cyz}^0 \\ -I_{czx}^0 & -I_{czy}^0 & I_{czz}^0 \end{bmatrix}}_{[T_c^0]} \underbrace{\begin{bmatrix} \Omega_x^0 \\ \Omega_y^0 \\ \Omega_z^0 \end{bmatrix}}_{[\Omega^0]} \qquad (10\text{-}21)$$

where $[T_c^0]$ is the inertia tensor (10-9) in the 0-system and $[\Omega^0]$ is the angular velocity vector in the same system in terms of the respective Euler angles.

General Equations of Motion

Since the position of the rigid body in space motion is specified by six coordinates (three linear and three angular), six independent scalar equations are necessary for the analytical determination of this motion. They are the derivatives of (10-19), (10-20) taken in vector form as

$$\mathbf{G}^* = \dot{\mathbf{G}}_{0c} = \mathbf{F} \qquad (10\text{-}22)$$

$$\mathbf{H}^* = \mathbf{r}_{0c} \times \dot{\mathbf{G}}_{0c} + \dot{\mathbf{H}}_c + \mathbf{\Omega} \times \mathbf{H}_c = \dot{\mathbf{H}}_{0c} + \mathbf{H}_c^* = \mathbf{M} \qquad (10\text{-}23)$$

where $\mathbf{H}_c^*$ is the total time derivative of $\mathbf{H}_c$, $\mathbf{F}$ is the resultant force function, and $\mathbf{M}$ is the resultant moment function.

The matrix forms of these equations are

$$m \begin{bmatrix} 1 & 0 & 0 \\ 0 & 1 & 0 \\ 0 & 0 & 1 \end{bmatrix} \begin{bmatrix} \ddot{x}_{0c}^0 \\ \ddot{y}_{0c}^0 \\ \ddot{z}_{0c}^0 \end{bmatrix} = \begin{bmatrix} \sum F_x^0 \\ \sum F_y^0 \\ \sum F_z^0 \end{bmatrix} \qquad (10\text{-}24)$$

$$m \begin{bmatrix} 0 & -z_{0c}^0 & y_{0c}^0 \\ z_{0c}^0 & 0 & -x_{0c}^0 \\ -y_{0c}^0 & x_{0c}^0 & 0 \end{bmatrix} \begin{bmatrix} \ddot{x}_{0c}^0 \\ \ddot{y}_{0c}^0 \\ \ddot{z}_{0c}^0 \end{bmatrix} + \begin{bmatrix} I_{cxx}^0 & -I_{cxy}^0 & -I_{cxz}^0 \\ -I_{cyx}^0 & I_{cyy}^0 & -I_{cyz}^0 \\ -I_{czx}^0 & -I_{czy}^0 & I_{czz}^0 \end{bmatrix} \begin{bmatrix} \dot{\Omega}_x^0 \\ \dot{\Omega}_y^0 \\ \dot{\Omega}_z^0 \end{bmatrix}$$

$$+ \begin{bmatrix} 0 & -\Omega_z^0 & \Omega_y^0 \\ \Omega_z^0 & 0 & -\Omega_x^0 \\ -\Omega_y^0 & \Omega_x^0 & 0 \end{bmatrix} \begin{bmatrix} I_{cxx}^0 & -I_{cxy}^0 & -I_{cxz}^0 \\ -I_{cyx}^0 & I_{cyy}^0 & -I_{cyz}^0 \\ -I_{czx}^0 & -I_{czy}^0 & I_{czz}^0 \end{bmatrix} \begin{bmatrix} \Omega_x^0 \\ \Omega_y^0 \\ \Omega_z^0 \end{bmatrix} = \begin{bmatrix} \sum M_x^0 \\ \sum M_y^0 \\ \sum M_z^0 \end{bmatrix} \qquad (10\text{-}25)$$

or symbolically,

$$m[I][\ddot{s}^0_{0c}] = [\textstyle\sum F^0] \tag{10-26}$$

$$m[r^0_{0c}][\ddot{s}^0_{0c}] + [T^0_c][\dot{\Omega}^0] + [\Gamma^0][T^0_c][\Omega^0] = [\textstyle\sum M^0] \tag{10-27}$$

where $[\sum F^0]$ and $[\sum M^0]$ are the resultant force and moment functions referred to the stationary axes X^0_0, Y^0_0, Z^0_0.

These equations are the distributed parameter model equivalents of the single particle equation (2-5), and this similarity allows again the application of the methods of single particle kinetics in the analysis of space motion of rigid bodies (problems of the first kind, and problems of the second kind, Section 2.2).

Euler's Equations of Motion

Equations (10-25) can be greatly simplified if the reference axes coincide with the principal axes of the body, for then the moments of inertia become the principal moments of inertia $I^p_{c,1}, I^p_{c,2}, I^p_{c,3}$ and the products of inertia vanish.   In the case of pure rotation, the resulting equations, called *Euler's equations*, are

$$I^p_{c,1}\dot{\Omega}^p_1 - (I^p_{c,2} - I^p_{c,3})\Omega^p_2\Omega^p_3 = \textstyle\sum M^p_1$$

$$I^p_{c,2}\dot{\Omega}^p_2 - (I^p_{c,3} - I^p_{c,1})\Omega^p_3\Omega^p_1 = \textstyle\sum M^p_2 \tag{10-28}$$

$$I^p_{c,3}\dot{\Omega}^p_3 - (I^p_{c,1} - I^p_{c,2})\Omega^p_1\Omega^p_2 = \textstyle\sum M^p_3$$

where $\Omega^p_1, \Omega^p_2, \Omega^p_3, \dot{\Omega}^p_1, \dot{\Omega}^p_2, \dot{\Omega}^p_3$ and $\sum M^p_1, \sum M^p_2, \sum M^p_3$ are respectively the scalar components of the angular velocity, of the angular acceleration and of the resultant moment of the body in the principal axes system.

Quasicoordinates

It must be pointed out that in (10-25) and (10-28) $\Omega_1, \Omega_2, \Omega_3$ are not just time derivatives of certain angles but nonintegrable combinations of time derivatives and trigonometric functions of the respective Euler angle system (Section 9.2).   They are called the quasicoordinates and their presence makes the solution of equations of space motion a formidable task.   Only a few special cases of this motion can be analyzed by elementary methods and are considered in this book.

10.3   ENERGY AND WORK

Kinetic Energy

The *total kinetic energy* T of the rigid body in space motion referred to the fixed point 0 is

$$T = \tfrac{1}{2}\int_m \mathbf{r}^*_{0m} \cdot \mathbf{r}^*_{0m}\, dm = \tfrac{1}{2}\int_m (\dot{\mathbf{r}}_{0c} + \boldsymbol{\Omega} \times \mathbf{r}_{cm}) \cdot (\dot{\mathbf{r}}_{0c} + \boldsymbol{\Omega} \times \mathbf{r}_{cm})\, dm$$

$$= \tfrac{1}{2}\dot{\mathbf{r}}_{0c} \cdot \dot{\mathbf{r}}_{0c}m + \tfrac{1}{2}\boldsymbol{\Omega} \cdot \mathbf{H}_c$$

$$= \tfrac{1}{2}\dot{r}^2_{0c}m + \tfrac{1}{2}(I_{cxx}\Omega^2_x + I_{cyy}\Omega^2_y + I_{czz}\Omega^2_z - 2I_{cxy}\Omega_x\Omega_y - 2I_{cyz}\Omega_y\Omega_z - 2I_{czx}\Omega_z\Omega_x)$$

$$= T_{0c} + T_c \tag{10-29}$$

where T_{0c} is the translatory energy (of the total mass concentrated at c) with respect to 0, and T_c is the rotary energy (of the distributed mass) with respect to c.

In matrix form,

$$T = \tfrac{1}{2}m \underbrace{\begin{bmatrix} \dot{x}^0_{0c} \\ \dot{y}^0_{0c} \\ \dot{z}^0_{0c} \end{bmatrix}^T}_{[\dot{s}^0_{0c}]^T} \underbrace{\begin{bmatrix} \dot{x}^0_{0c} \\ \dot{y}^0_{0c} \\ \dot{z}^0_{0c} \end{bmatrix}}_{[\dot{s}^0_{0c}]} + \tfrac{1}{2} \underbrace{\begin{bmatrix} \Omega^0_x \\ \Omega^0_y \\ \Omega^0_z \end{bmatrix}^T}_{[\Omega^0]^T} \underbrace{\begin{bmatrix} I^0_{cxx} & -I^0_{cxy} & -I^0_{cxz} \\ -I^0_{cyx} & I^0_{cyy} & -I^0_{cyz} \\ -I^0_{czx} & -I^0_{czy} & I^0_{cxz} \end{bmatrix}}_{[T^0_c]} \underbrace{\begin{bmatrix} \Omega^0_x \\ \Omega^0_y \\ \Omega^0_z \end{bmatrix}}_{[\Omega^0]} \qquad (10\text{-}30)$$

which can be written in the 0-system as shown above or in the l-system, but most conveniently in the p-system where the products of inertia vanish and $[T^p_c]$ becomes a diagonal matrix.

Mechanical Work

The *total mechanical work* U done by the forces moving the rigid body of mass m along a prescribed path in space from position 1 to position 2 is

$$U = \int_m \int_1^2 (\mathbf{r}^{**}_{0m}\, dm) \cdot d\mathbf{r}_{0m} = \int_m \int_1^2 (\mathbf{r}^{**}_{0c} + \mathbf{r}^{**}_{cm})\, dm \cdot d(\mathbf{r}_{0c} + \mathbf{r}_{cm})$$

$$= \tfrac{1}{2}m(\dot{r}^2_{0c,2} - \dot{r}^2_{0c,1}) + \tfrac{1}{2}[I_{cxx}(\Omega^2_{x,2} - \Omega^2_{x,1}) + I_{cyy}(\Omega^2_{y,2} - \Omega^2_{y,1})$$

$$+ I_{czz}(\Omega^2_{z,2} - \Omega^2_{z,1}) - 2I_{cxy}(\Omega_{x,2}\Omega_{y,2} - \Omega_{x,1}\Omega_{y,1})$$

$$- 2I_{cyz}(\Omega_{y,2}\Omega_{z,2} - \Omega_{y,1}\Omega_{z,1}) - 2I_{czx}(\Omega_{z,2}\Omega_{x,2} - \Omega_{z,1}\Omega_{x,1})]$$

$$= T_{0c,2} - T_{0c,1} + T_{c,2} - T_{c,1} = \Delta T_{0c} + \Delta T_c = U_{0c} + U_c \qquad (10\text{-}31)$$

where T_{0c} and T_c are the changes in the translatory and rotary energy of the body corresponding to the changes in position, and U_{0c} and U_c are the translatory and rotary work required to make this change. Equation $(10\text{-}31)$ is the general form of the *classical work-energy equation* which can be stated in matrix form as

$$\int_1^2 [F^0_c]^T[\dot{s}^0_{0c}]\, dt + \int_1^2 [M^0_c]^T[\Omega^0]\, dt = \tfrac{1}{2}m\{[\dot{s}^0_{0c,2}]^T[\dot{s}^0_{0c,2}] - [\dot{s}^0_{0c,1}]^T[\dot{s}^0_{0c,1}]\}$$

$$+ \tfrac{1}{2}\{[\Omega^0_2]^T[T^0_c][\Omega^0_2] - [\Omega^0_1]^T[T^0_c][\Omega^0_1]\} \qquad (10\text{-}32)$$

where $[F^0_c]$ and $[M^0_c]$ are the resultant force and moment vectors at c producing the required work, and the remaining symbols are those of $(10\text{-}31)$.

Conservation of Energy

If the forces and moments acting on the rigid body are conservative so that the whole system has a potential V, then $(8\text{-}21)$ is again valid and the total energy is constant (principle of conservation of energy).

Illustrative Problems

LINEAR AND ANGULAR MOMENTUM

10.1   Derive the linear momentum equation *(10-19)* for a rigid body in space motion (Fig. P-10.1).

The derivation of the vector form of *(10-19)* is identical to that given in Problem 8.1.

In matrix notation,

$$[G^0] = \int_m [s^{0*}_{0m}] \, dm$$

$$= [\dot{s}^0_{0c}] \int_m dm + \int_m [\dot{\pi}^{0I}][\dot{s}^0_{cm}] \, dm$$

$$+ \int_m [\pi^{0I}][\dot{\ddot{s}}^0_{cm}] \, dm$$

$$= [\dot{s}^0_{0c}]m = [G^0_{0c}]$$

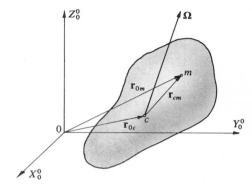

Fig. P-10.1

10.2   Derive the angular momentum equation *(10-20)* for a rigid body in space motion (Fig. P-10.1).

As in Problem 8.2, the total angular momentum of the body in Fig. P-10.1 is

$$\mathbf{H} = \int_m \mathbf{r}_{0m} \times \mathbf{r}^*_{0m} \, dm = \int_m (\mathbf{r}_{0c} + \mathbf{r}_{cm}) \times (\mathbf{r}^*_{0c} + \mathbf{r}^*_{cm}) \, dm \qquad (1)$$

where $\mathbf{r}_{0c} = \dot{\mathbf{r}}_{0c}$, $\mathbf{r}^*_{cm} = \mathbf{\Omega} \times \mathbf{r}_{cm}$ and $\mathbf{r}_{0c} \times \left(\mathbf{\Omega} \times \int_m \mathbf{r}_{cm} \, dm \right) = 0$, $\int_m \mathbf{r}_{cm} \times \dot{\mathbf{r}}_{0c} \, dm = \left(\int_m \mathbf{r}_{cm} \, dm \right)$ $\times \dot{\mathbf{r}}_{0c} = 0$.   Hence

$$\mathbf{H} = \mathbf{r}_{0c} \times \mathbf{G}_{0c} + \int_m \mathbf{r}_{cm} \times (\mathbf{\Omega} \times \mathbf{r}_{cm}) \, dm = \mathbf{H}_{0c} + \mathbf{H}_c \qquad (2)$$

where

$$\mathbf{H}_c = \int_m \mathbf{r}_{cm} \times (\mathbf{\Omega} \times \mathbf{r}_{cm}) \, dm = \int_m [\mathbf{\Omega}(\mathbf{r}_{cm} \cdot \mathbf{r}_{cm}) - \mathbf{r}_{cm}(\mathbf{\Omega} \cdot \mathbf{r}_{cm})] \, dm \qquad (3)$$

Since $\mathbf{r}_{cm} = x_{cm}\mathbf{i} + y_{cm}\mathbf{j} + z_{cm}\mathbf{k}$ and $\mathbf{\Omega} = \Omega_x \mathbf{i} + \Omega_y \mathbf{j} + \Omega_z \mathbf{k}$, equation *(3)* becomes

$$\mathbf{H} = (\Omega_x \mathbf{i} + \Omega_y \mathbf{j} + \Omega_z \mathbf{k}) \int_m (x^2_{cm} + y^2_{cm} + z^2_{cm}) \, dm - \int_m (x_{cm}\mathbf{i} + y_{cm}\mathbf{j} + z_{cm}\mathbf{k})(\Omega_x x_{cm} + \Omega_y y_{cm} + \Omega_z z_{cm}) \, dm$$

$$(4)$$

which is the origin of the moments and products of inertia defined by *(10-1)*.

In terms of *(10-1)*, equation *(4)* becomes

$$\mathbf{H}_c = (I_{cxx}\Omega_x - I_{cxy}\Omega_y - I_{cxz}\Omega_z)\mathbf{i} + (-I_{cyx}\Omega_x + I_{cyy}\Omega_y - I_{cyz}\Omega_z)\mathbf{j} + (-I_{czx}\Omega_x - I_{czy}\Omega_y + I_{czz}\Omega_z)\mathbf{k} \qquad (5)$$

where the superscript 0 of the stationary system is omitted in all terms.

10.3 Derive the matrix form of the angular momentum equation (*10-21*) for a rigid body in space motion (Fig. P-10.1).

By definition, the total angular momentum of the body is

$$[H^0] = \int_m [r^0_{0m}][\dot{s}^{0*}_{0m}]\,dm = \int_m (r^0_{0c} + r^0_{cm})(\dot{s}^{0*}_{0c} + \dot{s}^{0*}_{cm})\,dm \tag{1}$$

where $[\dot{s}^{0*}_{0c}] = [\dot{s}^0_{0c}]$, $[\dot{s}^{0*}_{cm}] = [\Gamma^0][\dot{s}^0_{cm}]$ and $[r^0_{0c}][\Gamma^0]\int_m [\dot{s}^0_{cm}]\,dm = [0]$, $\int_m [r^0_{cm}][\dot{s}^0_{0c}]\,dm =$

$\left(\int_m [r^0_{cm}]\,dm\right)[\dot{s}^0_{0c}] = [0]$.   Hence

$$[H^0] = [r^0_{0c}][\dot{s}^0_{0c}]m + \int_m [r^0_{cm}][\Gamma^0][\dot{s}^0_{cm}]\,dm = [H^0_{0c}] + [H^0_c] \tag{2}$$

where

$$[H^0_c] = \int_m \underbrace{\begin{bmatrix} 0 & -z^0_{cm} & y^0_{cm} \\ z^0_{cm} & 0 & -x^0_{cm} \\ -y^0_{cm} & x^0_{cm} & 0 \end{bmatrix}}_{[r^0_{cm}]} \underbrace{\begin{bmatrix} 0 & -\Omega^0_z & \Omega^0_y \\ \Omega^0_z & 0 & -\Omega^0_x \\ -\Omega^0_y & \Omega^0_x & 0 \end{bmatrix}}_{[\Gamma^0]} \underbrace{\begin{bmatrix} x^0_{cm} \\ y^0_{cm} \\ z^0_{cm} \end{bmatrix}}_{[\dot{s}^0_{cm}]}\,dm$$

$$= \begin{bmatrix} I^0_{cxx}\Omega^0_x & -I^0_{cxy}\Omega^0_y & -I^0_{cxz}\Omega^0_z \\ -I^0_{cyx}\Omega^0_x & I^0_{cyy}\Omega^0_y & -I^0_{cyz}\Omega^0_z \\ -I^0_{czx}\Omega^0_x & -I^0_{czy}\Omega^0_y & I^0_{czz}\Omega^0_z \end{bmatrix} = \underbrace{\begin{bmatrix} I^0_{cxx} & -I^0_{cxy} & -I^0_{cxz} \\ -I^0_{cyx} & I^0_{cyy} & -I^0_{cyz} \\ -I^0_{czx} & -I^0_{czy} & I^0_{czz} \end{bmatrix}}_{[T^0_c]} \underbrace{\begin{bmatrix} \Omega^0_x \\ \Omega^0_y \\ -\Omega^0_z \end{bmatrix}}_{[\Omega^0]} \tag{3}$$

INERTIA TENSOR
10.4 Derive the transformation relationships (*10-10*) and (*10-11*) for the inertia tensors $[T^0_0]$ and $[T^l_0]$.

In the 0-system (as in equation (3) of Problem 10.3),

$$[H^0_0] = [T^0_0][\Omega^0] \tag{1}$$

In the *l*-system,

$$[H^l_0] = [T^l_0][\Omega^l] \tag{2}$$

Since $[H^l_0] = [\pi^{l0}][H^0_0]$, $[\Omega^l] = [\pi^{l0}][\Omega^0]$, equation (2) can be written as

$$[\pi^{l0}][H^0_0] = [T^l_0][\pi^{l0}][\Omega^0] \tag{3}$$

and on multiplying by $[\pi^{0l}]$,

$$[H^0_0] = \underbrace{[\pi^{0l}][T^l_0][\pi^{l0}]}_{[T^0_0]}[\Omega^0] \tag{4}$$

Similarly, with $[H_0^0] = [\pi^{0l}][H_0^l]$, $[\Omega^0] = [\pi^{0l}][\Omega^l]$, equation (1) can be written as

$$[\pi^{0l}][H_0^l] = [T_0^0][\pi^{0l}][\Omega^l] \tag{5}$$

and on multiplying by $[\pi^{l0}]$,

$$[H_0^l] = \underbrace{[\pi^{l0}][T_0^0][\pi^{0l}]}_{[T_0^l]}[\Omega^l] \tag{6}$$

10.5 Derive the determinant equation (10-14), the roots of which are the principal inertia functions.

If Ω is given and coincides with one of the principal axes, then the angular momentum of the body is

$$[H_0^p] = [T_0^p][\Omega^p] \tag{1}$$

where

$$[T_0^p] = \begin{bmatrix} I_{0,1}^p & & \\ & I_{0,2}^p & \\ & & I_{0,3}^p \end{bmatrix}, \qquad [\Omega^p] = \begin{bmatrix} \Omega^p \\ 0 \\ 0 \end{bmatrix} \tag{2, 3}$$

Equation (1) in terms of (2) and (3) in the p-system is

$$\begin{bmatrix} H_{0x}^p \\ H_{0y}^p \\ H_{0z}^p \end{bmatrix} = \begin{bmatrix} I_{0,1}^p & & \\ & I_{0,2}^p & \\ & & I_{0,3}^p \end{bmatrix} \begin{bmatrix} \Omega^p \\ 0 \\ 0 \end{bmatrix} = \begin{bmatrix} I_{0,1}^p \Omega^p \\ 0 \\ 0 \end{bmatrix} \tag{4}$$

and in the 0-system is

$$\begin{bmatrix} H_{0x}^0 \\ H_{0y}^0 \\ H_{0z}^0 \end{bmatrix} = I_{0,1}^p \begin{bmatrix} \Omega_x^0 \\ \Omega_y^0 \\ \Omega_z^0 \end{bmatrix} \tag{5}$$

where $\Omega_x^0, \Omega_y^0, \Omega_z^0$ are the scalar components of Ω^p in X_0^0, Y_0^0, Z_0^0 respectively.
But (5) is also given as

$$\begin{bmatrix} H_{0x}^0 \\ H_{0y}^0 \\ H_{0z}^0 \end{bmatrix} = \begin{bmatrix} I_{0xx}^0 & -I_{0xy}^0 & -I_{0xz}^0 \\ -I_{0yx}^0 & I_{0yy}^0 & -I_{0yz}^0 \\ -I_{0zx}^0 & -I_{0zy}^0 & I_{0zz}^0 \end{bmatrix} \begin{bmatrix} \Omega_x^0 \\ \Omega_y^0 \\ \Omega_z^0 \end{bmatrix} \tag{6}$$

On substituting (5) in (6),

$$I_{0,1}^p \begin{bmatrix} \Omega_x^0 \\ \Omega_y^0 \\ \Omega_z^0 \end{bmatrix} = \begin{bmatrix} I_{0xx}^0 & -I_{0xy}^0 & -I_{0xz}^0 \\ -I_{0yx}^0 & I_{0yy}^0 & -I_{0yz}^0 \\ -I_{0zx}^0 & -I_{0zy}^0 & I_{0zz}^0 \end{bmatrix} \begin{bmatrix} \Omega_x^0 \\ \Omega_y^0 \\ \Omega_z^0 \end{bmatrix}$$

or

$$
\underbrace{\begin{bmatrix} I^0_{0xx} - I^p_{0,\,1} & -I^0_{0xy} & -I^0_{0xz} \\ -I^0_{0yx} & I^0_{0yy} - I^p_{0,\,1} & -I^0_{0yz} \\ -I^0_{0zx} & -I^0_{0zy} & I^0_{0zz} - I^p_{0,\,1} \end{bmatrix}}_{[D^0_0]} \underbrace{\begin{bmatrix} \Omega^0_x \\ \Omega^0_y \\ \Omega^0_z \end{bmatrix}}_{[\Omega^0]} = \begin{bmatrix} 0 \\ 0 \\ 0 \end{bmatrix}
\tag{7}
$$

where $I^p_{0,\,1}$ may be also $I^p_{0,\,2}$ or $I^p_{0,\,3}$ depending on the position of Ω^p in (3).

For (7) to be satisfied, the determinant of the coefficient matrix $[D^0_0]$ must be zero. This condition furnishes the determinant equation (10-14), the roots of which are the principal moments of inertia.

10.6 Derive the direction cosines of the principal axes given by (10-15).

The direction cosines of the principal axis X^p_0 in Problem 10.5 are

$$\cos(X^0_0, X^p_0) = \Omega^0_x/\Omega^p = \alpha_1, \qquad \cos(Y^0_0, X^p_0) = \Omega^0_y/\Omega^p = \beta_1, \qquad \cos(Z^0_0, X^p_0) = \Omega^0_z/\Omega^p = \gamma_1 \quad (1)$$

In terms of (1), equations (7) of Problem 10.5 are

$$
\begin{aligned}
&[(I^0_{0xx} - I^p_{0,\,1})\alpha_1 - I^0_{0xy}\beta_1 - I^0_{0xz}\gamma_1]\Omega^p = 0 \\
&[-I^0_{0yx}\alpha_1 + (I^0_{0yy} - I^p_{0,\,1})\beta_1 - I^0_{0yx}\gamma_1]\Omega^p = 0 \\
&[-I^0_{0zx}\alpha_1 - I^0_{0zy}\beta_1(I^0_{0zz} - I^p_{0,\,1})\gamma_1]\Omega^p = 0
\end{aligned}
\tag{2}
$$

which after cancelling Ω^p and eliminating α_1 reduce to

$$
\begin{aligned}
&[(I^0_{0xx} - I^p_{0,\,1})(I^0_{0yy} - I^p_{0,\,1}) - (I^0_{0xy})^2]\beta_1 + [(I^0_{0xx} - I^p_{0,\,1})I^0_{0yz} + I^0_{0yx}I^0_{0xz}]\gamma_1 = 0 \\
&[(I^0_{0xx} - I^p_{0,\,1})I^0_{0zy} + I^0_{0zx}I^0_{0xy}]\beta_1 + [(I^0_{0zz} - I^p_{0,\,1})(I^0_{0xx} - I^p_{0,\,1}) - (I^0_{0zx})^2]\gamma_1 = 0
\end{aligned}
\tag{3}
$$

After multiplying the first equation of (3) by β_1, the second equation of (3) by γ_1, and subtracting,

$$\beta^2_1 = \frac{(I^0_{0zz} - I^p_{0,\,1})(I^0_{0xx} - I^p_{0,\,1}) - (I^0_{0zx})^2}{(I^0_{0xx} - I^p_{0,\,1})(I^0_{0yy} - I^p_{0,\,1}) - (I^0_{0xy})^2}\gamma^2_1 = \frac{b_1}{c_1}\gamma^2_1 \tag{4}$$

Similarly, after eliminating β_1 and repeating the above procedure,

$$\alpha^2_1 = \frac{(I^0_{0yy} - I^p_{0,\,1})(I^0_{0zz} - I^p_{0,\,1}) - (I^0_{0yz})^2}{(I^0_{0xx} - I^p_{0,\,1})(I^0_{0yy} - I^p_{0,\,1}) - (I^0_{0xy})^2}\gamma^2_1 = \frac{a_1}{c_1}\gamma^2_1 \tag{5}$$

From the orthogonality condition,

$$\alpha^2_1 + \beta^2_1 + \gamma^2_1 = 1$$

which in terms of (4) and (5) yields

$$\gamma_1 = \pm\sqrt{\frac{c_1}{a_1 + b_1 + c_1}} = \pm\sqrt{\frac{c_1}{d_1}} \tag{6}$$

By cyclic substitution,

$$\alpha_1 = \pm\sqrt{\frac{a_1}{d_1}}, \qquad \beta_1 = \pm\sqrt{\frac{b_1}{d_1}}$$

Similarly, the direction cosines of Y^p_0 and Z^p_0 are respectively

$$\alpha_2 = \pm\sqrt{\frac{a_2}{d_2}}, \qquad \beta_2 = \pm\sqrt{\frac{b_2}{d_2}}, \qquad \gamma_2 = \pm\sqrt{\frac{c_2}{d_2}}$$

$$\alpha_3 = \pm\sqrt{\frac{a_3}{d_3}}, \qquad \beta_3 = \pm\sqrt{\frac{b_3}{d_3}}, \qquad \gamma_3 = \pm\sqrt{\frac{c_3}{d_3}}$$

where the subscripts 2 and 3 require the substitution of $I^p_{0,2}$ and $I^p_{0,3}$ in (2), respectively.

10.7 Consider a rigid body of a known inertia tensor in the X^0_0, Y^0_0, Z^0_0 axes. Find its moment of inertia about the axis X^l_0 of given direction cosines α, β, γ (Fig. P-10.7).

By (10-11),

$$I^l_{0xx} = \begin{bmatrix} \alpha & \beta & \gamma \end{bmatrix} \begin{bmatrix} I^0_{0xx} & -I^0_{0xy} & -I^0_{0xz} \\ -I^0_{0yx} & I^0_{0yy} & -I^0_{0yz} \\ -I^0_{0zx} & -I^0_{0zy} & I^0_{0zz} \end{bmatrix} \begin{bmatrix} \alpha \\ \beta \\ \gamma \end{bmatrix}$$

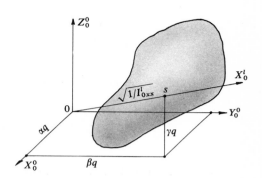

Fig. P-10.7

$$= I^0_{0xx}\alpha^2 + I^0_{0yy}\beta^2 + I^0_{0zz}\gamma^2$$
$$- 2(I^0_{0xy}\alpha\beta + I^0_{0yz}\beta\gamma + I^0_{0zx}\gamma\alpha) \qquad (1)$$

where the inertia functions in the 0-system are constants and I^l_{0xx}, α, β, γ change with the position of X^l_0.
    With the notation

$$q = \sqrt{1/I^l_{0xx}}, \qquad x^0_{0s} = \alpha q, \qquad y^0_{0s} = \beta q, \qquad z^0_{0s} = \gamma q$$

equation (1) reduces to

$$1 = I^0_{0xx}(x^0_{0s})^2 + I^0_{0yy}(y^0_{0s})^2 + I^0_{0zz}(z^0_{0s})^2 - 2(I^0_{0xy}x^0_{0s}y^0_{0s} + I^0_{0yz}y^0_{0s}z^0_{0s} + I^0_{0zx}z^0_{0s}x^0_{0s}) \qquad (2)$$

which is the equation of a quadratic surface. Since $I^l_{0xx} \neq \infty$, this surface must be an ellipsoid of inertia in the 0-system.
    If (2) is written in the principal axes ($I^p_{0xy} = I^p_{0yz} = I^p_{0zx} = 0$), it becomes

$$I = I^p_{0,1}(x^p_{0s})^2 + I^p_{0,2}(y^p_{0s})^2 + I^p_{0,3}(z^p_{0s}) \qquad (3)$$

and with

$$q_1 = \sqrt{1/I^p_{0,1}}, \qquad q_2 = \sqrt{1/I^p_{0,2}}, \qquad q_3 = \sqrt{1/I^p_{0,3}}$$

reduces to

$$1 = \left(\frac{x^p_{0s}}{q_1}\right)^2 + \left(\frac{y^p_{0s}}{q_2}\right)^2 + \left(\frac{z^p_{0s}}{q_3}\right)^2$$

where q_1, q_2, q_3 are the semiaxes of the ellipsoid of inertia.

ROTATION ABOUT A FIXED AXIS

10.8 Derive the equations of pure rotation of a rigid body about a fixed axis Z_0^0 (Fig. P-10.8).

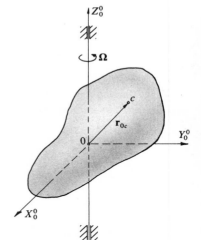

In the case of pure rotation about Z_0^0,

$$\Omega_x^0 = 0, \qquad \Omega_y^0 = 0, \qquad \Omega_z^0 = \Omega \qquad (1)$$

$$\dot{x}_{0c}^0 = -y_{0c}^0\Omega, \qquad \dot{y}_{0c}^0 = x_{0c}^0\Omega, \qquad \dot{z}_{0c}^0 = 0 \qquad (2)$$

$$\ddot{x}_{0c}^0 = -y_{0c}^0\dot{\Omega} - x_{0c}^0(\Omega)^2, \quad \ddot{y}_{0c}^0 = x_{0c}^0\dot{\Omega} - y_{0c}^0(\Omega)^2, \quad \ddot{z}_{0c}^0 = 0 \qquad (3)$$

The force equations of motion (*10-24*) are

$$m[-x_{0c}^0(\Omega^2) - y_{0c}^0\dot{\Omega}] = \sum F_x^0$$
$$m[x_{0c}^0\dot{\Omega} - y_{0c}^0(\Omega)^2] = \sum F_y^0 \qquad (4)$$
$$0 = \sum F_z^0$$

The moment equations of motion (*10-25*) are

$$I_{cyz}^0(\Omega)^2 - I_{cxz}^0\dot{\Omega} = \sum M_x^0$$
$$-I_{cxz}^0(\Omega)^2 - I_{cyz}^0\dot{\Omega} = \sum M_y^0 \qquad (5)$$
$$I_{czz}^0\dot{\Omega} = \sum M_z^0$$

Fig. P-10.8

The rigid body in this state of motion is called a rotor.
When the mass center of the rotor falls on the axis of rotation,

$$\sum F_x^0 = 0, \qquad \sum F_y^0 = 0, \qquad \sum F_z^0 = 0 \qquad (6)$$

and the rotor is said to be statically balanced.
When the axis of rotation is one of the principal axes of the body,

$$\sum M_x^p = 0, \qquad \sum M_y^p = 0, \qquad \sum M_z^p = I_{czz}^p\dot{\Omega} \qquad (7)$$

and the rotor is said to be dynamically balanced.

10.9 A circular disk of radius a, constant thickness, and mass m is mounted on a rigid shaft of negligible mass as shown in Fig. P-10.9a. Find the bearing reactions of the shaft which rotates with constant angular velocity Ω about X_c^0. Note the angle of X_c^0 and X_c^p is ψ = constant.

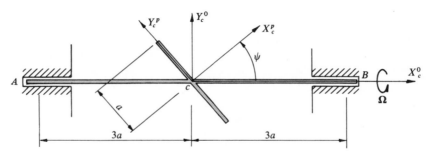

Fig. P-10.9a

The principal inertia tensor of the disk (see Appendix) is

$$[T_c^p] = \begin{bmatrix} I_{c,1}^p & & \\ & I_{c,2}^p & \\ & & I_{c,3}^p \end{bmatrix} = \tfrac{1}{4}ma^2 \begin{bmatrix} 2 & & \\ & 1 & \\ & & 1 \end{bmatrix}$$

and its inertia tensor in the 0-system which rotates about X_c^0 is

$$[T_c^0] = [\pi^{0p}][T_c^p][\pi^{p0}] = \tfrac{1}{4}ma^2 \begin{bmatrix} \cos\psi & -\sin\psi & 0 \\ \sin\psi & \cos\psi & 0 \\ 0 & 0 & 1 \end{bmatrix} \begin{bmatrix} 2 & & \\ & 1 & \\ & & 1 \end{bmatrix} \begin{bmatrix} \cos\psi & \sin\psi & 0 \\ -\sin\psi & \cos\psi & 0 \\ 0 & 0 & 1 \end{bmatrix}$$

$$= \tfrac{1}{4}ma^2 \begin{bmatrix} \cos^2\psi + 1 & \cos\psi\sin\psi & 0 \\ \cos\psi\sin\psi & \sin^2\psi + 1 & 0 \\ 0 & 0 & 1 \end{bmatrix}$$

The moment equations of motion (10-25) modified for rotation about X_c^0 are

$$\tfrac{1}{4}ma^2 \begin{bmatrix} 0 & 0 & 0 \\ 0 & 0 & -\Omega \\ 0 & \Omega & 0 \end{bmatrix} \begin{bmatrix} \cos^2\psi + 1 & \cos\psi\sin\psi & 0 \\ \cos\psi\sin\psi & \sin^2\psi + 1 & 0 \\ 0 & 0 & 1 \end{bmatrix} \begin{bmatrix} \Omega \\ 0 \\ 0 \end{bmatrix} = \begin{bmatrix} \sum M_x^0 \\ \sum M_y^0 \\ \sum M_z^0 \end{bmatrix}$$

$$\tfrac{1}{4}ma^2 \begin{bmatrix} 0 \\ 0 \\ (\Omega)^2 \cos\psi\sin\psi \end{bmatrix} = \begin{bmatrix} \sum M_x^0 \\ \sum M_y^0 \\ \sum M_z^0 \end{bmatrix}$$

The bearing reactions due to $\sum M_z^0$ are (Fig. 10-9b)

$$R_{Ay}^0 = -R_{By}^0 = \tfrac{1}{24}ma(\Omega)^2 \cos\psi\sin\psi$$

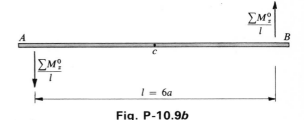

Fig. P-10.9b

10.10 Solve Problem 10.9 using Euler's equations of motion (10-28).

The angular velocities in the p-system are

$$\Omega_1^p = \Omega\cos\psi, \qquad \Omega_2^p = -\Omega\sin\psi, \qquad \Omega_3^p = 0$$

By (10-28),

$$0 = \sum M_1^p, \qquad 0 = \sum M_2^p, \qquad \tfrac{1}{4}ma^2(\Omega)^2 \cos\psi\sin\psi = \sum M_3^p$$

where $\sum M_3^p = \sum M_z^0$.   Then

$$R_{Ay}^0 = -R_{By}^0 = \frac{\sum M_3^p}{l} = \tfrac{1}{24}ma(\Omega)^2 \cos\psi\sin\psi$$

MOMENT-FREE ROTATION OF AN UNSYMMETRICAL BODY

10.11 Find the moment-free equations of rotation of an unsymmetrical rigid body about a fixed point 0.

Referred to the p-system of the body, the Euler equations of rotation (10-28) are

$$I_1\dot{\Omega}_1 = (I_2 - I_3)\Omega_2\Omega_3$$
$$I_2\dot{\Omega}_2 = (I_3 - I_1)\Omega_3\Omega_1 \qquad (1)$$
$$I_3\dot{\Omega}_3 = (I_1 - I_2)\Omega_1\Omega_2$$

where the superscript p is omitted.

Since $\mathbf{M} = 0$, $\mathbf{H}$ must be constant which implies that its magnitude

$$H = \sqrt{\mathbf{H} \cdot \mathbf{H}} = \sqrt{(I_1\Omega_1)^2 + (I_2\Omega_2)^2 + (I_3\Omega_3)^2} = \text{constant} \qquad (2)$$

and the direction of $\mathbf{H}$ is constant.

Also, with zero moment the change in kinetic energy is zero and

$$\mathbf{\Omega} \cdot \mathbf{H} = I_1\Omega_1^2 + I_2\Omega_2^2 + I_3\Omega_3^2 = 2T = \text{constant} \qquad (3)$$

Equations (2) and (3) provide auxiliary conditions which are frequently useful in the solution of particular problems.

10.12 Show the geometric representation of Problem 10.11.

Equation (3) of Problem 10.11 indicates that the tip of $\mathbf{\Omega}$ (Fig. P-10.12) is always touching a fixed plane, called the invariable plane. This plane is normal to $\mathbf{H}$, and the line of action of $\mathbf{H}$ (which has a fixed direction) is called the invariable line.

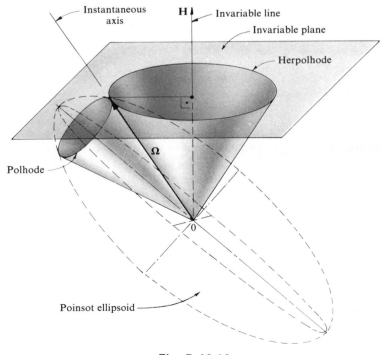

Fig. P-10.12

If the terminus of $\mathbf{\Omega}$ is given by coordinates

$$x = \Omega_1, \qquad y = \Omega_2, \qquad z = \Omega_3 \tag{1}$$

in the p-axes with origin at 0, then (2) of Problem 10.11 becomes

$$I_1 x^2 + I_2 y^2 + I_3 z^2 = H^2 \tag{2}$$

and (3) of the same problem is

$$I_1^2 x^2 + I_2^2 y^2 + I_3^2 z^2 = 2T \tag{3}$$

where T is the rotary kinetic energy of the body.

Equations (2) and (3) define two concentric ellipsoids rigidly attached to the body.   In order to satisfy both conditions, the tip of $\mathbf{\Omega}$ must trace the intersection of these two surfaces, called the polhode.

The ellipsoid defined by (3) written in a modified form as

$$\frac{x^2}{2T/I_1} + \frac{y^2}{2T/I_2} + \frac{z^2}{2T/I_3} = 1 \tag{4}$$

is called the Poinsot ellipsoid.

Since the tip of $\mathbf{\Omega}$ lies on the Poinsot ellipsoid and also on the invariable plane, the invariable plane must be a fixed tangential plane on which the ellipsoid rolls without slipping about the pivot 0.   The trace of the ellipsoid on the invariable plane is called the herpolhode and the trace of the invariable plane on the ellipsoid is called the polhode.

The cone generated by $\mathbf{\Omega}$ on the herpolhode is called the space cone, and the cone generated by $\mathbf{\Omega}$ on the polhode is called the body cone.

Since the herpolhode and the polhode at a given instant have a common point, the line connecting this point and the pivot 0 is the instantaneous axis of rotation of these two cones, and the moving body cone rolls on the fixed space cone about the instantaneous axis which is their line of contact.

If the body cone is external to the space cone, the motion is called direct precession.   If the body cone is internal to the space cone, the motion is called retrograde precession.

MOMENT-FREE ROTATION OF A SYMMETRICAL BODY

10.13 For a rigid body with two of its principal moments of inertia equal, $I_{c,1}^p = I_{c,2}^p$, find Euler's equations of moment-free rotation (10-28).

Since all components are in the p-system, the superscript p and the subscript c can be omitted.   Then by (10-28) with $I_1 = I_2$,

$$I_1 \dot{\Omega}_1 - (I_1 - I_3)\Omega_2\Omega_3 = 0 \tag{1}$$
$$I_2 \dot{\Omega}_2 - (I_3 - I_1)\Omega_3\Omega_1 = 0 \tag{2}$$
$$I_3 \dot{\Omega}_3 = 0 \tag{3}$$

From (3),

$$\Omega_3 = \omega_3 = \text{constant} \tag{4}$$

and with

$$\frac{I_1 - I_3}{I_1}\omega_3 = \tau = \text{constant} \tag{5}$$

equations (*1*) and (*2*) become

$$\dot{\Omega}_1 - \tau\Omega_2 = 0, \qquad \dot{\Omega}_2 + \tau\Omega_1 = 0 \tag{6), (7}$$

On differentiating (*6*) with respect to t and substituting for $\dot{\Omega}_2$ from (*7*),

$$\ddot{\Omega}_1 + \tau^2\Omega_1 = 0 \tag{8}$$

The integral of (*8*) is

$$\Omega_1 = A_1 \cos \tau t + B_1 \sin \tau t$$

where A_1, B_1 are computed from the initial conditions of motion.

At $t = 0$, for $\Omega_1(0) = \omega_1$ and $\dot{\Omega}_1(0) = 0$, $A_1 = \omega_1$, $B_1 = 0$, and

$$\Omega_1 = \omega_1 \cos \tau t \tag{9}$$

Then from (*7*),

$$\Omega_2 = \omega_1 \sin \tau t \tag{10}$$

The angular velocity in the p-system is then

$$\boldsymbol{\Omega} = \Omega_1 \mathbf{i}^p + \Omega_2 \mathbf{j}^p + \Omega_3 \mathbf{k}^p = (\omega_1 \cos \tau t)\mathbf{i}^p + (\omega_1 \sin \tau t)\mathbf{j}^p + \omega_3 \mathbf{k}^p \tag{11}$$

From (*11*),

$$\omega_{12} = \sqrt{\Omega_1^2 + \Omega_2^2} = \text{constant} \tag{12}$$

$$\Omega = \sqrt{\Omega_1^2 + \Omega_2^2 + \Omega_3^2} = \text{constant} \tag{13}$$

and

$$\tan \tau t = \Omega_2/\Omega_1 \tag{14}$$

Since $M = 0$, the angular momentum

$$\mathbf{H} = I_1\boldsymbol{\Omega}_1 + I_2\boldsymbol{\Omega}_2 + I_3\boldsymbol{\Omega}_3 = \text{constant} \tag{15}$$

From Fig. P-10.13,

$$\cos \alpha = \Omega_3/\Omega = \text{constant} \tag{16}$$

which shows that $\boldsymbol{\Omega}$ precesses along a right circular cone (body cone) and its tip traces a circular polhode.

The precession frequency of $\boldsymbol{\Omega}$ (number of revolutions per unit of time) is

$$f = \frac{\tau}{2\pi} = \frac{I_3 - I_1}{2\pi I_1}\omega_3 \tag{17}$$

as is apparent from Fig. P-10.13.

Since all vectors are in the p-system, only relative motion is described (Problem 10.15).

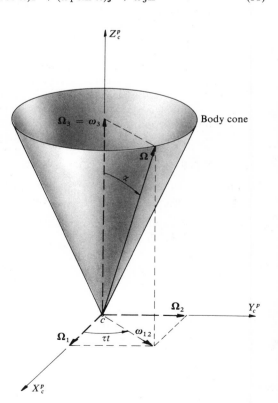

Fig. P-10.13

10.14 Using the results of Problem 10.13, compute the precession frequency of the earth rotating about its axis.

In the motion of the earth, $\mathbf{\Omega}$ is slightly inclined with $\alpha = 0.2$ sec of arc. The ratio of $I_3/I_1 = 1.00327$, as given by the geometry of the earth.

By (5) of Problem 10.13, $\tau = [(I_3 - I_1)/I_1]\omega_3 = 0.00327\omega_3$ where $\omega_3 = 2\pi$ rad/day.

Then (17) of Problem 10.13 gives $f = \tau/2\pi = (I_3 - I_1)/I_1 = 0.00327$ rad/day, and the period of precession is $P = 1/f = 305$ days. The observed precession of the earth is about 430 days. This disagreement is attributed to the nonrigidity of the earth.

EULER ANGLE SYSTEM

10.15 Describe the moment-free motion of Problem 10.13 in the stationary coordinate system.

Let the axes X_c^0, Y_c^0, Z_c^0 be stationary and the axes X_c^p, Y_c^p, Z_c^p be the rotating principal axes of the body. Next introduce the third system of axes X_c^5, Y_c^5, Z_c^5 defined in Table P-9.2 (Euler angle system B).

The geometric relations of these three systems is shown in Fig. P-10.15a where the angles ϕ, θ and ψ are the Euler angles.

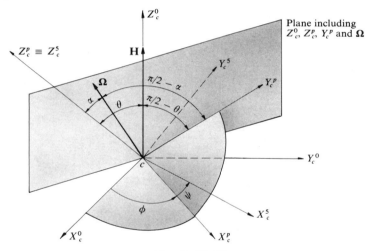

Fig. P-10.15a

Since in a moment-free rotation $\mathbf{H}$ is a constant and fixed vector, $\mathbf{H}$ is chosen as acting along Z_c^0, which now becomes the invariable line.

The scalar components of $\mathbf{H}$ in the p-system are

$$H_x^p = 0, \qquad H_y^p = H \sin\theta, \qquad H_z^p = H \cos\theta \tag{1}$$

Since Z_c^p and Z_c^5 are collinear and X_c^p, Y_c^p, X_c^5, Y_c^5 are in the same plane, the 5-system is also a principal system.

Since $H_x^p = 0$, Ω_x^p is also zero and $\mathbf{\Omega}$ must lie in the $Y_c^p Z_c^p$ plane. Then in terms of the position angle α (Problem 10.13),

$$\Omega_x^p = 0, \qquad \Omega_y^p = \Omega \sin\alpha, \qquad \Omega_z^p = \Omega \cos\alpha \tag{2}, (3), (4)$$

and

$$H_x^p = I_{xx}^p \Omega_x^p = 0 \tag{5}$$

$$H_y^p = I_{yy}^p \Omega_y^p = I_2 \Omega \sin \alpha \qquad (6)$$

$$H_z^p = I_{zz}^p \Omega_z^p = I_3 \Omega \cos \alpha \qquad (7)$$

where I_2, I_3 are the principal moments of inertia in the p-system and also in the 5-system.

From (1) and (3),

$$\frac{H_y^p}{H_z^p} = \tan \theta = \frac{I_2}{I_3} \tan \alpha \qquad (8)$$

which gives the relation between θ and α.

If $I_2 > I_3$, then $\alpha < \theta$ (slender body), the precession is direct and the body cone rolls on the outside of the space cone (Fig. P-10.15b).

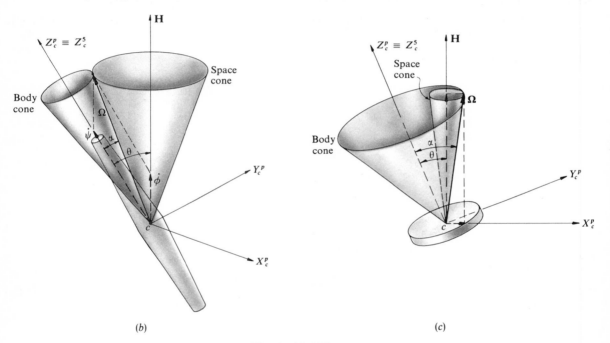

(b)   (c)

Fig. P-10.15b,c

If $I_2 < I_3$, then $\alpha > \theta$ (flatter body), the precession is retrograde and the body cone rolls on the inside of the space cone (Fig. P-10.15c).

From Fig. P-10.15a,

$$\Omega_1^p = 0 \qquad (9)$$

$$\Omega_2^p = \dot{\phi} \sin \theta \qquad (10)$$

$$\Omega_3^p = \dot{\phi} \cos \theta + \dot{\psi} \qquad (11)$$

where $\dot{\phi}$ is the angular rate of precession of $\boldsymbol{\Omega}$ about the invariable line and $\dot{\psi}$ is the angular rate of spin.

Equating the right-hand terms of (3) and (10),

$$\dot{\phi} = \Omega \frac{\sin \alpha}{\sin \theta} \qquad (12)$$

which in terms of (8) becomes

$$\dot{\phi} = \Omega\sqrt{1 + \frac{I_3^2 - I_2^2}{I_2^2}\cos^2\alpha} \tag{13}$$

where Ω, α, I_2 and I_3 are given constant quantities.

The transformation to the 0-system is then given by $[\Omega^0] = [\pi^{0l}][\Omega^l]$.

GYROSCOPIC PRECESSION

10.16 Derive the equations of motion of a spinning top having a fixed point and on which there is exerted a moment due to gravity (motion of a heavy top) as shown in Fig. P-10.16.

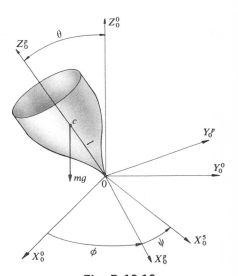

Fig. P-10.16

The moments with respect to the p-system are

$$M_{0x}^p = mgl\sin\theta, \qquad M_{0y}^p = 0, \qquad M_{0z}^p = 0 \qquad (1), (2), (3)$$

In terms of (9), (10) and (11) of Problem 10.15, the components of the angular momentum of the body are

$$H_{0x}^p = I_1^p\Omega_1^p = I_1^p\dot{\theta} \tag{4}$$
$$H_{0y}^p = I_2^p\Omega_2^p = I_2^p\dot{\phi}\sin\theta \tag{5}$$
$$H_{0z}^p = I_3^p\Omega_3^p = I_3^p(\dot{\phi}\cos\theta + \dot{\psi}) \tag{6}$$

where the moments of inertia are in the p-system with origin at 0, and $\dot{\theta} \neq 0$ (compare equation (9), Problem 9.15) since $M_{0x}^p \neq 0$.

The equation of motion in axes rotating with angular velocity

$$\omega = \Omega_1^p i^p + \Omega_2^p j^p + (\Omega_3^p - \dot{\psi})k^p \tag{7}$$

is

$$\mathbf{H}^* = \dot{\mathbf{H}} + \boldsymbol{\omega} \times \mathbf{H} = \mathbf{M} \tag{8}$$

which yields

$$I_1\dot{\Omega}_1 + (I_3 - I_2)\Omega_3\Omega_1 + I_3\dot{\psi}\Omega_2 = mgl\sin\theta \tag{9}$$

$$I_2\dot{\Omega}_2 + (I_1 - I_3)\Omega_1\Omega_3 - I_3\dot{\psi}\Omega_1 = 0 \tag{10}$$

$$I_3\dot{\Omega}_3 = 0 \tag{11}$$

where all quantities are in the p-system and $\Omega_3 = A = $ constant.

For the symmetrical top ($I_1 = I_2$) in terms of the Euler angles ϕ, θ and ψ, the moment equations of motion are

$$I_1\ddot{\theta} + I_3 A\dot{\phi}\sin\theta - I_1\dot{\phi}^2\cos\theta\sin\theta = mgl\sin\theta \tag{12}$$

$$I_1(\ddot{\phi}\sin\theta + \dot{\phi}\cos\theta) - I_3 A\dot{\theta} + I\dot{\theta}\dot{\phi}\cos\theta = 0 \tag{13}$$

$$\dot{\phi}\cos\theta + \dot{\psi} = A \tag{14}$$

where $\dot{\phi}$ = velocity of precession, $\dot{\theta}$ = velocity of nutation, and $\dot{\psi}$ = velocity of spin. Equation (13) can be written in a more compact form as

$$\frac{d}{dt}(I_1\dot{\phi}\sin^2\theta + I_3A\cos\theta) = 0$$

so that

$$I_1\dot{\phi}\sin^2\theta + I_3A\cos\theta = B = \text{constant} \tag{15}$$

Equations (14) and (15) are keys to special solutions shown in Problems 10.17 and 10.18.

10.17 Consider a special case of Problem 10.16, called the steady precession characterized by $\theta =$ constant.

In this case, $\dot{\theta} = \ddot{\theta} = 0$, and ($12$) of Problem 10.16 reduces to

$$I_3A\dot{\phi} - I_1\dot{\phi}^2\cos\theta = mgl$$

from which

$$\dot{\phi} = \frac{I_3A \pm \sqrt{(I_3A)^2 - 4mglI_1\cos\theta}}{2I_1\cos\theta}$$

and for $(I_3A)^2 > 4mglI_1\cos\theta$ two values of $\dot{\phi}$ exist.
For large A and small $\dot{\phi}$,

$$\dot{\phi} = \frac{mgl}{I_3A}$$

which is the formula given for gyroscopic motion in elementary texts.

10.18 Derive the energy equation $T + V = E$ for the motion of Problem 10.16.

If the contact friction of the tip at 0 is disregarded,

$$\underbrace{\tfrac{1}{2}(I_1\Omega_1^2 + I_2\Omega_2^2 + I_3\Omega_3^2)}_{T} + \underbrace{mgl\cos\theta}_{V} = E \tag{1}$$

and in the Euler angles,

$$\underbrace{\tfrac{1}{2}(I_1\dot{\theta}^2 + I_2\dot{\phi}^2\sin^2\theta + I_3A^2)}_{T} + \underbrace{mgl\cos\theta}_{V} = E \tag{2}$$

In terms of $\dot{\phi}$ given by (15) of Problem 10.16 and for a symmetrical top ($I_1 = I_2$), equation (2) becomes

$$\tfrac{1}{2}I_1\dot{\theta}^2 + \frac{(B - I_3A\cos\theta)^2}{2I_1\sin^2\theta} + \tfrac{1}{2}I_3A^2 + mgl\cos\theta = E \tag{3}$$

which contains only θ and $\dot{\theta}$ as unknowns.

Letting $u = \cos\theta$, $\dot{u} = -(\sin\theta)\dot{\theta} = -\dot{\theta}\sqrt{1 - u^2}$, equation (3) becomes

$$\dot{u}^2 = (1 - u^2)\frac{2E - I_3 A^2 - mglu}{I_1} - \frac{B - I_3 Au}{I_1^2} \tag{4}$$

or symbolically

$$\frac{du}{dt} = \sqrt{f(u)}$$

from which

$$t = \int \frac{du}{\sqrt{f(u)}} + \text{constant} \tag{5}$$

Since $f(u)$ is a cubic polynomial, the integration can be carried out in terms of elliptic functions which are periodic.

10.19 Discuss the properties of $f(u)$ in Problem 10.18 and describe the respective motion.

For t to be real, $f(u)$ must be positive and the limits of θ are determined as the roots of

$$f(u) = 0$$

which can be conveniently written as

$$(\alpha - \beta u)(1 - u^2) - (a - bu)^2 = 0$$

where

$$\alpha = (2E - I_3 A^2)/I_1, \qquad \beta = 2mg/I_1, \qquad a = B/I_1, \qquad b = I_3 A/I_1$$

Here, u may have only the values between 0 and $+1$ (since θ must lie between 0° and 90°).

The plot of $f(u)$ in Fig. P-10.19a shows that there are two distinct roots, θ_1 and θ_2, between which the axis of the top nutates. If $\theta_1 = \theta_2$, there is no nutation and the motion becomes steady precession (Problem 10.17).

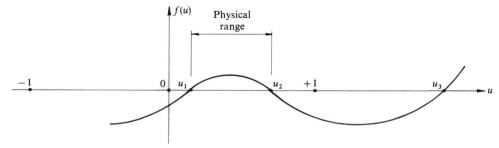

Fig. P-10.19a

If $\theta_1 \neq \theta_2$, the top tip of the body traces one of the three typical curves which depend on the precession equation

$$\dot{\phi} = \frac{a - b\cos\theta}{1 - \cos^2\theta}$$

derived from (*15*) of Problem 10.16.   These three cases are:

    (1) $a > b \cos \theta_2$, precession is the same at the bounding circles (Fig. P-10.19*b*).

    (2) $a = b \cos \theta_2$, precession is zero at the top bounding circle (Fig. P-10.19*c*).

    (3) $b \cos \theta_2 > a > b \cos \theta_1$, precession is negative at the top bounding circle and positive at the bottom bounding circle (Fig. P-10.19*d*).

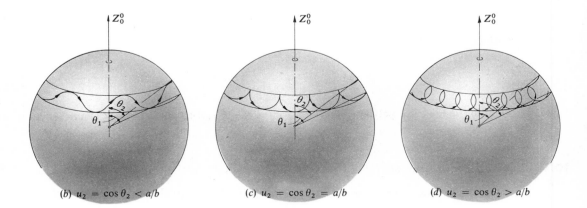

(*b*) $u_2 = \cos \theta_2 < a/b$ (*c*) $u_2 = \cos \theta_2 = a/b$ (*d*) $u_2 = \cos \theta_2 > a/b$

Fig. P-10.19*b*,*c*,*d*

Problems

INERTIA TENSOR

10.20 For the cube of mass *m* and side *a* (Fig. P-10.20), find (*a*) the inertia tensor in the 0-system and (*b*) the principal moments of inertia and the direction cosines of the principal axes.

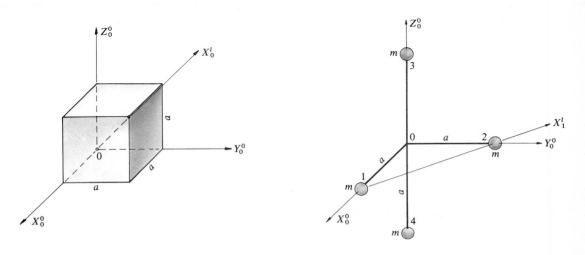

Fig. P-10.20   **Fig. P-10.21**

10.21   Each of the four spheres of the assembly of Fig. P-10.21 has a mass m and a diameter so small that its centroidal moment of inertia may be disregarded.   Neglecting the mass of the bars to which the spheres are attached, find the inertia tensor of this assembly in the 0-system.   Given: m, a.

10.22   For the assembly of Fig. P-10.21, find the principal moments of inertia and the direction cosines of the principal axes.

10.23   Find the moment of inertia of the cube of Problem 10.20 about its diagonal axis X_0^l.

10.24   Find the moment of inertia of the assembly of Fig. P-10.21 about the axis X_1^l.

10.25   Compute the radii of gyration of the assembly of Fig. P-10.21 in the 0-system.

ANGULAR MOMENTUM

10.26   A straight bar $\overline{12}$ with two balls of mass m fixed at its ends is rigidly attached to a vertical shaft $\overline{03}$ (Fig. P-10.26).   The entire assembly rotates with velocity $\mathbf{\Omega}$ about the Z_0^p axis.   Find the angular momentum of the assembly.   Given: $m, a, \mathbf{\Omega}$.   Disregard the mass of the bars.

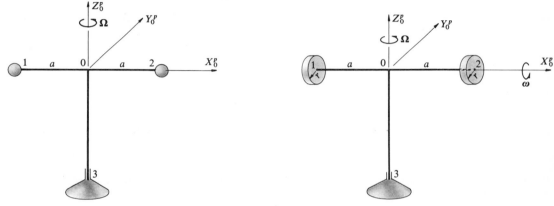

Fig. P-10.26   **Fig. P-10.27**

10.27   The assembly of Fig. P-10.27 consists of a rigid T-frame and two uniform disks each of mass m and radius r.   The frame rotates with velocity $\mathbf{\Omega}$ about Z_0^p and the disks rotate independently with velocity ω about X_0^p.   Find the angular momentum of the assembly.   Given: $m, a, \mathbf{\Omega}, \omega$ and I_{0zz}^p = moment of inertia of the T-frame about Z_0^p.

10.28   The cube of Problem 10.20 rotates about the fixed origin 0 with velocity $\mathbf{\Omega} = 10\mathbf{i}^0 + 20t\mathbf{j}^0 + 30t^2\mathbf{k}^0$.   Find its angular momentum about X_0^l.

10.29   The assembly of Problem 10.21 rotates with velocity $\mathbf{\Omega} = 100t\mathbf{i}^l$ about the X_1^l axis.   Find the linear and angular momentum of this assembly with respect to the 0-system.

ROTATION ABOUT A FIXED AXIS

10.30   A thin rectangular plate of weight W rotates with constant velocity $\mathbf{\Omega}$ about its diagonal as shown in Fig. P-10.30.   Find the moment required for this rotation.   Given: a, b, m, $\mathbf{\Omega} = \Omega_x \mathbf{i}^0$.

10.31   Determine the reactions of the bearings at A and B in Problem 10.30.   Given: $l = \overline{AB}$.

10.32   Formulate the equations of motion of the cube in Problem 10.28.

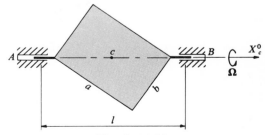

Fig. P-10.30

10.33 Formulate the equations of motion of the assembly in Problem 10.29.

ROTATION ABOUT A FIXED POINT

10.34 A rigid straight bar of mass m and length l is hinged at 0 to a vertical shaft that rotates at a constant angular speed as shown in Fig. P-10.34.   Find the relationship of θ to Ω.   Given: l, m, Ω.

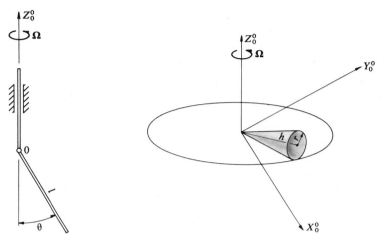

Fig. P-10.34   Fig. P-10.35

10.35 A rigid right cone rolls without slipping and precesses about Z_0^0 with constant angular speed Ω (Fig. P-10.35).   Find the moment required to sustain this motion.   Given: h, r, m, Ω.

10.36 A helicopter blade of mass m and length l rotates with constant speed Ω about the vertical shaft (Fig. P-10.36).   Find the relationship of the lift angle θ to Ω.   Given: m, c, l, Ω.   Neglect the masses of the supporting bars $\overline{01}, \overline{03}$ and of the vertical shaft.

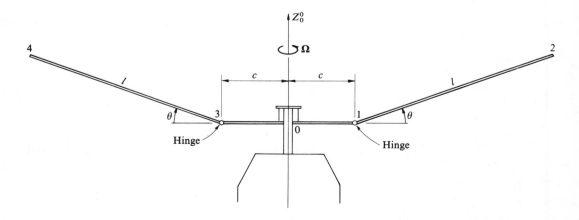

Fig. P-10.36

GYROSCOPIC PRECESSION

10.37 A simple gyroscope consists of a heavy circular disk of mass m and radius r, mounted at the center of a thin rod of mass $m/4$ that extends a distance l on each side of the disk as shown in Fig. P-10.37. If this gyroscope is spinning at constant $\dot{\psi}$ about Z_0^g under a constant angle θ, determine its frequency of precession. Given: $m = 40$ kg$_m$, $r = 20$ cm, $l = 40$ cm, $\dot{\psi} = 1000$ rpm, $\theta = 45°$. Assume 0 is fixed.

10.38 Find the condition under which the heavy top of Problem 10.17 (if started in a vertical position) will remain in the vertical position so that $\theta = 0$ and $\dot{\theta} = 0$ (sleeping top).

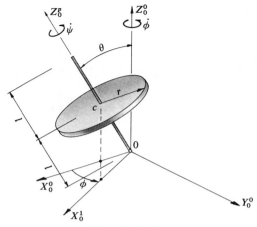

Fig. P-10.37

ENERGY AND WORK

10.39 Derive the kinetic energy equation (*10-29*) and its matrix form (*10-30*).

10.40 Find the kinetic energy of the assembly of Problem 10.26.

10.41 Find the kinetic energy of the plate in Problem 10.30.

10.42 Derive the mechanical work equation (*10-31*).

10.43 A uniform rigid sphere of mass m and radius r rolls without slipping on an inclined plane (Fig. P-10.43). Using the classical work-energy equation (*10-32*), find the equations of motion of the sphere. Given: m, r, α = angle of the plane with the horizontal; $\dot{x}(0), \dot{y}(0)$ = initial velocities of the center of the sphere.

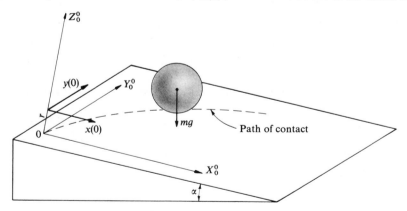

Fig. P-10.43

Chapter 11

Linear Vibrations of Mechanical Systems

11.1 BASIC CONCEPTS

Definition of Vibration

When the motion of a particle or of a body continually repeats itself, the motion is called *vibration* (oscillation). The vibration of a string, the oscillation of a pendulum, and the roll of a ship are examples of vibration. The analytical study of vibrations of mechanical systems is a large field and only an introduction to this topic will be given.

Assumptions and Causes

In addition to the basic assumptions of mechanics, elementary vibration analysis assumes that:

(1) The particle (or the body) oscillates about its position of static equilibrium.

(2) The governing equations of motion are linear differential equations with constant coefficients.

Then the principle of *superposition of causes and effects* is valid and the respective motion is called *linear vibration*.

The causes producing and/or sustaining the vibration are the *initial conditions*, the *disturbing forces*, the *restoring forces*, and the *retarding (damping) forces*.

The initial conditions are the displacement and the velocity (or both) imposed on the particle at $t = 0$. The disturbing forces are the causes tending to displace the particle, the retarding forces are the causes tending to retard (damp) the motion, and finally the restoring forces tend to return the particle to the datum position.

Mechanical Models

For the analysis, it is often advantageous to represent the vibrating mechanical system by an *ideal mechanical model* which closely approximates the behavior of the real system and is more adaptable to mathematical treatment. Only lumped mass mechanical models are considered here. For their construction three elements are used: *rigid block*, *elastic spring*, and *viscoelastic dashpot (damper)*.

The combination of these elements leads to a large variety of models which are classified according to number of degrees of freedom.

Only two single-degree freedom models are used in this book: the *Hookean model* (Sections 11.2 and 11.3) and the *Kelvin model* (Sections 11.4 and 11.5).

11.2   FREE VIBRATION WITHOUT DAMPING

Rectilinear Free Vibration

The simplest type of vibration is the rectilinear free vibration of the *linear Hookean model* of Fig. 11-1.   This model consists of a lumped mass block attached by an elastic linear spring to a rigid support.   It has one linear degree of freedom (oscillates longitudinally along X), and its *differential equation of motion* derived from the condition of dynamic equilibrium is

$$m\ddot{x} + \kappa_\delta x = 0 \qquad (11\text{-}1)$$

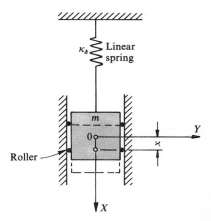

where x = linear displacement,
$\ddot{x}$ = linear acceleration,
m = lumped mass,
κ_δ = linear spring constant.

Fig. 11-1   Linear Hookean model.

The *linear spring constant* κ_δ, often called the *linear stiffness*, is defined as the force produced in the spring by a unit displacement.   Since the force F_δ and the displacement x are related by

$$F_\delta = \kappa_\delta x \qquad (11\text{-}2)$$

the Hookean model of Fig. 11-1 is called the *linear elastic model*.

The solution of (*11-1*) is

$$x = x_0 \cos p_\delta t + \frac{\dot{x}_0}{p_\delta} \sin p_\delta t \qquad (11\text{-}3)$$

where

$$p_\delta = \sqrt{\frac{\kappa_\delta}{m}} \qquad (11\text{-}4)$$

is called the *natural circular frequency*, x_0 is the initial linear displacement, and $\dot{x}_0$ is the initial linear velocity of the block (Problem 11.1).

Angular Free Vibration

The second type of free vibration is the angular (torsional) free vibration of the *angular Hookean model* of Fig. 11-2.   This model consists of a lumped mass block attached by an elastic angular spring to a rigid support.   It has one angular degree of freedom (oscillates angularly about the Z axis) and its *differential equation of motion* derived from the condition of dynamic equilibrium is

$$I\ddot{\theta} + \kappa_\theta \theta = 0 \qquad (11\text{-}5)$$

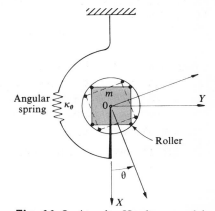

where θ = angular displacement,
$\ddot{\theta}$ = angular acceleration,
I = mass moment of inertia about the Z axis,
κ_θ = angular spring constant.

Fig. 11-2   Angular Hookean model.

The *angular spring constant* κ_θ, also called the *angular stiffness*, is defined as the moment produced in the spring by a unit rotation. Since the relationship between the moment M_θ and the rotation θ is

$$M_\theta = \kappa_\theta \theta \qquad (11\text{-}6)$$

the Hookean model of Fig. 11-2 is called an *angular elastic model*.

The solution of (*11-5*) is

$$\theta = \theta_0 \cos p_\theta t + \frac{\dot\theta_0}{p_\theta} \sin p_\theta t \qquad (11\text{-}7)$$

where

$$p_\theta = \sqrt{\frac{\kappa_\theta}{I}} \qquad (11\text{-}8)$$

is called the *natural circular frequency*, θ_0 is the initial angular displacement, and $\dot\theta_0$ is the initial angular velocity.

Graphs of Motion

The variation of x given by (*11-3*) can be represented graphically as a superposition of two curves (Fig. 11-3a,b) or by one curve (Fig. 11-3c) defined by

$$x = A_\delta \cos(p_\delta t - \alpha_\delta) \qquad \text{or} \qquad x = A_\delta \sin(p_\delta t + \beta_\delta) \qquad (11\text{-}9a), (11\text{-}9b)$$

where

$$A_\delta = \sqrt{(x_0)^2 + (\dot x_0/p_\delta)^2} \qquad (11\text{-}10)$$

is the maximum linear displacement, called the *amplitude*, and

$$\alpha_\delta = \tan^{-1}\frac{\dot x_0}{p_\delta x_0}, \qquad \beta_\delta = \tan^{-1}\frac{p_\delta x_0}{\dot x_0} \qquad (11\text{-}11), (11\text{-}12)$$

are the *phase angles* defining the shift of the cosine and sine curves on the $p_\delta t$ axis respectively (Problems 11.3 and 11.4).

Similar relations can be derived for the angular free vibration.

Characteristics of Motion

In the motions described above, the *displacement varies harmonically* with time (harmonic motion) and *repeats itself* after a definite interval (periodic motion).

The distinct characteristics of this motion are:

(1) The *amplitude A* is the greatest displacement from the equilibrium position.

(2) The *period* τ of the motion is the time required for a complete cycle, after which the motion repeats itself:

$$\tau = 2\pi/p \qquad (11\text{-}13)$$

where p is the natural circular frequency given by (*11-4*) and (*11-8*) respectively.

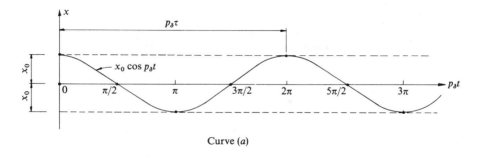

Curve (a)

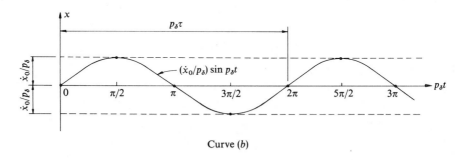

Curve (b)

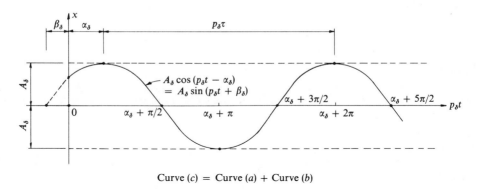

Curve (c) = Curve (a) + Curve (b)

Fig. 11-3   Displacement curves: free vibration without damping.

(3) The *frequency f* is the number of complete cycles per unit time:

$$f = 1/\tau = p/2\pi \qquad\qquad (11\text{-}14)$$

(4) The *sum of the phase angles* of the motion is

$$\alpha + \beta = \pi/2 = \tau p/4 \qquad\qquad (11\text{-}15)$$

which is one quarter of a cycle.

Energy Equations

In the absence of the disturbing forces and the damping forces, the energy of the vibration system consisting of the kinetic and potential energies is

$$T_\delta + V_\delta = \tfrac{1}{2}(m\dot{x}^2 + \kappa_\delta x^2) = \text{constant} \qquad (11\text{-}16)$$

or

$$T_\theta + V_\theta = \tfrac{1}{2}(I\dot{\theta}^2 + \kappa_\theta\theta^2) = \text{constant} \qquad (11\text{-}17)$$

and their time derivatives equal zero (Problem 11.9).

11.3   FORCED VIBRATION WITHOUT DAMPING

Rectilinear Forced Vibration

If the block of the Hookean model of Fig. 11-1 is acted upon by a *disturbing force P(t)*, the *differential equation of motion*, derived again from the condition of dynamic equilibrium, is

$$m\ddot{x} + \kappa_\delta x = P(t) \qquad (11\text{-}18)$$

and its solution is

$$x = x_0 \cos p_\delta t + \frac{\dot{x}_0}{p_\delta} \sin p_\delta t + \Phi_\delta(t) \qquad (11\text{-}19)$$

where $\Phi_\delta(t)$ is a particular function satisfying $(11\text{-}18)$.

In general, $\Phi_\delta(t)$ is a convolution integral found by the method of Laplace transforms.   In the simple cases considered in this book, $\Phi_\delta(t)$ can be found by elementary methods or by inspection (Problems 11.9 and 11.10).

Angular Forced Vibration

If the block of the Hookean model of Fig. 11-2 is acted upon by a *disturbing moment M(t)*, the *differential equation of motion* is

$$I\ddot{\theta} + \kappa_\theta\theta = M(t) \qquad (11\text{-}20)$$

and its solution is

$$\theta = \theta_0 \cos p_\theta t + \frac{\dot{\theta}_0}{p_\theta} \sin p_\theta t + \Phi_\theta(t) \qquad (11\text{-}21)$$

where $\Phi_\theta(t)$ is again a particular function satisfying $(11\text{-}20)$.

Graphs of Motion

The variation of the displacement x given by $(11\text{-}18)$ can also be represented graphically as a superposition of the free vibration curve of Fig. 11-3c and the graph of $\Phi_\delta(t)$.   A similar superposition can be used in the case of angular forced vibration.

11.4   VIBRATION WITH DAMPING
Damping Force and Moment
The vibrations discussed in Section 11.2 were assumed to continue indefinitely with constant amplitude and frequency.   Real vibrating systems show that their internal and external friction will eventually dampen out all motion and the systems will return to their initial state of static equilibrium.

The true nature of damping is a complicated phenomenon, which is still a subject of investigation. An *approximate damping force* (based on the assumption of viscous damping) is usually given as

$$D_\delta = \eta_\delta \dot{x} \qquad\qquad (11\text{-}22)$$

where $D_\delta =$ damping force, $\eta_\delta =$ linear coefficient of damping, $\dot{x} =$ linear velocity.

Thus the damping force is assumed to be proportional to the linear velocity.   A similar relation can be assumed in the case of angular vibration in terms of D_θ, η_θ and $\dot{\theta}$.

Rectilinear Free Motion
For the study of rectilinear free vibration with damping, the *Kelvin model* of Fig. 11-4 below is used. This model consists of a lumped mass block attached by an elastic linear spring and a viscoelastic linear dashpot to a rigid support. It has one degree of freedom (oscillates longitudinally along the X axis) and its *differential equation of motion* is

$$m\ddot{x} + \eta_\delta \dot{x} + \kappa_\delta x = 0 \qquad\qquad (11\text{-}23)$$

where x = linear displacement, m = lumped mass,
$\quad\quad\quad \dot{x}$ = linear velocity, η_δ = linear dashpot constant,
$\quad\quad\quad \ddot{x}$ = linear acceleration, κ_δ = linear spring constant.

Equation (11-23) is frequently given in a more convenient form as

$$\ddot{x} + 2\gamma_\delta \dot{x} + p_\delta^2 x = 0 \qquad\qquad (11\text{-}24)$$

where $2\gamma_\delta = \eta_\delta/m$ and $p_\delta^2 = \kappa_\delta/m$.

The solution of (11-24) takes on one of the three forms given below, depending on the relationship of γ_δ and p_δ.

(a)   *Underdamped motion,* $\gamma_\delta^2 < p_\delta^2$, $\lambda_\delta = \sqrt{p_\delta^2 - \gamma_\delta^2}$:

$$x = e^{-\gamma_\delta t}\left(x_0 \cos \lambda_\delta t + \frac{\dot{x}_0 + \gamma_\delta x_0}{\lambda_\delta} \sin \lambda_\delta t \right) \qquad\qquad (11\text{-}25)$$

(b)   *Critically damped motion,* $\gamma_\delta^2 = p_\delta^2$, $\lambda_\delta = 0$:

$$x = e^{-\gamma_\delta t}[x_0(1 + \gamma_\delta t) + \dot{x}_0 t] \qquad\qquad (11\text{-}26)$$

(c)   *Overdamped motion,* $\gamma_\delta^2 > p_\delta^2$, $\lambda_\delta = \sqrt{\gamma_\delta^2 - p_\delta^2}$:

$$x = e^{-\gamma_\delta t}\left(x_0 \cosh \gamma_\delta t + \frac{\dot{x}_0 + \gamma_\delta x_0}{\lambda_\delta} \sinh \lambda_\delta t \right) \qquad\qquad (11\text{-}27)$$

where λ_δ is the *damped circular frequency* and x_0, $\dot{x}_0$ are the initial conditions (Problems 11.13–11.15).

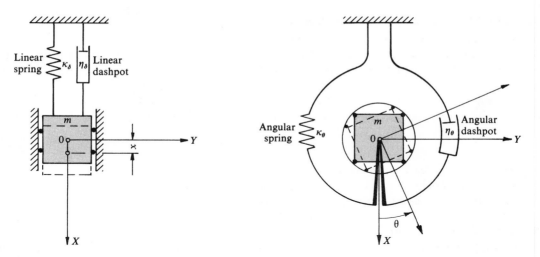

Fig. 11-4 Linear Kelvin model.   **Fig. 11-5** Angular Kelvin model.

Angular Free Motion

The equations of the angular free vibration with damping (Fig. 11-5), written in terms of θ, θ_0, $\dot{\theta}_0$, I, γ_θ, λ_θ, are formally identical to their rectilinear counterparts (*11-25*)–(*11-27*).

Graphs of Motion

Equations (*11-25*), (*11-26*) and (*11-27*) are plotted in Fig. 11-6.   Curve (*a*) shows that the underdamped vibration is oscillatory with diminishing amplitude but equal periods.   Curves (*b*) and (*c*) show that the critically damped and overdamped motions are no longer oscillatory and decrease exponentially with time.   The critically damped motion is the top limit of the periodic motion during which the system reaches rest in the shortest time.

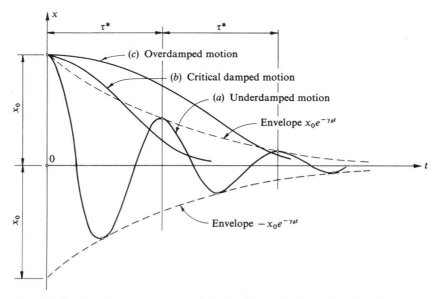

Fig. 11-6   Displacement curves: free vibration with damping, $\dot{x}_0 = 0$.

11.5   FORCED VIBRATION WITH DAMPING

The most general case of vibration is the forced vibration with damping, which can be again recti-linear or angular (torsional).   If the *Kelvin model* of Fig. 11-5 is assumed to be acted upon by a disturbing force $P(t)$, the *differential equation of motion* becomes

$$m\ddot{x} + \eta_\delta \dot{x} + \kappa_\delta x = P(t) \tag{11-28}$$

and its solution is

$$x = x_c + x_p \tag{11-29}$$

where x_c is one of the *complementary solutions* introduced before [equations *(11-25)*–*(11-27)*] and $x_p = \Phi_\delta^*(t)$ is a particular function obtained by the methods discussed in reference to *(11-19)*.

The closed form of $\Phi_\delta^*(t)$ can be obtained in simple cases by elementary methods.   In general, how-ever, numerical or transformation methods must be employed.

As before, the differential equation and the displacement equation of the angular forced vibration with damping are similar to *(11-28)* and *(11-29)* respectively.

Illustrative Problems

RECTILINEAR FREE VIBRATION WITHOUT DAMPING

11.1   Derive the displacement equation of free rectilinear vibration of the Hookean model of Fig. P-11.1*a*.

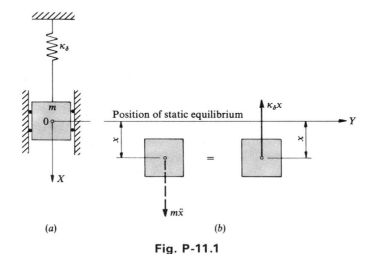

(a)   (b)

Fig. P-11.1

From the dynamic equilibrium (Problem 8.7) of the free-body sketch of Fig. P-11.1*b*,

$$m\ddot{x} = -\kappa_\delta x \tag{1}$$

or

$$\ddot{x} + p_\delta^2 x = 0 \tag{2}$$

where $p_\delta^2 = \kappa_\delta/m$.   The general solution of (2) can be obtained by several methods, but the method of trial functions is the most convenient one and is used here.   Let

$$x = Ce^{st} \tag{3}$$

be the assumed solution; then (2) becomes

$$s^2(Ce^{st}) + p_\delta^2(Ce^{st}) = 0 \tag{4}$$

which on dividing by Ce^{st} reduces to

$$s^2 + p_\delta^2 = 0 \tag{5}$$

called the characteristic equation, whose roots are

$$s_{1,2} = \pm ip \tag{6}$$

where for convenience the subscript δ is dropped.

Since (2) is a linear second-order differential equation, the total solution consists of two functions, i.e.

$$x = C_1 e^{ipt} + C_2 e^{-ipt} \tag{7}$$

Recalling that

$$e^{ipt} = \cos pt + i \sin pt, \qquad e^{-ipt} = \cos pt - i \sin pt \tag{8}$$

equation (7) can be written as

$$x = (C_1 + C_2)\cos pt + i(C_1 - C_2)\sin pt \tag{9}$$

and with $C_1 + C_2 = \overline{C}_1,\ i(C_1 - C_2) = \overline{C}_2$ it becomes

$$x = \overline{C}_1 \cos pt + \overline{C}_2 \sin pt \tag{10}$$

where $\overline{C}_1, \overline{C}_2$ are the constants of integration to be determined from the initial conditions.
Since at $t = 0$ we have $x(0) = x_0$ and $\dot{x}(0) = \dot{x}_0$, then

$$\overline{C}_1 = x_0, \qquad \overline{C}_2 = \frac{\dot{x}_0}{p} \tag{11}$$

and the solution (10) is

$$x = x_0 \cos pt + \frac{\dot{x}_0}{p} \sin pt \tag{12}$$

11.2 Show that equations (11-3), (11-9a) and (11-9b) are equivalent, i.e. they are different forms of the general solution of equation (11-1).

By trigonometry,

$$x = A \cos(pt - \alpha) \qquad (11\text{-}9a)$$

$$= A(\cos pt \cos \alpha + \sin pt \sin \alpha)$$

$$= x_0 \cos pt + \frac{\dot{x}_0}{p} \sin pt \qquad (11\text{-}3)$$

where $x_0 = A \cos \alpha$ and $\dot{x}_0/p = A \sin \alpha$.   Then

$$A = \sqrt{x_0^2 + (\dot{x}_0/p)^2} \qquad (1)$$

and

$$\tan \alpha = \dot{x}_0/x_0 p \qquad (2)$$

Similarly,

$$x = A \sin(pt + \beta) \qquad (11\text{-}9b)$$

$$= A(\sin pt \cos \beta + \cos pt \sin \beta)$$

$$= x_0 \cos pt + \frac{\dot{x}_0}{p} \sin pt \qquad (11\text{-}3)$$

where now $x_0 = A \sin \beta$ and $\dot{x}_0/p = A \cos \beta$.   Then (1) is still valid here and

$$\tan \beta = x_0 p/\dot{x}_0 \qquad (3)$$

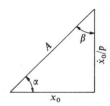

Note that (3) is the reciprocal of (2).   The relations (1)–(3) are represented graphically in Fig. P-11.2.   It follows from the figure that $\alpha + \beta = \pi/2$.   Angles α and β are called *phase angles* and they indicate the shift of the curve in Fig. 11-3c.

Fig. P-11.2

11.3   Discuss the characteristics of the motion analyzed in Problems 11.1 and 11.2.

The first and second time derivatives of the equations of motion (11-9a) and (11-9b) respectively are:

$$\dot{x} = -Ap \sin(pt - \alpha), \qquad \ddot{x} = -Ap^2 \cos(pt - \alpha) \qquad (1), (2)$$
$$\dot{x} = Ap \cos(pt + \beta), \qquad \ddot{x} = -Ap^2 \sin(pt + \beta) \qquad (3), (4)$$

Since the displacement is maximum when the velocity is zero, from (1),

$$\sin(pt - \alpha) = 0 \qquad \text{if } pt = \alpha$$

and from (3),

$$\cos(pt + \beta) = 0 \qquad \text{if } pt = \alpha$$

Then by (11-9a) or (11-9b),

$$x_{\max} = A \cos(\alpha - \alpha) = A \sin(\alpha + \beta) = A$$

If $pt = \pi - \alpha$,

$$x_{\max} = -A$$

and if $pt = 2\pi - \alpha$,

$$x_{\max} = A$$

The maximum displacements $\pm A$ are the *amplitudes* given analytically by (1) of Problem 11.2.

The angular distance between two positive amplitudes is then 2π; the motion corresponding to 2π is called the cycle; and the time required to complete a cycle is called the period τ.

Since the motion is continuous,

$$p\tau = pt_n - pt_{n-1} = 2n\pi - \alpha - 2(n-1)\pi + \alpha = 2\pi$$

from which

$$\tau = 2\pi/p$$

The inverse of τ is called the *frequency f*.   Analytically,

$$f = 1/\tau = p/2\pi$$

which gives the number of cycles per unit time.

The displacement equations

$$x = A \cos (pt - \alpha) \qquad \text{and} \qquad x = A \sin (pt + \beta)$$

can be also represented by the rotating vector **A** as shown in Fig. P-11.3.

Since p is the angular velocity of **A** in the respective circle, it is called the natural circular frequency.

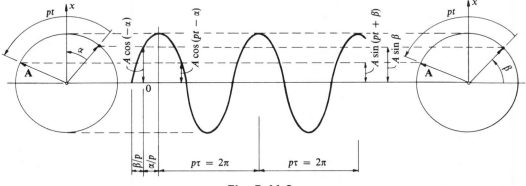

Fig. P-11.3

11.4 Express the natural frequency of the vibrating block of Problem 11.1 in terms of the static deflection.

The static deflection of the block is

$$\delta_0 = W/\kappa_\delta = mg/\kappa_\delta$$

Using $g = 386$ in./sec^2 and expressing δ_0 in inches, the natural frequency is

$$f_\delta = \frac{p_\delta}{2\pi} = \frac{\sqrt{\kappa_\delta/m}}{2\pi} = \frac{\sqrt{386/\delta_0}}{6.28319} = \frac{3.127}{\sqrt{\delta_0}}\text{cycles/sec}$$

If for example $\delta_0 = 0.01$ in, $f_\delta = 31.27$ cycles/sec.

11.5   Find the natural circular frequency of free rectilinear vibration of a rigid sphere of weight W attached to the top of a flexible column of length l (Fig. P-11.5); $\kappa_\delta = 3EI/l^3$ where E = modulus of elasticity of the column's material, and I = moment of the column's cross section about the axis normal to the motion.   Neglect the mass of the column.

By (*11-4*),

$$P_\delta = \sqrt{\frac{\kappa_\delta}{m}} = \sqrt{\frac{3EIg}{Wl^3}}$$

If $E = 30 \times 10^6$ lb/in², $I = 100$ in⁴, $l = 100$ in. and $W = 386$ lb, the natural circular frequency of the sphere is

$$p_\delta = \sqrt{\frac{3(30)\,(10)^6(100)\,(386)}{386(100)^3}} = 94.86 \text{ rad/sec}$$

and the natural frequency is

$$f_\delta = \frac{p_\delta}{2\pi} = \frac{94.86}{6.283} = 15.1 \text{ cycles/sec}$$

Fig. P-11.5

11.6   Find the amplitude and phase angles of the motion of Problem 11.5.   The initial conditions are $x_0 = 1$ in., $\dot{x}_0 = 94.86$ in./sec.

By (*11-12*), the amplitude is

$$A_\delta = \sqrt{x_0^2 + (\dot{x}_0/p_\delta)^2} = \sqrt{2} = 1.41 \text{ in.}$$

and the phase angles are

$$\alpha_\delta = \tan^{-1}\frac{\dot{x}_0}{x_0 p_\delta} = \tan^{-1} 1 = \pi/4$$

$$\beta_\delta = \tan^{-1}\frac{x_0 p_\delta}{\dot{x}_0} = \tan^{-1} 1 = \pi/4$$

ANGULAR FREE VIBRATION WITHOUT DAMPING

11.7   The simple pendulum of Fig. P-11.7, consisting of a sphere of weight W suspended by a piano wire of negligible mass and length l, swings in the XY plane.   The motion began at $\theta = \theta_0$. Neglecting the elongation of the wire, find the equation of motion of the pendulum.

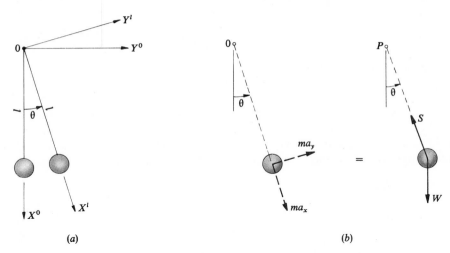

Fig. P-11.7

From Fig. P-11.7b,

$$ma_x \cong -S + W \cos \theta, \qquad ma_y = -W \sin \theta \qquad (1), (2)$$

where a_x, a_y are the linear accelerations of m in the X^l, Y^l direction and S is the tensile force in the wire.
From the condition of rigidity, $a_x \cong 0$; and from the geometry of the motion, $a_y = l\ddot{\theta}$. Hence

$$S \cong W \cos \theta \qquad \text{and} \qquad ml\ddot{\theta} + W \sin \theta = 0 \qquad (3), (4)$$

Equation (3) is a static equation (condition of constraint) and equation (4) is the differential equation of motion in angular coordinate θ.
For small values of θ, $\sin \theta \cong \theta$, and (4) reduces to

$$\ddot{\theta} + \frac{W}{ml}\theta = 0 \qquad (5)$$

where $W/ml = g/l = p_\theta^2$.
The angular amplitude is θ_0 and so the solution of (5) is

$$\theta = \theta_0 \cos p_\theta t$$

The period of motion is $\tau_\theta = 2\pi/\sqrt{g/l}$.
If θ is not a very small angle, then $\sin \theta \neq \theta$, and the differential equation (4) is a nonlinear equation. Its solution then must be expressed in terms of elliptic functions.

11.8 Derive the equation of rolling motion of the ship of Fig. P-11.8. Given: W = weight of ship, R = distance of the metacenter b to the mass center c of the ship, I_{czz} = mass moment of inertia of the ship about its longitudinal centroidal axis.

During any and all angular deviations θ of the ship, the buoyant force $F_b = -W$ and the gravity force $F_g = W$ produce a couple C, which is the source of rolling.

The point of action of F_b is called the metacenter b and $R = \overline{cb}$ is called the metacenter height.

In terms of R and W, the couple is

$$C = -WR \sin \theta \qquad (1)$$

From the condition of dynamic equilibrium,

$$I_{czz}\ddot{\theta} = -WR \sin \theta \qquad (2)$$

For small values of θ, $\sin \theta \cong \theta$ and (2) reduces to

$$\ddot{\theta} + \frac{WR}{I_{czz}}\theta = 0 \qquad (3)$$

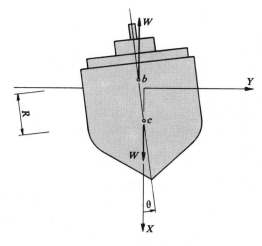

Fig. P-11.8

where $WR/I_{czz} = p_\theta^2$.

Formally the solution of the rolling of the ship parallels the solution of Problem 11.7. For large θ, equation (2) becomes a nonlinear differential equation and its solution must again be expressed in terms of elliptic functions.

ENERGY METHOD

11.9 Using the principle of conservation of energy find the natural circular frequency of small vibration of the assembly of Fig. P-11.9. Given: κ_δ = linear spring constant, W = weight of disk, R = radius of disk, I_{czz} = mass moment of inertia, h = vertical distance between the center of the disk c and the pin connecting the linear spring to the disk. Assume rolling without slipping and neglect the mass of the springs.

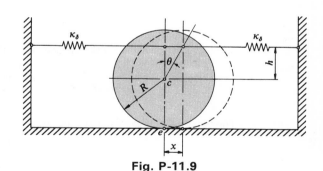

Fig. P-11.9

The kinetic energy of the system is

$$T = \tfrac{1}{2}m\dot{x}^2 + \tfrac{1}{2}I_{czz}\dot{\theta}^2 = \tfrac{1}{2}mR^2\dot{\theta}^2 + \tfrac{1}{4}mR^2\dot{\theta}^2 = \tfrac{3}{4}mR^2\dot{\theta}^2 \qquad (1)$$

where $m = W/g$ and $I_{czz} = mR^2/2$ (see Appendix).

The potential energy of the system is

$$V = 2(\tfrac{1}{2}\kappa_\delta x^2) = \kappa_\delta(R\theta + h\sin\theta)^2 = \kappa_\delta(R + h)^2\theta^2 \qquad (2)$$

where $\sin\theta = \theta$ (for a small angle).

By (11-17),

$$T + V = \text{constant} \qquad (3)$$

and

$$dT/dt + dV/dt = 0 \qquad (4)$$

In terms of (1) and (2), equation (4) becomes

$$\tfrac{3}{2}mR^2\dot\theta\ddot\theta + 2\kappa_\delta(R+h)^2\theta\dot\theta = 0 \qquad \text{from which} \qquad \ddot\theta + \frac{4\kappa_\delta(R+h)^2}{3mR^2}\theta = 0$$

The required natural circular frequency is $p_\theta = \sqrt{\dfrac{4\kappa_\delta(R+h)^2}{3mR^2}}.$

11.10 Using the principle of conservation of energy find the equations of motion of the cylinder of radius r, mass m and mass moment of inertia I_{czz}, which rolls without slipping on a cylindrical surface of radius R (Fig. P-11.10). Assume small oscillatory motion.

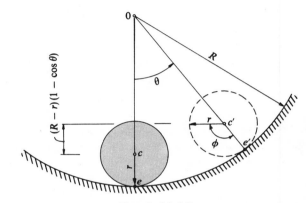

Two angular coordinates θ and ϕ are introduced: θ defines the rotation of radius $R - r$ about 0 and ϕ defines the rotation of radius r about c.

Since e is the instantaneous center (no slipping),

$$(R - r)\dot\theta = r\dot\phi$$

and the kinetic energy of the rolling cylinder with respect to e is

$$T = \tfrac{1}{2}I_{ezz}\dot\phi^2 = \tfrac{1}{2}\left(mr^2 + \frac{mr^2}{2}\right)\frac{(R-r)^2}{r^2}\dot\theta^2 = \tfrac{3}{4}m(R-r)^2\dot\theta^2 \qquad (1)$$

The potential energy of the cylinder is

$$V = mg\underbrace{(R-r)(1-\cos\theta)}_{h} \qquad (2)$$

where h is the vertical change in position of c.

As in Problem 11.9,

$$dT/dt + dV/dt = 0$$

which in terms of (1) and (2) becomes

$$\ddot\theta + \frac{2g\sin\theta}{3(R-r)} = 0$$

or for small θ,

$$\ddot\theta + \frac{2g}{3(R-r)}\theta = 0$$

Fig. P-11.10

The natural circular frequency of this oscillation is $p_\theta = \sqrt{\dfrac{2g}{3(R-r)}}$.

FORCED VIBRATION WITHOUT DAMPING

11.11 Consider the Hookean model of Fig. P-11.11 acted upon by a constant disturbing force P.   Find the displacement equation of this motion.

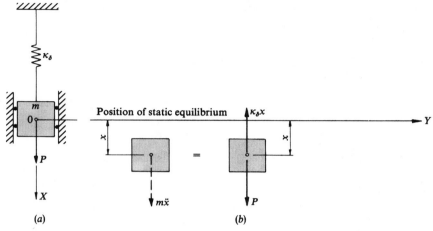

Fig. P-11.11

From the condition of dynamic equilibrium of Fig. P-11.1b,

$$m\ddot{x} = -\kappa_\delta x + P \tag{1}$$

or

$$\ddot{x} + p_\delta^2 x = P/m \tag{2}$$

The general solution of (2) is

$$x = x_c + x_p$$

where $x_c = \overline{C}_1 \cos p_\delta t + \overline{C}_2 \sin p_\delta t$ and $x_p = P/\kappa_\delta$.

If at $t = 0$ we have $x(0) = x_0$ and $\dot{x}(0) = \dot{x}_0$, then

$$\overline{C}_1 = x_0 - \frac{P}{\kappa_\delta}, \qquad \overline{C}_2 = \frac{\dot{x}_0}{p_\delta}$$

and the solution of (2) is

$$x = x_0 \cos pt + \frac{\dot{x}_0}{p} \sin pt + \frac{P}{\kappa}(1 - \cos pt)$$

where again for convenience the subscript δ is omitted.

For $x_0 = 0$ and $\dot{x}_0 = 0$, $x = P(1 - \cos pt)/\kappa$ which shows that under these conditions, the displacement is never negative. It has a minimum value of zero at $t = 0$, a medium value P/κ at $t = \pi/2p$ and a maximum value $2P/\kappa$ at $t = \pi/p$.

The dynamic load factor (DLF) is the ratio

$$\frac{x_{\text{dynamic}}}{x_{\text{static}}} = \frac{p(1 - \cos pt)/\kappa}{P/\kappa} = (1 - \cos pt)$$

which shows that DLF is nondimensional and independent of P.

11.12 Consider Problem 11.11 with $P(t) = P \sin \Omega t$ where P is a constant and Ω is a constant circular frequency. Find the displacement equation of this motion.

As in Problem 11.11,

$$m\ddot{x} + \kappa_\delta x = P \sin \Omega t \tag{1}$$

or

$$\ddot{x} + p_\delta^2 x = \frac{P}{m} \sin \Omega t \tag{2}$$

Let

$$x_c = \overline{C}_1 \cos pt + \overline{C}_2 \sin pt \tag{3}$$

$$x_p = \overline{C}_3 \sin \Omega t \tag{4}$$

where again the subscript δ is omitted.

Differentiating and substituting (4) into (2) gives

$$\overline{C}_3 = \frac{P}{m\kappa(p^2 - \Omega^2)}$$

If at $t = 0$ we have $x(0) = x_0$ and $\dot{x}(0) = \dot{x}_0$, then

$$\overline{C}_1 = x_0, \qquad \overline{C}_2 = \frac{\dot{x}_0}{p} - \frac{P}{m(p^2 - \Omega^2)}$$

and the solution of (2) becomes

$$x = x_0 \cos pt + \frac{\dot{x}_0}{p} \sin pt + \frac{P}{m(p^2 - \Omega^2)} (\sin \Omega t - \sin pt)$$

For $x_0 = 0$ and $\dot{x}_0 = 0$,

$$x = \frac{P(\sin \Omega t - \sin pt)}{m(p^2 - \Omega^2)}$$

FREE VIBRATION WITH DAMPING

11.13 Derive the displacement equation of free vibration of the Kelvin model of Fig. 11-4.   Consider underdamped motion.

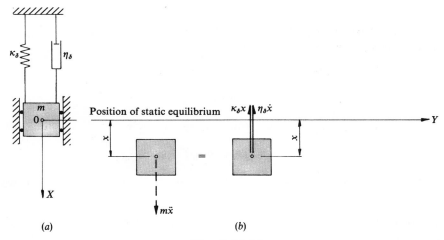

Fig. P-11.13

From the dynamic equilibrium (Problem 8.7) of the free-body sketch of Fig. P-11.13b,

$$m\ddot{x} = -\eta_\delta \dot{x} - \kappa_\delta x \tag{1}$$

or

$$\ddot{x} + 2\gamma_\delta \dot{x} + p_\delta^2 x = 0 \tag{2}$$

where $2\gamma_\delta = \eta_\delta/m$ and $p_\delta^2 = \kappa_\delta/m$.

In terms of the trial function $x = Ce^{st}$, equation (2) yields the characteristic equation

$$s^2 + 2\gamma s + p^2 = 0 \tag{3}$$

where the subscript δ is omitted.   The roots of (3) are

$$s_{1,2} = -\gamma \pm \sqrt{\gamma^2 - p^2} \tag{4}$$

If $\gamma^2 < p^2$, then $s_{1,2} = -\gamma \pm i\lambda$ where $\lambda = \sqrt{p^2 - \gamma^2}$ and the solution of (2) is

$$x = C_1 e^{(-\gamma + i\lambda)t} + C_2 e^{(-\gamma - i\lambda)t} = e^{-\gamma t}(C_1 e^{i\lambda t} + C_2 e^{-i\lambda t}) = e^{-\gamma t}(\overline{C}_1 \cos \lambda t + \overline{C}_2 \sin \lambda t) \tag{5}$$

where $\overline{C}_1 = C_1 + C_2$ and $\overline{C}_2 = i(C_1 - C_2)$.

If at $t = 0$ we have $x(0) = x_0$ and $\dot{x}(0) = \dot{x}_0$, then

$$\overline{C}_1 = x_0, \qquad \overline{C}_2 = \frac{\dot{x}_0 + \gamma x_0}{\lambda}$$

and the solution (5) becomes

$$x = e^{-\gamma t}\left(x_0 \cos \lambda t + \frac{\dot{x}_0 + \gamma x_0}{\lambda} \sin \lambda t\right) \tag{6}$$

The motion defined by (6) is called *underdamped* and its graph is shown in Fig. 11-6.

11.14 Derive the displacement equation of free vibration of the Kelvin model of Fig. P-11.13.   Consider critically damped motion.

If $\gamma^2 = p^2$ in (4) of Problem 11.13, then $s_{1,2} = -\gamma$ and

$$x = (C_1 + C_2 t)e^{-\gamma t}$$

If at $t = 0$ we have $x(0) = x_0$ and $\dot{x}(0) = \dot{x}_0$, then $C_1 = x_0$, $C_2 = \dot{x}_0 + \gamma x_0$ yielding

$$x = e^{-\gamma t}[x_0(1 + \gamma t) + \dot{x}_0 t] \tag{1}$$

The motion defined by (1) is called *critically damped motion* and its graph is shown in Fig. 11-6.

11.15 Derive the displacement equation of free vibration of the Kelvin model of Fig. P-11.13.   Consider the overdamped motion.

If $\gamma^2 > p^2$ in (4) of Problem 11.13, then $s_{1,2} = -\gamma \pm \lambda$ where $\lambda = \sqrt{\gamma^2 - p^2}$ and so

$$x = C_1 e^{(-\gamma + \lambda)t} + C_2 e^{(-\gamma - \lambda)t} = e^{-\gamma t}(C_1 e^{\lambda t} + C_2 e^{-\lambda t}) \tag{1}$$

Recalling that

$$e^{\lambda t} = \cosh \lambda t + \sinh \lambda t, \qquad e^{-\lambda t} = \cosh \lambda t - \sinh \lambda t$$

equation (1) can be written as

$$x = e^{-\gamma t}[(C_1 + C_2) \cosh \lambda t + (C_1 - C_2) \sinh \lambda t] = e^{-\gamma t}(\overline{C}_1 \cosh \lambda t + \overline{C}_2 \sinh \lambda t)$$

where $\overline{C}_1 = C_1 + C_2$ and $\overline{C}_2 = C_1 - C_2$.
If at $t = 0$ we have $x(0) = x_0$ and $\dot{x}(0) = \dot{x}_0$, then $\overline{C}_1 = x_0$, $\overline{C}_2 = (\dot{x}_0 + \gamma x_0)/\lambda$ and the solution is

$$x = e^{-\gamma t}\left(x_0 \cosh \lambda t + \frac{\dot{x}_0 + \gamma x_0}{\lambda} \sinh \lambda t\right) \tag{2}$$

Equation (2) establishes *overdamped motion* and its graph is shown in Fig. 11-6.

FORCED VIBRATION WITH DAMPING

11.16 Consider the Kelvin model of Fig. P-11.16a acted upon by a disturbing force $P(t) = P \sin \Omega t$ where P is a constant and Ω is the constant circular frequency.   Find the displacement equation of this motion.

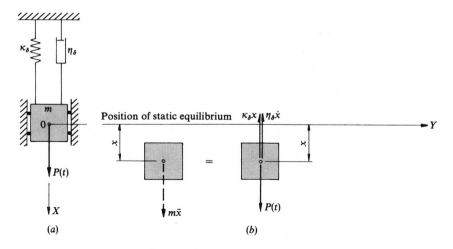

Fig. P-11.16

From the condition of dynamic equilibrium of Fig. P-11.16b,

$$m\ddot{x} = -\eta_\delta\dot{x} - \kappa_\delta x + P\sin\Omega t \tag{1}$$

or

$$\ddot{x} + 2\gamma_\delta\dot{x} + p_\delta^2 x = \frac{P}{m}\sin\Omega t \tag{2}$$

The general solution of (2) is

$$x = x_c + x_p \tag{3}$$

where

$$x_c = e^{-\gamma t}(\overline{C}_1\cos\lambda t + \overline{C}_2\sin\lambda t) \tag{4}$$

is the solution of Problem 11.13 and

$$x_p = \overline{C}_3\cos\Omega t + \overline{C}_4\sin\Omega t \tag{5}$$

is the assumed particular solution.
Substituting (5) into (2) gives

$$\left(-\Omega^2\overline{C}_4 - 2\gamma\Omega\overline{C}_3 + p^2\overline{C}_4 - \frac{P}{m}\right)\sin\Omega t + (-\Omega^2\overline{C}_3 + 2\gamma\Omega\overline{C}_4 + p^2\overline{C}_3)\cos\Omega t = 0 \tag{6}$$

Equation (6) is satisfied when the factors of $\sin\Omega t$ and $\cos\Omega t$ are both zero, i.e.

$$\overline{C}_4(p^2 - \Omega^2) - 2\overline{C}_3\gamma\Omega = P/m \qquad \text{and} \qquad 2\overline{C}_4\gamma\Omega + \overline{C}_3(p^2 - \Omega^2) = 0$$

from which

$$\overline{C}_3 = -\frac{(P/m)(2\gamma\Omega)}{(p^2 - \Omega^2)^2 + (2\gamma\Omega)^2}, \qquad \overline{C}_4 = \frac{(P/m)(p^2 - \Omega^2)}{(p^2 - \Omega^2)^2 + (2\gamma\Omega)^2} \tag{7}$$

As in Problem 11.2, the amplitude of x_p is

$$A^* = \sqrt{\overline{C}_3^2 + \overline{C}_4^2} = \frac{(P/m)}{\sqrt{(p^2 - \Omega^2)^2 + (2\gamma\Omega)^2}} \tag{8}$$

and the tangents of the phase angles are

$$\tan \alpha^* = \overline{C}_4/\overline{C}_3, \qquad \tan \beta^* = \overline{C}_3/\overline{C}_4$$

The complete solution is then

$$x = e^{-\gamma t}\left(x_0 \cos \lambda t + \frac{\dot{x}_0 + \gamma x_0}{\lambda} \cos \lambda t\right) + A^* \cos (\Omega t - \alpha^*)$$

Since the first term (Fig. 11-6) dies out with time (transient motion), the system will eventually be in a state of steady vibration with circular frequency Ω and period $\tau = 2\pi/\Omega$.

Problems

VIBRATION WITHOUT DAMPING

11.17 Find the equation of free rectilinear vibration of the system of Fig. P-11.17. Given: W, $\kappa_{\delta 1} = \kappa_1$, $\kappa_{\delta 2} = \kappa_2$, x_0, $\dot{x}_0$.

11.18 A cylinder of weight W and radius r is suspended as shown in Fig. P-11.18. Neglecting the mass of the loop, derive the equations of free angular vibration of the cylinder. Given: W, r, κ_δ, θ_0, $\dot{\theta}_0$.

11.19 A rigid bar of length $l = 3a$ and mass m is supported by springs as shown in Fig. P-11.19. Find the equation of free angular vibration of this bar. Given: W, a, $\kappa_{\delta 1} = \kappa_{\delta 2} = \kappa$, θ_0, $\dot{\theta}_0$.

11.20 Consider Problem 11.12 with $P(t) = P \cos \Omega t$, where P and Ω are given constants. Find the displacement equation of this motion.

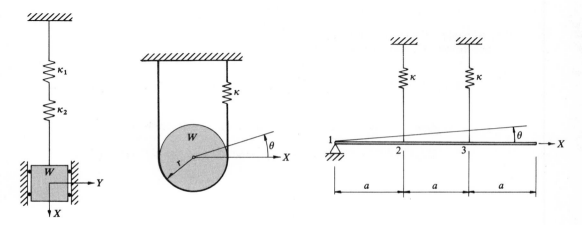

Fig. P-11.17   Fig. P-11.18   Fig. P-11.19

ENERGY METHOD

11.21 Using the energy method, solve Problem 11.17.

11.22 Using the energy method, solve Problem 11.18.

11.23 Using the energy method, solve Problem 11.19.

11.24 Using the energy method, solve Problem 11.20.

VIBRATION WITH DAMPING

11.25 For the system of Fig. P-11.25 find the equation of motion.   Given: $W, \kappa_\delta, \eta_\delta, x_0, \dot{x}_0$.

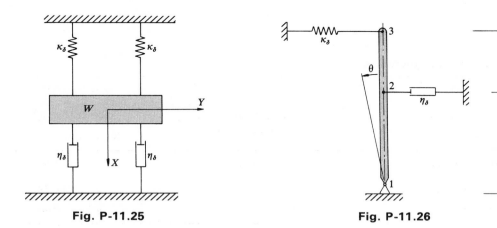

| Fig. P-11.25 | Fig. P-11.26 |

11.26 The rigid bar of $W = 100$ lb and $l = 100$ in. is hinged at 1, supported by a damper at 2 and by a spring at 3, as shown in Fig. P-11.26.   The dashpot coefficient $\eta_\delta = 1$ lb-sec/ft, and the spring constant $\kappa_\delta = 10$ lb/ft. Determine the damping type of the angular vibration of this bar (about 1).

11.27 Consider the Kelvin model of Fig. P-11.16a acted upon by a disturbing force $P(t) = P \cos \Omega t$ where P and Ω are constants.   Find the displacement equation of this motion.

Appendix A

Numerical Constants and Approximations

Table A-1 Numerical Constants

$\pi = 3.14159$	$e = 2.71828$	$g = 9.80665^*$
$\ln \pi = 1.14473$ $\log \pi = 0.49715$	$\ln e = 1.00000$ $\log e = 0.43429$	$\ln g = 2.28308$ $\log g = 0.99152$
$1/\pi = 0.31831$	$1/e = 0.36788$	$1/g = 0.10197$
$\sqrt{\pi} = 1.77245$ $\sqrt[3]{\pi} = 1.46459$	$\sqrt{e} = 1.64872$ $\sqrt[3]{e} = 1.39561$	$\sqrt{g} = 3.13155$ $\sqrt[3]{g} = 2.14046$

*Acceleration of gravity in meters/second^2.

Table A-2 Numerical Approximations

$\pi \cong \frac{22}{7} = 3.14286$ $(\varepsilon = 0.05\%)$	$e \cong \frac{19}{7} = 2.71429$ $(\varepsilon = 0.15\%)$	$g \cong \frac{51}{52} \times 10 = 9.80769$ $(\varepsilon = 0.01\%)$

Table A-3 Algebraic Approximations $(x^2 < 1, \ n = 1, 2, 3, \ldots, \ r = 2, 3, 4, \ldots)$

$$(1 \pm x)^n = 1 \pm nx + \frac{n(n-1)}{2!}x^2 \pm \frac{n(n-1)(n-2)}{3!}x^3 + \cdots$$

$$\frac{1}{(1 \pm x)^n} = 1 \mp nx + \frac{n(n+1)}{2!}x^2 \mp \frac{n(n+1)(n+2)}{3!}x^3 + \cdots$$

$$\sqrt[r]{(1 \pm x)^n} = 1 \pm n\left(\frac{x}{r}\right) + \frac{n(n-r)}{2!}\left(\frac{x}{r}\right)^2 \pm \frac{n(n-r)(n-2r)}{3!}\left(\frac{x}{r}\right)^3 + \cdots$$

$$\frac{1}{\sqrt[r]{(1 \pm x)^n}} = 1 \mp n\left(\frac{x}{r}\right) + \frac{n(n+r)}{2!}\left(\frac{x}{r}\right)^2 \mp \frac{n(n+r)(n+2r)}{3!}\left(\frac{x}{r}\right)^3 + \cdots$$

Table A-4   Transcendental Approximations $(-\infty < x < \infty)$

$$e^x = 1 + \frac{x}{1!} + \frac{x^2}{2!} + \frac{x^3}{3!} + \cdots$$

$$\sin x = x - \frac{x^3}{3!} + \frac{x^5}{5!} - \frac{x^7}{7!} + \cdots$$

$$\cos x = 1 - \frac{x^2}{2!} + \frac{x^4}{4!} - \frac{x^6}{6!} + \cdots$$

$$e^{-x} = 1 - \frac{x}{1!} + \frac{x^2}{2!} - \frac{x^3}{3!} + \cdots$$

$$\sinh x = x + \frac{x^3}{3!} + \frac{x^5}{5!} + \frac{x^7}{7!} + \cdots$$

$$\cosh x = 1 + \frac{x^2}{2!} + \frac{x^4}{4!} + \frac{x^6}{6!} + \cdots$$

$$\ln x = 2\left\{ \frac{x-1}{x+1} + \frac{1}{3}\left(\frac{x-1}{x+1}\right)^3 + \frac{1}{5}\left(\frac{x-1}{x+1}\right)^5 + \frac{1}{7}\left(\frac{x-1}{x+1}\right)^7 + \cdots \right\} \qquad (x > 0)$$

Appendix B

Conversion Factors

NOTATION

The conversion factors listed in this appendix are expressed in the *modified form of scientific notation* in which the power of 10 is given by its signed exponent only. For example,

$$1 \text{ centimeter} = 3.28084\,(-02) \text{ foot} = 3.28084 \times 10^{-2} \text{ foot} = 0.032084 \text{ foot}$$
$$1 \text{ mile} \qquad = 5.28000\,(+03) \text{ foot} = 5.28000 \times 10^{3} \text{ foot} \quad = 5280 \text{ foot}$$

LENGTH

centimeter	3.28084 ($-$02) foot
centimeter	3.93701 ($-$01) inch
centimeter	1.00000 ($-$02) meter
foot	3.04800 ($+$01) centimeter
foot	1.20000 ($+$01) inch
foot	3.04800 ($-$01) meter
inch	2.54000 ($+$00) centimeter
inch	8.33333 ($-$02) foot
inch	2.54000 ($-$02) meter
kilometer	3.28084 ($+$03) foot
kilometer	1.00000 ($+$03) meter
kilometer	6.21371 ($-$01) mile (U.S. Statute)
kilometer	5.39957 ($-$01) mile (U.S. Nautical)
meter	1.00000 ($+$02) centimeter
meter	3.93701 ($+$01) inch
meter	3.28084 ($+$00) foot
mile (U.S. Statute)	5.28000 ($+$03) foot
mile (U.S. Statute)	1.60934 ($+$00) kilometer
mile (U.S. Statute)	8.68975 ($-$01) mile (U.S. Nautical)
mile (U.S. Nautical)	6.07610 ($+$03) foot
mile (U.S. Nautical)	1.85200 ($+$00) kilometer
mile (U.S. Nautical)	1.15078 ($+$00) mile (U.S. Statute)

AREA, STATIC MOMENT OF LINE

centimeter^2 .... 1.07639 (-03) foot^2
centimeter^2 .... 1.55000 (-01) inch^2
centimeter^2 .... 1.00000 (-04) meter^2

foot^2.......................... 9.29030 $(+02)$ centimeter^2
foot^2.......................... 1.44000 $(+02)$ inch^2
foot^2.......................... 9.29030 (-02) meter^2

inch^2.......................... 6.45160 $(+00)$ centimeter^2
inch^2.......................... 6.94444 (-03) foot^2
inch^2.......................... 6.45160 (-04) meter^2

meter^2 .... 1.00000 $(+04)$ centimeter^2
meter^2 .... 1.55000 $(+03)$ inch^2
meter^2 .... 1.07639 $(+01)$ foot^2

VOLUME, STATIC MOMENT OF AREA

centimeter^3 .... 3.53147 (-05) foot^3
centimeter^3 .... 6.10238 (-02) inch^3
centimeter^3 .... 1.00000 (-06) meter^3

foot^3.......................... 2.83168 $(+04)$ centimeter^3
foot^3.......................... 1.72800 $(+03)$ inch^3
foot^3.......................... 2.83168 (-02) meter^3

inch^3.......................... 1.63871 $(+01)$ centimeter^3
inch^3.......................... 5.78704 (-04) foot^3
inch^3.......................... 1.63871 (-05) meter^3

meter^3 .... 1.00000 $(+06)$ centimeter^3
meter^3 .... 6.10238 $(+04)$ inch^3
meter^3 .... 3.53147 $(+01)$ foot^3

STATIC MOMENT OF VOLUME, MOMENT OF INERTIA OF AREA

centimeter^4 .... 1.15862 (-06) foot^4
centimeter^4 .... 2.40251 (-02) inch^4
centimeter^4 .... 1.00000 (-08) meter^4

foot^4.......................... 8.63098 $(+05)$ centimeter^4
foot^4.......................... 2.07360 $(+04)$ inch^4
foot^4.......................... 8.63098 (-03) meter^4

inch^4.......................... 4.16231 $(+01)$ centimeter^4
inch^4.......................... 4.82253 (-05) foot^4
inch^4.......................... 4.16231 (-07) meter^4

meter^4 .... 1.00000 $(+08)$ centimeter^4
meter^4 .... 2.40251 $(+06)$ inch^4
meter^4 .... 1.15862 $(+02)$ foot^4

MOMENT OF INERTIA OF VOLUME

centimeter^5 . . . . 3.80124 (-08) foot^5
centimeter^5 . . . . 9.45872 (-03) inch^5
centimeter^5 . . . . 1.00000 (-10) meter^5

foot^5 . . . . 2.63072 $(+07)$ centimeter^5
foot^5 . . . . 2.48832 $(+05)$ inch^5
foot^5 . . . . 2.63072 (-03) meter^5

inch^5 . . . . 1.05723 $(+02)$ centimeter^5
inch^5 . . . . 4.01878 (-06) foot^5
inch^5 . . . . 1.05723 (-08) meter^5

meter^5 . . . . 1.00000 $(+10)$ centimeter^5
meter^5 . . . . 9.45872 $(+07)$ inch^5
meter^5 . . . . 3.80124 $(+02)$ foot^5

FORCE

dyne . . . . 1.01972 (-06) kilogram-force
dyne . . . . 1.00000 (-05) newton
dyne . . . . 2.24810 (-06) pound-force

kilogram-force . . . . 9.80665 $(+05)$ dyne
kilogram-force . . . . 9.80665 $(+00)$ newton
kilogram-force . . . . 2.20462 $(+00)$ pound-force

newton . . . . 1.00000 $(+05)$ dyne
newton . . . . 1.01972 (-01) kilogram-force
newton . . . . 2.24810 (-01) pound-force

pound-force . . . . 4.44822 $(+05)$ dyne
pound-force . . . . 4.53592 (-01) kilogram-force
pound-force . . . . 4.44822 $(+00)$ newton

MOMENT OF FORCE, WORK

dyne $\times$ centimeter . . . . 1.01972 (-08) kilogram-force $\times$ meter
dyne $\times$ centimeter . . . . 1.00000 (-07) newton $\times$ meter
dyne $\times$ centimeter . . . . 7.37567 (-08) pound-force $\times$ foot

kilogram-force $\times$ meter . . . . 9.80655 $(+07)$ dyne $\times$ centimeter
kilogram-force $\times$ meter . . . . 9.80655 $(+00)$ newton $\times$ meter
kilogram-force $\times$ meter . . . . 7.23301 $(+00)$ pound-force $\times$ foot

newton $\times$ meter . . . . 1.00000 $(+07)$ dyne $\times$ centimeter
newton $\times$ meter . . . . 7.37567 (-01) pound-force $\times$ foot
newton $\times$ meter . . . . 1.01972 (-01) kilogram-force $\times$ meter

pound-force $\times$ foot . . . . 1.35582 $(+07)$ dyne $\times$ centimeter
pound-force $\times$ foot . . . . 1.38255 (-01) kilogram-force $\times$ meter
pound-force $\times$ foot . . . . 1.35582 $(+00)$ newton $\times$ meter

STRESS, PRESSURE

kilogram-force/centimeter^2 . . . . 1.00000 (+04) kilogram-force/meter^2
kilogram-force/centimeter^2 . . . . 2.04816 (+03) pound-force/foot^2
kilogram-force/centimeter^2 . . . . 1.42233 (+01) pound-force/inch^2

kilogram-force/meter^2 . . . . 1.00000 (−04) kilogram-force/centimeter^2
kilogram-force/meter^2 . . . . 2.04816 (−01) pound-force/foot^2
kilogram-force/meter^2 . . . . 1.42233 (−03) pound-force/inch^2

pound-force/foot^2. . . . . 4.88243 (−04) kilogram-force/centimeter^2
pound-force/foot^2. . . . . 4.88243 (+00) kilogram-force/meter^2
pound-force/foot^2. . . . . 6.94444 (−03) pound-force/inch^2

pound-force/inch^2 . . . . 7.03069 (−02) kilogram-force/centimeter^2
pound-force/inch^2 . . . . 7.03069 (+02) kilogram-force/meter^2
pound-force/inch^2 . . . . 1.44000 (+02) pound-force/foot^2

Appendix C
Inertia Functions of Solids

1. Slender Straight Bar

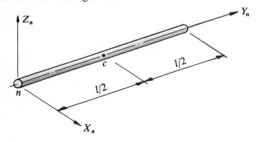

$$I_{nxx} = \frac{ml^2}{3}$$

$$I_{nyy} = 0$$

$$I_{nzz} = \frac{ml^2}{3}$$

$$I_{cxx} = \frac{ml^2}{12}$$

$$I_{cyy} = 0$$

$$I_{czz} = \frac{ml^2}{12}$$

2. Rectangular Parallelepiped

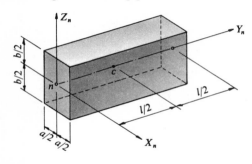

$$I_{nxx} = \frac{m(b^2 + 4l^2)}{12}$$

$$I_{nyy} = \frac{m(a^2 + b^2)}{12}$$

$$I_{nzz} = \frac{m(a^2 + 4l^2)}{12}$$

$$I_{cxx} = \frac{m(b^2 + l^2)}{12}$$

$$I_{cyy} = \frac{m(a^2 + b^2)}{12}$$

$$I_{czz} = \frac{m(a^2 + l^2)}{12}$$

3. Right Circular Cylinder

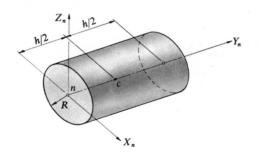

$$I_{nxx} = \frac{m(3R^2 + 4h^2)}{12}$$

$$I_{nyy} = \frac{mR^2}{2}$$

$$I_{nzz} = \frac{m(3R^2 + 4h^2)}{12}$$

$$I_{cxx} = \frac{m(3R^2 + h^2)}{12}$$

$$I_{cyy} = \frac{mR^2}{2}$$

$$I_{czz} = \frac{m(3R^2 + h^2)}{12}$$

4. Right Circular Cone

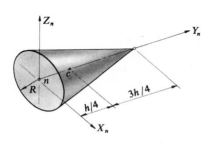

$$I_{nxx} = \frac{m(3R^2 + 2h^2)}{20}$$

$$I_{nyy} = \frac{3mR^2}{10}$$

$$I_{nzz} = \frac{m(3R^2 + 2h^2)}{20}$$

$$I_{cxx} = \frac{3m(4R^2 + h^2)}{80}$$

$$I_{cyy} = \frac{3mR^2}{10}$$

$$I_{czz} = \frac{3m(4R^2 + h^2)}{80}$$

5. Hemisphere

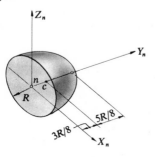

$$I_{nxx} = \frac{2mR^2}{5}$$

$$I_{nyy} = \frac{2mR^2}{5}$$

$$I_{nzz} = \frac{2mR^2}{5}$$

$$I_{cxx} = \frac{83mR^2}{320}$$

$$I_{cyy} = \frac{2mR^2}{5}$$

$$I_{czz} = \frac{83mR^2}{320}$$

Selected References and Bibliography

KINEMATICS OF PARTICLES

Goodman, L. E., and W. H. Warner: *Dynamics*, Wadsworth, Belmont, Calif., 1961.
Halfman, R. L.: *Dynamics—Particles, Rigid Bodies, and Systems*, Addison-Wesley, Reading, Mass., 1962.
Higdon, A., and W. B. Stiles: *Dynamics*, Prentice-Hall, Englewood Cliffs, N.J., 1962.
Pestel, E. C., and W. T. Thomson: *Dynamics*, McGraw-Hill, New York, 1968.

KINETICS OF PARTICLES

Greenwood, D. T.: *Principles of Dynamics*, Prentice-Hall, Englewood Cliffs, N. J., 1965.
Housner, G. W., and D. E. Hudson: *Dynamics*, 2nd ed., Van Nostrand, Princeton, N. J., 1959.
Thomson, W. T.: *Introduction to Space Dynamics*, Wiley, New York, 1961.
Timoshenko, S. P., and D. H. Young: *Engineering Mechanics*, 3rd ed., McGraw-Hill, New York, 1951.

MOVING REFERENCE SYSTEMS

Crandall, S. H., D. C. Karnopp, E. D. Kurtz, Jr., and D. C. Pridmore-Brown: *Dynamics of Mechanical and Electromechanical Systems*, McGraw-Hill, New York, 1968.
Meriam, J. L.: *Dynamics*, Wiley, New York, 1966.
Pipes, L. A.: *Matrix Methods for Engineering*, Prentice-Hall, Englewood Cliffs, N.J., 1963.

KINEMATICS OF RIGID BODIES

Goldstein, H.: *Classical Mechanics*, Addison-Wesley, Reading, Mass., 1950.
Greenwood, D. T.: *Principles of Dynamics*, Prentice-Hall, Englewood Cliffs, N.J., 1961.
Halfman, R. L.: *Dynamics—Particles, Rigid Bodies, and Systems*, Addison-Wesley, Reading, Mass., 1962.
Synge, J. L., and B. A. Griffith: *Principles of Mechanics*, 3rd ed., McGraw-Hill, New York, 1959.

KINETICS OF RIGID BODIES

Goodman, L. E., and W. H. Warner: *Dynamics*, Wadsworth, Belmont, Calif., 1961.
McMillan, W. D.: *Dynamics of Rigid Bodies*, Dover, New York, 1936.
Shames, I. H.: *Dynamics*, Prentice-Hall, Englewood Cliffs, N.J., 1960.
Yeh, H., and J. I. Abrahams: *Principles of Mechanics of Solids and Fluids*, Vol. I., McGraw-Hill, New York, 1960.

LINEAR VIBRATIONS

Meirovitch, L.: *Analytical Methods in Vibrations*, Macmillan, New York, 1967.
Thomson, W. T.: *Vibration Theory and Applications*, Prentice-Hall, Englewood Cliffs, N.J., 1965.
Timoshenko, S.: *Vibration Problems in Engineering*, 3rd ed., Van Nostrand, Princeton, N.J., 1955.

Answers to Selected Problems

CHAPTER 1

1.24 $\dot{x} = R\omega - b\omega \cos \omega t, \quad \dot{y} = b\omega \sin \omega t \qquad ds = \omega\sqrt{R^2 - 2Rb \cos \omega t + b^2}$
$\ddot{x} = b\omega^2 \sin \omega t, \qquad \ddot{y} = b\omega^2 \cos \omega t \qquad \tan \phi = (R - b \cos \omega t)/(b \sin \omega t)$

1.26 $\rho = \dfrac{(a^2 \sin^2 \omega t + b^2)^{3/2}}{ab \cos^3 \omega t}, \quad x_k = \dfrac{a^2 + b^2}{a \cos^3 \omega t}, \quad y_k = -\dfrac{(a^2 + b^2) \tan^3 \omega t}{b}$

1.28 $\rho = \dfrac{(a^2 \sin^2 \omega t + b^2 \cos^2 \omega t)^{3/2}}{ab}, \quad x_k = \dfrac{a^2 - b^2}{a} \cos \omega t, \quad y_k = -\dfrac{a^2 - b^2}{b} \sin^3 \omega t$

1.30 $\mathbf{r} = [(5t^2 + 50t + 30)\mathbf{i}]\text{ L}, \quad \mathbf{v} = [(10t + 50)\mathbf{i}]\text{ L/T}, \quad \mathbf{a} = [10\mathbf{i}]\text{ L/T}^2$

1.32 $\begin{bmatrix} 1 \\ s(t) \\ v(t) \end{bmatrix} = \begin{bmatrix} 1 & 0 & 0 \\ gt^2/2 & 1 & t \\ gt & 0 & 1 \end{bmatrix} \begin{bmatrix} 1 \\ s_0 \\ v_0 \end{bmatrix}$

1.34 $\begin{bmatrix} 1 \\ s(t) \\ v(t) \end{bmatrix} = \begin{bmatrix} 1 & 0 & 0 \\ gt^2/2 & 1 & -t \\ gt & 0 & -1 \end{bmatrix} \begin{bmatrix} 1 \\ s_0 \\ v_0 \end{bmatrix}$

1.36 $\dot{\mathbf{r}} = -(a\omega \sin \omega t)\mathbf{i} + (b\omega \cos \omega t)\mathbf{j}, \quad \ddot{\mathbf{r}} = -(a\omega^2 \cos \omega t)\mathbf{i} - (b\omega^2 \sin \omega t)\mathbf{j}$

1.38 $\dot{\mathbf{r}} = (R\omega - b\omega \cos \omega t)\mathbf{i} + (b\omega \sin \omega t)\mathbf{j}, \quad \ddot{\mathbf{r}} = (b\omega^2 \sin \omega t)\mathbf{i} + (b\omega^2 \cos \omega t)\mathbf{j}$

1.40 $t_l = 72.9 \text{ sec}, \quad l = 25{,}770 \text{ m}, \quad v_l = 505.2 \text{ m/sec}$

1.42 $\mathbf{v} = 2at\,\mathbf{e}_r + 2at^3\mathbf{e}_\theta, \quad \mathbf{a} = (2a - 4at^4)\mathbf{e}_r + (10at^2)\mathbf{e}_\theta$

1.44 $\mathbf{e}_t = (t/\sqrt{t^2 + 4})\mathbf{i} + (2/\sqrt{t^2 + 4})\mathbf{j}, \quad \mathbf{e}_n = (2/\sqrt{t^2 + 4})\mathbf{i} - (t/\sqrt{t^2 + 4})\mathbf{j}$

1.46 $\mathbf{e}_t = \dfrac{a \sin \omega t}{A}\mathbf{i} + \dfrac{b}{A}\mathbf{j}, \quad \mathbf{e}_n = \dfrac{b}{A}\mathbf{i} - \dfrac{a \sin \omega t}{A}\mathbf{j}, \quad \dot{s} = \dfrac{A}{\cos^2 \omega t}, \quad A = \sqrt{a^2 \sin^2 \omega t + b^2}$

1.48 $\dot{\mathbf{r}}_{21} = (228.8\mathbf{j})\text{ m/sec}, \quad t_{\text{collision}} = 4.62 \text{ sec}$

1.50 $\dot{\mathbf{r}}_{12} = \pm 2R\omega\mathbf{j} \text{ at } t = 0, \pi/\omega; \quad \dot{\mathbf{r}}_{12} = \mp R\omega\mathbf{i} \text{ at } t = \pi/2\omega, 3\pi/2\omega$

1.52 $v_m = A/t_p, \quad \alpha = \cos^{-1}(B/A), \quad A = \sqrt{(l - v_p t_p)^2 + (h + gt_p^2/2)^2}, \quad B = l - v_p t_p$

CHAPTER 2

2.42 $\mathbf{F} = [(-1000 \cos \pi t/10)\mathbf{i} + (-1000 \sin \pi t/10)\mathbf{j}]$ kg

2.44 $t = 10$ sec

2.46 $\mathbf{r} = \left[\left(\dfrac{500}{\pi^2} \cos \pi t/10\right)\mathbf{i} + \left(\dfrac{200}{\pi^2} \sin \pi t/10 + 2\pi t\right)\mathbf{j}\right]$ m

2.48 $x = \left(\dfrac{25}{9} t^4\right)$ ft

2.50 $h = (\sqrt{2egt_1^2 + e^2} - e)/2g$

2.52 $x = \dfrac{ag}{a+b}\mu_k$ (if the inertia moment is neglected)

2.54 (L.I.) $= 6 \times 10^6$ kg$_m$-km/hr

2.56 $G_{1x} = 0$, $G_{2x} = 0$, $G_{1y} = -12{,}650$ kg$_m$-m/sec, $G_{2y} = 12{,}650$ kg$_m$-m/sec
(L.I.) $= 25{,}300$ kg$_m$-m/sec

2.58 $H = 0$

2.60 $U = 5.75 \times 10^6$ m-kg

2.62 $N = 3W \sin \theta$

2.64 $t = 2\sqrt{\dfrac{l}{g}} \ln \dfrac{l_2 + \sqrt{l + l_1}}{\sqrt{2l_1}}$

2.66 $U = (\tan^{-1}\tfrac{11}{17})$ L-F

CHAPTER 3

3.32 $\mathbf{e}_t = \dfrac{\cos(\ln t) - \sin(\ln t)}{\sqrt{51}}\mathbf{i} + \dfrac{\cos(\ln t) + \sin(\ln t)}{\sqrt{51}}\mathbf{j} + \dfrac{7}{\sqrt{51}}\mathbf{k}$

$\mathbf{e}_n = \dfrac{-\cos(\ln t) - \sin(\ln t)}{\sqrt{2}}\mathbf{i} + \dfrac{\cos(\ln t) - \sin(\ln t)}{\sqrt{2}}\mathbf{j}$

$\mathbf{e}_b = \dfrac{7[-\cos(\ln t) + \sin(\ln t)]}{\sqrt{102}}\mathbf{i} + \dfrac{7[-\cos(\ln t) - \sin(\ln t)]}{\sqrt{102}}\mathbf{j} + \dfrac{2}{\sqrt{102}}\mathbf{k}$

3.34 $\rho_1 = 51t/\sqrt{2}$, $\rho_2 = 51t/7$

3.36 $\mathbf{v} = \mathbf{i} + t\mathbf{j} + (t^2/2)\mathbf{k}$, $\mathbf{a} = \mathbf{j} + t\mathbf{k}$

3.38 $\mathbf{r} = (100 + 20t)\mathbf{i} + (200 + 40t)\mathbf{j} + (300 + 60t + 5t^3/3)\mathbf{k}$

3.40 $\mathbf{a} = \left(-\dfrac{4000t^2}{10 + t}\right)\mathbf{e}_c + \left(\dfrac{2000 + 400t}{10 + t}\right)\mathbf{e}_\theta + 60\mathbf{e}_z$

3.42 $\phi_1 = \pi/2 - \phi_2$, $\dot{\phi}_1 = -\dot{\phi}_2$, $\ddot{\phi}_1 = -\ddot{\phi}_2$

3.44 $\rho_1 = \dfrac{20/t}{10\sqrt{101}}$, $\rho_2 = \dfrac{201t}{100}$

3.46 $\mathbf{r} = (t^2\sqrt{14})\mathbf{e}_v$, $\theta = \tan^{-1} 2$, $\phi = \tan^{-1}\dfrac{\sqrt{5}}{3}$

CHAPTER 4

4.22 $\ddot{x} = 10$ $\qquad$ $\ddot{y} = 20$ $\qquad$ $\ddot{z} = 30$

$\dot{x} = 10t$ $\qquad$ $\dot{y} = 20t + 6$ $\qquad$ $\dot{z} = 30t$

$x = 5t^2 + 4$ $\qquad$ $y = 10t^2 + 6t + 5$ $\qquad$ $z = 15t^2$

4.24

$$
\begin{bmatrix} 1 \\ x(t) \\ y(t) \\ z(t) \\ \dot{x}(t) \\ \dot{y}(t) \\ \dot{z}(t) \end{bmatrix}
=
\left[\begin{array}{c|ccc|ccc} 1 & 0 & 0 & 0 & 0 & 0 & 0 \\ 5t^2 & 1 & 0 & 0 & t & 0 & 0 \\ 10t^2 & 0 & 1 & 0 & 0 & t & 0 \\ 15t^2 & 0 & 0 & 1 & 0 & 0 & t \\ \hline 10t & 0 & 0 & 0 & 1 & 0 & 0 \\ 20t & 0 & 0 & 0 & 0 & 1 & 0 \\ 30t & 0 & 0 & 0 & 0 & 0 & 1 \end{array} \right]
\begin{bmatrix} 1 \\ 4 \\ 5 \\ 0 \\ 0 \\ 6 \\ 0 \end{bmatrix}
$$

where $t = 10$.

4.26

$$
\begin{bmatrix} 1 \\ x(10) \\ y(10) \\ z(10) \\ \dot{x}(10) \\ \dot{y}(10) \\ \dot{z}(10) \end{bmatrix}
=
\begin{bmatrix} 1 \\ 504 \\ 1065 \\ 1500 \\ 100 \\ 206 \\ 300 \end{bmatrix},
\quad
\begin{bmatrix} 1 \\ x(20) \\ y(20) \\ z(20) \\ \dot{x}(20) \\ \dot{y}(20) \\ \dot{z}(20) \end{bmatrix}
=
\begin{bmatrix} 1 \\ 2004 \\ 4125 \\ 6000 \\ 200 \\ 406 \\ 600 \end{bmatrix},
\quad
\begin{bmatrix} 1 \\ x(30) \\ y(30) \\ z(30) \\ \dot{x}(30) \\ \dot{y}(30) \\ \dot{z}(30) \end{bmatrix}
=
\begin{bmatrix} 1 \\ 4504 \\ 9160 \\ 13,500 \\ 300 \\ 606 \\ 900 \end{bmatrix}
$$

4.28 $N = \pi W$

4.30 $\phi_2 = 0,\ v_2 = v_1$

4.32 $v = \sqrt{[(R - e)g]/\mu_k},\ \phi = \tan^{-1} \mu_k$

4.34 $v_2 = v_1(R_1/R_2)$

4.38 $\dot{\theta} = 2\sqrt{(g/l)(\cos \theta_0 - \cos \theta)},\ \ddot{\theta} = (2g \sin \theta)/l$

CHAPTER 5

5.18 $x_{0c} = 0,\ y_{0c} = -\left[h - \dfrac{W_a c}{W_a + W_b} + \dfrac{1}{2}\left(\dfrac{W_b - W_a}{W_a + W_b}\right)^2 gt^2\right]$

5.20 $\dot{\mathbf{r}}_{0c} = \left[-\left(\dfrac{W_b - W_a}{W_a + W_b}\right)^2 gt\right]\mathbf{j}$

5.22 $\mathbf{G} = [(-333.3t)\mathbf{j}]$ lb-sec

5.24 $\mathbf{H} = [(-1000t)\mathbf{k}]$ lb-ft-sec

5.26 (L.I.) $= [-333.3(t_2 - t_1)\mathbf{j}]$ lb-sec

5.28 (A.I.) $= [-1000(t_2 - t_1)\mathbf{j}]$ lb-ft-sec

5.30 $\displaystyle\int_1^2 F_s \cdot d\mathbf{r}_s = \dfrac{1}{m}(\dot{x}_{s,2}^2 - \dot{x}_{s,1}^2 + \dot{y}_{s,2}^2 - \dot{y}_{s,1}^2 + \dot{z}_{s,2}^2 - \dot{z}_{s,1}^2)$

5.32 $\displaystyle\int_1^2 F_s \cdot d\mathbf{r}_s = \tfrac{1}{2}m[(r_{s,2}\dot{\phi}_{s,2})^2 - (r_{s,1}\dot{\phi}_{s,1})^2 + (r_{s,2}\dot{\theta}_{s,2} \sin \phi_{s,2})^2 - (r_{s,1}\dot{\theta}_{s,1} \sin \phi_{s,1})^2 + (\dot{r}_{s,2})^2 - (\dot{r}_{s,1})^2]$

CHAPTER 6

6.22 $\mathbf{v}_{0m} = \dot{\mathbf{r}}_{0m} + \boldsymbol{\omega} \times \mathbf{r}_{0m}$, $\mathbf{a}_{0m} = \ddot{\mathbf{r}}_{0m} + \dot{\boldsymbol{\omega}} \times \mathbf{r}_{0m} + 2\boldsymbol{\omega} \times \dot{\mathbf{r}}_{0m} + \boldsymbol{\omega} \times (\boldsymbol{\omega} \times \mathbf{r}_{0m})$
where $\mathbf{r}_{0m}, \dot{\mathbf{r}}_{0m}, \ddot{\mathbf{r}}_{0m}$ are given by (1-19), page 5, $\boldsymbol{\omega} = \omega_z\mathbf{k}$, $\dot{\boldsymbol{\omega}} = \dot{\omega}_z\mathbf{k}$, and $\dot{\theta}_z \neq \omega_z$, $\ddot{\theta}_z \neq \dot{\omega}_z$.

6.24 $\begin{bmatrix} x_{0m}^{*\theta} \\ y_{0m}^{*\theta} \end{bmatrix} = \begin{bmatrix} \dot{r}_{0m} \\ 0 \end{bmatrix} + \begin{bmatrix} 0 & -\dot{\theta}_z - \omega_z \\ \dot{\theta}_z + \omega_z & 0 \end{bmatrix}\begin{bmatrix} r_{0m} \\ 0 \end{bmatrix}$

$\begin{bmatrix} x_{0m}^{**\theta} \\ y_{0m}^{**\theta} \end{bmatrix} = \begin{bmatrix} \ddot{r}_{0m} \\ 0 \end{bmatrix} + 2\begin{bmatrix} 0 & -\dot{\theta}_z - \omega_z \\ \dot{\theta}_z + \omega_z & 0 \end{bmatrix}\begin{bmatrix} \dot{r}_{0m} \\ 0 \end{bmatrix} + \begin{bmatrix} -\dot{\theta}_z^2 - \omega_z^2 & -\ddot{\theta}_z - \dot{\omega}_z \\ \ddot{\theta}_z + \dot{\omega}_z & -\dot{\theta}_z^2 - \omega_z^2 \end{bmatrix}\begin{bmatrix} r_{0m} \\ 0 \end{bmatrix}$

6.26 $\mathbf{r}_{0m}^* = 10(1 + 5\sin t)\,[(-\sin t)\mathbf{i} + (\cos t)\mathbf{j}]$
$\mathbf{r}_{0m}^{**} = -10[2(1 + 5\sin t)\cos t + 5\cos t \sin t]\mathbf{i} - 10[2(1 + 5\sin t)\sin t - 5\cos^2 t]\mathbf{j}$

6.28 $\mathbf{r}_{0m}^* = (-100t - 50t\sin 5t^2)\mathbf{i}^0 + (50t\cos 5t^2)\mathbf{j}^0$
$\mathbf{r}_{0m}^{**} = (-100 - 50\sin 5t^2 - 500t\cos 5t^2)\mathbf{i}^0 + (50\cos 5t^2 - 500t\sin 5t^2)\mathbf{j}^0$

6.30 Equation (3-22), page 55.

6.32 Equation (1-21), page 6.

6.34 Equation (3-33), page 58.

6.36 Table 6-1, page 121.

6.38 $2[\Gamma]\,[\dot{s}_{cm}^l] = \begin{bmatrix} 1.04882 \\ -1.24180 \\ 0.47786 \end{bmatrix}$, $[\Gamma]^2[s_{cm}^l] = \begin{bmatrix} -0.71313 \\ 0.00419 \\ 0.38177 \end{bmatrix}$

6.40 $[v_{cm}^l] = \begin{bmatrix} 1.15853 \\ 2.45970 \\ 2.69993 \end{bmatrix}$, $[a_{cm}^l] = \begin{bmatrix} 0.87599 \\ 4.08746 \\ 5.47780 \end{bmatrix}$

CHAPTER 7

7.22 $\mathbf{v}_{0m} = \dot{x}_{0n}\mathbf{i} + \dot{y}_{0n}\mathbf{j} = \dot{x}_{0m}\mathbf{i} + \dot{y}_{0m}\mathbf{j}$

7.24 $\mathbf{a}_{0m} = \ddot{x}_{0n}\mathbf{i} + \ddot{y}_{0n}\mathbf{j} = \ddot{x}_{0m}\mathbf{i} + \ddot{y}_{0m}\mathbf{j}$

7.26 $\begin{bmatrix} x_{0m}^* \\ y_{0m}^* \end{bmatrix} = \begin{bmatrix} \dot{x}_{0n} \\ \dot{y}_{0n} \end{bmatrix} = \begin{bmatrix} \dot{x}_{0m} \\ \dot{y}_{0m} \end{bmatrix}$, $\begin{bmatrix} x_{0m}^{**} \\ y_{0m}^{**} \end{bmatrix} = \begin{bmatrix} \ddot{x}_{0n} \\ \ddot{y}_{0n} \end{bmatrix} = \begin{bmatrix} \ddot{x}_{0m} \\ \ddot{y}_{0m} \end{bmatrix}$

7.28 $v_{em,t} = R_1\dot{\theta}_z$, $\Omega = \dot{\theta}_z$, $\dot{\Omega} = \ddot{\theta}_z$, $a_{em,t} = -\dfrac{R_1^2}{R_2 - R_1}\dot{\theta}_z^2$, $a_{em,r} = R_1\ddot{\theta}_z$

7.30 $\mathbf{v}_{0c} = (\tfrac{1}{2}l\dot{\theta}_z)\,[(\sin\theta_z)\mathbf{i} + (\cos\theta_z)\mathbf{j}]$
$\mathbf{a}_{0c} = \tfrac{1}{2}l[(\ddot{\theta}_z\sin\theta_z + \dot{\theta}_z^2\cos\theta_z)\mathbf{i} + (\ddot{\theta}_z\cos\theta_z - \dot{\theta}_z^2\sin\theta_z)\mathbf{j}]$
$\theta_z = \cos^{-1}(\tfrac{1}{2}t^2)$, $\dot{\theta}_z = -\dfrac{2t}{l\sin\theta_z}$, $\ddot{\theta}_z = -\dfrac{2(\sin\theta_z - t\dot{\theta}_z\cos\theta_z)}{l\sin^2\theta_z}$

7.32 $\mathbf{r}_{14} = (-5\sin\theta_z + 30\sin\psi_z)\mathbf{i} + (5\cos\theta_z + 30\sin\psi_z)\mathbf{j}$
$\theta_z = t$, $\omega_{12} = \dot{\theta}_z = 1$, $\dot{\omega}_{12} = \ddot{\theta}_z = 0$
$\psi_z = \tan^{-1}\dfrac{1 - \cos\theta_z}{4 + \sin\theta_z}$, $\omega_{24} = \dot{\psi}_z = \dfrac{\dot{\theta}_z\sin\theta_z}{4 + \sin\theta_z}$, $\dot{\omega}_{24} = \ddot{\psi}_z = \dfrac{4\dot{\theta}_z\cos\theta_z}{(4 + \sin\theta_z)^2}$

7.34 $x_{0m}^0 = x_{0n}^0 + x_{nm}^l \cos \theta_z - y_{nm}^l \sin \theta_z, \quad y_{0m}^0 = y_{0n}^0 + x_{nm}^l \sin \theta_z + y_{nm}^l \cos \theta_z$

$x_{0m}^{*0} = \dot{x}_{0n}^0 + (\dot{x}_{nm}^l \cos \theta_z - \dot{y}_{nm}^l \sin \theta_z) - (x_{nm}^l \sin \theta_z + y_{nm}^l \cos \theta_z)\dot{\theta}_z$

$y_{0m}^{*0} = \dot{y}_{0n}^0 + (\dot{x}_{nm}^l \sin \theta_z + \dot{y}_{nm}^l \cos \theta_z) + (x_{nm}^l \cos \theta_z - y_{nm}^l \sin \theta_z)\dot{\theta}_z$

$x_{0m}^{**0} = \ddot{x}_{0n}^0 + (\ddot{x}_{nm}^l \cos \theta_z - \ddot{y}_{nm}^l \sin \theta_z) - 2(\dot{x}_{nm}^l \sin \theta_z + \dot{y}_{nm}^l \cos \theta_z)\dot{\theta}_z$
$\qquad\qquad - (x_{nm}^l \cos \theta_z - y_{nm}^l \sin \theta_z)\dot{\theta}_z^2 - (x_{nm}^l \sin \theta_z + y_{nm}^l \cos \theta_z)\ddot{\theta}_z$

$y_{0m}^{**0} = \ddot{y}_{0n}^0 + (\ddot{x}_{nm}^l \sin \theta_z + \ddot{y}_{nm}^l \cos \theta_z) + 2(\dot{x}_{nm}^l \cos \theta_z - \dot{y}_{nm}^l \sin \theta_z)\dot{\theta}_z$
$\qquad\qquad - (x_{nm}^l \sin \theta_z + y_{nm}^l \cos \theta_z)\dot{\theta}_z^2 + (x_{nm}^l \cos \theta_z - y_{nm}^l \sin \theta_z)\ddot{\theta}_z$

7.36 $\theta_z = -t^2/4, \quad \dot{\theta}_z = -t/2, \quad \ddot{\theta}_z = -1/2$

$$\mathbf{v}_{0m} = 10t\,\mathbf{i}^0 + (2 - 3t)\mathbf{i}^l + \begin{vmatrix} \mathbf{i}^l & \mathbf{j}^l & \mathbf{k}^l \\ 0 & 0 & -t/2 \\ 2t - 3t^2/2 & 10 & 0 \end{vmatrix}$$

7.38 $\left[\dot{s}_{0c}^0\right] = \begin{bmatrix} 10t \\ 0 \end{bmatrix}, \qquad \left[\pi^{0l}\right] = \begin{bmatrix} \cos t^2/4 & \sin t^2/4 \\ -\sin t^2/4 & \cos t^2/4 \end{bmatrix}$

$\left[\dot{s}_{cm}^l\right] = \begin{bmatrix} 2 - 3t \\ 0 \end{bmatrix}, \qquad [\Gamma] = \begin{bmatrix} 0 & t/2 \\ -t/2 & 0 \end{bmatrix}$

$\left[s_{cm}^l\right] = \begin{bmatrix} 2t - 3t^2/2 \\ 0 \end{bmatrix}, \quad [\Delta] = \begin{bmatrix} -1/4 & t/2 \\ -t/2 & -1/4 \end{bmatrix}$

7.40 $\mathbf{v}_{0n} = (-72.2\mathbf{i} + 15.1\mathbf{j})$ in./sec, $\boldsymbol{\omega}_{0n} = (5.6\mathbf{k})$ rad/sec, $\dot{\boldsymbol{\omega}}_{0n} = (67.4\mathbf{k})$ rad/sec^2

CHAPTER 8

8.20 $\dot{\theta}_z = 2Pt/mr, \quad \ddot{\theta}_z = 2P/mr$

8.22 $v = \sqrt{2g(h - \mu b)} + v_0$

8.24 $R_{cx} = P \sin \theta_z, \quad R_{cy} = mg + P \cos \theta_z, \quad \theta_z$ measured from the horizontal.

8.26 $\ddot{x}_{01} = \dfrac{[\mu_2 W_2 - \mu_1(W_1 + W_2)]g}{W_1}, \quad \ddot{x}_{02} = \dfrac{(P - \mu_2 W_2)g}{W_2}$

8.28 $\ddot{\theta}_{\text{disk}} = -\dfrac{4P}{r(4m_1 + m_2)}, \quad \ddot{\theta}_{\text{bar}} = \dfrac{6P(2m_1 + m_2)}{lm_2(4m_1 + m_2)}$

8.30 $\cos \theta_z = \frac{3}{5} + l\dot{\theta}_{1z}^2/5g$

8.32 $\dot{\theta}_z = \sqrt{\dfrac{24gb \sin \theta_z}{l^2 + 12b^2} + \dot{\theta}_{1z}^2}$

8.34 $\ddot{y}_{23} = \dfrac{(4W_1 - 8W_3)g}{3W_1 + 4W_2 + 8W_3}$

8.36 $\dot{\theta}_z = \sqrt{\dfrac{24gb \sin \theta_z}{l^2 + 12b^2} + \dot{\theta}_{1z}^2}$

CHAPTER 9

9.18 $\begin{bmatrix} \dot{\mathbf{i}}^l \\ \dot{\mathbf{j}}^l \\ \dot{\mathbf{k}}^l \end{bmatrix} = -\begin{bmatrix} 0 & -\Omega_z^l & \Omega_y^l \\ \Omega_z^l & 0 & -\Omega_x^l \\ -\Omega_y^l & \Omega_x^l & 0 \end{bmatrix} \begin{bmatrix} \mathbf{i}^l \\ \mathbf{j}^l \\ \mathbf{k}^l \end{bmatrix}$

where $\Omega_x^l = \dot{\theta} \sin \phi - \dot{\psi} \sin \theta \cos \phi, \quad \Omega_y^l = \dot{\theta} \cos \phi + \dot{\psi} \sin \theta \sin \phi, \quad \Omega_z^l = \dot{\phi} + \dot{\psi} \cos \theta.$

9.20　$\Omega = (\dot\theta \sin\phi - \dot\psi \sin\theta \cos\phi)\mathbf{i}^l + (\dot\theta \cos\phi + \dot\psi \sin\theta \sin\phi)\mathbf{j}^l + (\dot\phi + \dot\psi \cos\theta)\mathbf{k}^l$

9.22　$\mathbf{v}_{0m} = [(-40\pi)\mathbf{j}^0 + (30\pi)\mathbf{k}^0]$ m/sec

9.24　$\begin{bmatrix} x_{0m}^{*0} \\ y_{0m}^{*0} \\ z_{0m}^{*0} \end{bmatrix} = \begin{bmatrix} 0 \\ -40\pi \\ 30\pi \end{bmatrix}$ m/sec,　$\begin{bmatrix} x_{0m}^{**0} \\ y_{0m}^{**0} \\ z_{0m}^{**0} \end{bmatrix} = \begin{bmatrix} 0 \\ -300\pi^2 \\ -400\pi^2 \end{bmatrix}$ m/sec^2

9.26　$[s_{0m}^{*l}] = \begin{bmatrix} h\dot\phi \sin\alpha \cos\psi \\ -h\dot\phi \sin\alpha \sin\psi + R\dot\phi \cos\alpha + R\dot\psi \\ -R\dot\phi \sin\alpha \cos\psi \end{bmatrix}$,　$[s_{0m}^{*0}] = [\pi^{0l}][s_{0m}^{*l}]$

where $[\pi^{0l}]$ is given in Problem 9.2, page 187.

9.28　$[s_{cm}^{*0}] = [\pi^{0l}][\Gamma^l][s_{cm}^l]$,　$[\Gamma^l] = \begin{bmatrix} 0 & -\Omega^l & \Omega^l \\ \Omega^l & 0 & -\Omega^l \\ -\Omega^l & \Omega^l & 0 \end{bmatrix}$,　$[s_{cm}^l] = \begin{bmatrix} 0 \\ R \\ 0 \end{bmatrix}$

where $\Omega_x^l = \dot\phi \sin\theta \sin\psi$, $\Omega_y^l = \dot\phi \sin\theta \cos\psi$, $\Omega_z^l = \dot\psi + \dot\phi \cos\theta$ and $[\pi^{0l}]$ is given in Problem 9.2, page 187.

9.30　$\mathbf{v}_{0m} = (\dot\phi l \sin\theta)\mathbf{i}^l + (v)\mathbf{k}^l$,　$\mathbf{a}_{0m} = (2\dot\phi v \sin\theta)\mathbf{i}^l + (\dot\phi^2 l \sin\theta \cos\theta)\mathbf{j}^l + (-\dot\phi^2 l \sin^2\theta)\mathbf{k}^l$

9.32　$\mathbf{v}_{0m} = \left(v + \dot\psi R \cos\dfrac{\pi}{4}\right)\mathbf{j}^l$,　$\mathbf{a}_{0m} = \left(-2\dot\psi v \sin\dfrac{\pi}{4}\right)\mathbf{i}^l - \left(2\dot\psi v \cos\dfrac{\pi}{4} + \dot\psi^2 R \cos^2\dfrac{\pi}{4}\right)\mathbf{k}^l$

CHAPTER 10

10.20　$[T_0^0] = \dfrac{ma^2}{12} \begin{bmatrix} 8 & -3 & -3 \\ -3 & 8 & -3 \\ -3 & -3 & 8 \end{bmatrix}$,　$I_{0,1}^p = \dfrac{ma^2}{6}$,　$I_{0,2}^p = I_{0,3}^p = \dfrac{11ma^2}{12}$

X_0^0 is the diagonal of the cube; Y_0^p, Z_0^p are any two orthogonal axes in the plane through 0 and normal to X_0^p.

For example: $[\pi^{0p}] = \begin{bmatrix} \dfrac{1}{\sqrt{3}} & -\dfrac{1}{\sqrt{2}} & -\dfrac{\sqrt{2}}{2\sqrt{3}} \\ \dfrac{1}{\sqrt{3}} & \dfrac{1}{\sqrt{2}} & -\dfrac{\sqrt{2}}{2\sqrt{3}} \\ \dfrac{1}{\sqrt{3}} & 0 & \dfrac{\sqrt{3}}{2} \end{bmatrix}$

10.22　$I_{0,1}^p = I_{0xx}^0 = 3a^2m$, $I_{0,2}^p = I_{0yy}^0 = 3a^2m$, $I_{0,3}^p = I_{0zz}^0 = 2a^2m$, $X_0^p \equiv X_0^0$, $Y_0^p \equiv Y_0^0$, $Z_0^p \equiv Z_0^0$

10.24　$I_{1xx}^l = 2(\tfrac{1}{4}a^2 + a^2)m = \tfrac{5}{2}ma^2$

10.26　$\mathbf{H}_0 = \Omega(2a^2m) = (2a^2m\Omega)\mathbf{k}$

10.28　$\begin{bmatrix} H_{0x}^0 \\ H_{0y}^0 \\ H_{0z}^0 \end{bmatrix} = \dfrac{ma}{12} \begin{bmatrix} 8 & -3 & -3 \\ -3 & 8 & -3 \\ -3 & -3 & 8 \end{bmatrix} \begin{bmatrix} 10 \\ 20t \\ 30t^2 \end{bmatrix}$,　$\mathbf{H}_{0x} = \dfrac{ma^2}{12}(80 - 60t - 90t^2)\mathbf{i}$

10.30　$M_{cz}^0 = \dfrac{m(a^2 - b^2)ab\Omega_x^2}{12(a^2 + b^2)}$,　Z_c^0 normal to the plate and rotates with the plate

10.32
$$\begin{bmatrix} M_{0x}^0 \\ M_{0y}^0 \\ M_{cz}^0 \end{bmatrix} = \frac{ma}{12} \begin{bmatrix} 8 & -3 & -3 \\ -3 & 8 & -3 \\ -3 & -3 & 8 \end{bmatrix} \begin{bmatrix} 0 \\ 20 \\ 60t \end{bmatrix} + \begin{bmatrix} 0 & -30t^2 & 20t \\ 30t^2 & 0 & -10 \\ -20t & 10 & 0 \end{bmatrix} \begin{bmatrix} 8 & -3 & -3 \\ -3 & 8 & -3 \\ -3 & -3 & 8 \end{bmatrix} \begin{bmatrix} 10 \\ 20t \\ 30t^2 \end{bmatrix}$$

10.34 $\cos \theta = 3g/2l\Omega^2$

10.36 $\cot \theta = (\Omega^2 l/g)(c/l + \frac{2}{3} \cos \theta)$

10.38 $u_1 = u_2 = +1, \ u_1 = (I_3 A)^2/2I_1 mgl - 1$

CHAPTER 11

11.18 $p_\theta = \sqrt{2kg/Wr}$

11.20 $x = x_0 \cos p_\delta t + \dfrac{\dot{x}_0}{p_\delta} \sin p_\delta t + \dfrac{P(\cos \Omega t - \cos p_\delta t)}{m(p_\delta^2 - \Omega^2)}$

11.22 Same as in Problem 11.18.

11.24 Same as in Problem 11.20.

11.26 Underdamped vibration.

Index